DEMOGRAPHY OF THE NORTHERN SPOTTED OWL

Eric D. Forsman, Stephen DeStefano,
Martin G. Raphael, and R. J. Gutiérrez, editors

Proceedings of a Workshop
Fort Collins, Colorado,
December 1993

Sponsor:
USDA Forest Service

Studies in Avian Biology No. 17
A PUBLICATION OF THE COOPER ORNITHOLOGICAL SOCIETY

Cover drawing of Northern Spotted Owl by Viktor Bahktin

STUDIES IN AVIAN BIOLOGY

Edited by

John T. Rotenberry
Department of Biology
University of California
Riverside, California 92521

Studies in Avian Biology is a series of works too long for *The Condor,* published at irregular intervals by the Cooper Ornithological Society. Manuscripts for consideration should be submitted to the editor. Style and format should follow those of previous issues.

Price $20.00 including postage and handling. All orders cash in advance; make checks payable to Cooper Ornithological Society. Send orders to Cooper Ornithological Society, % Western Foundation of Vertebrate Zoology, 439 Calle San Pablo, Camarillo, CA 93010.

ISBN: 0-935868-83-6

Library of Congress Catalog Card Number: 96-085058
Printed at Allen Press, Inc., Lawrence, Kansas 66044
Issued: 26 June 1996

CONTENTS

LIST OF AUTHORS

DAVID R. ANDERSON
Colorado Cooperative Fish and Wildlife
  Research Unit
National Biological Service
Colorado State University
Fort Collins, CO 80523

LAWRENCE S. ANDREWS
Oregon Cooperative Wildlife Research Unit
104 Nash Hall
Oregon State University
Corvallis, OR 97330

ROBERT G. ANTHONY
National Biological Service
Oregon Cooperative Wildlife Research Unit
Oregon State University
Corvallis, OR 97330

DOUGLAS K. BARRETT
USDA Forest Service
Pacific Northwest Research Station
3200 SW Jefferson Way
Corvallis, OR 97331

GREGORY M. BENNETT
Oregon Cooperative Wildlife Research Unit
Department of Fisheries and Wildlife
Oregon State University
Corvallis, OR 97331

MARK BROWN
Arizona Game and Fish Department
9140 East County 10½ Street
Yuma, AZ 85365

KENNETH P. BURNHAM
Colorado Cooperative Fish and Wildlife
  Research Unit
National Biological Service
Colorado State University
Fort Collins, CO 80523

STEPHEN DeSTEFANO
Oregon Cooperative Wildlife Research Unit
Department of Fisheries and Wildlife
Oregon State University
Corvallis, OR 97330
(present address: National Biological Service
Cooperative Fish and Wildlife Research Unit
104 Biological Sciences East
University of Arizona
Tucson, AZ 85271)

ERIC D. FORSMAN
USDA Forest Service
Pacific Northwest Research Station
3200 SW Jefferson Way
Corvallis, OR 97331

RAYMOND K. FORSON
USDA Forest Service
Pacific Northwest Research Station
3200 SW Jefferson Way
Corvallis, OR 97331

ALAN B. FRANKLIN
Colorado Cooperative Fish and Wildlife
  Research Unit
Department of Fishery and Wildlife Biology
Colorado State University
Fort Collins, CO 80523

R. J. GUTIÉRREZ
Department of Wildlife
Humboldt State University
Arcata, CA 95521

D. SCOTT HOPKINS
USDI Bureau of Land Management
Salem District Office
1717 Fabry Road
Salem, OR 97306

RICHARD HOLTHAUSEN
USDA Forest Service
104 Nash Hall
Oregon State University
Corvallis, OR 97331

CHRIS J. LARSON
Oregon Cooperative Wildlife Research Unit
Department of Fisheries and Wildlife
Oregon State University
Corvallis, OR 97331

JOSEPH B. LINT
USDI Bureau of Land Management
777 Garden Valley Blvd.
Roseburg, OR 97470

WAYNE D. LOGAN
USDI Bureau of Land Management
Salem District Office
1717 Fabry Road
Salem, OR 97306

PETER J. LOSCHL
USDA Forest Service
Pacific Northwest Research Station
3200 SW Jefferson Way
Corvallis, OR 97331

KEVIN J. MAURICE
USDA Forest Service
Pacific Northwest Research Station
3200 SW Jefferson Way
Corvallis, OR 97331

E. Charles Meslow
National Biological Service
Oregon Cooperative Wildlife Research Unit
Oregon State University
Corvallis, OR 97330
(present address: Wildlife Management
  Institute
8035 NW Oxbow Dr.
Corvallis, OR 97330)

Gary S. Miller
Oregon Cooperative Wildlife Research Unit
Department of Fisheries and Wildlife
Oregon State University
Corvallis, OR 97331
(present address: US Fish and Wildlife Service
2600 SE 98th Ave., Suite 100
Portland, OR 97266)

Barry R. Noon
USDA Forest Service
Redwood Sciences Laboratory
1700 Bayview Dr.
Arcata, CA 95521

John P. Perkins
Oregon Cooperative Wildlife Research Unit
104 Nash Hall
Oregon State University
Corvallis, OR 97330

Martin G. Raphael
USDA Forest Service
Pacific Northwest Research Station
3625 93rd Ave. SW
Olympia, WA 98512

Janice A. Reid
USDA Forest Service
Pacific Northwest Research Station
Roseburg Field Office
777 Garden Valley Blvd.
Roseburg, OR 97470

Susan E. Salmons
USDA Forest Service
Pacific Southwest Forest and Range
  Experiment Station
1700 Bayview Dr.
Arcata, CA 95521

D. Erran Seaman
National Biological Service
Olympic Field Unit
600 E. Park Ave.
Port Angeles, WA 98362

Stephen M. Small
Oregon Cooperative Wildlife Research Unit
Department of Fisheries and Wildlife
Oregon State University
Corvallis, OR 97331

Stan G. Sovern
USDA Forest Service
Pacific Northwest Research Station
3200 SW Jefferson Way
Corvallis, OR 97331

Keith A. Swindle
Oregon Cooperative Wildlife Research Unit
Department of Fisheries and Wildlife
Oregon State University
Corvallis, OR 97330

Margaret Taylor
USDA Forest Service
Pacific Northwest Research Station
3200 SW Jefferson Way
Corvallis, OR 97331

James A. Thrailkill
Oregon Cooperative Wildlife Research Unit
104 Nash Hall
Oregon State University
Corvallis, OR 97330

Frank F. Wagner
Oregon Cooperative Wildlife Research Unit
Department of Fisheries and Wildlife
Oregon State University
Corvallis, OR 97331

James P. Ward, Jr.
Department of Biology
Colorado State University
Fort Collins, CO 80523

Gary C. White
Department of Fishery and Wildlife Biology
Colorado State University
Fort Collins, CO 80523

Cynthia J. Zabel
USDA Forest Service
Pacific Southwest Forest and Range
  Experiment Station
1700 Bayview Dr.
Arcata, CA 95521

Joseph J. Zisa
USDA Forest Service
Pacific Northwest Research Station
3200 SW Jefferson Way
Corvallis, OR 97331

Studies in Avian Biology No. 17:1, 1996.

PREFACE

A large number of mark-recapture studies of Northern Spotted Owls (*Strix occidentalis caurina*) were initiated during 1985–1990, with the primary objective of evaluating trends in vital rates of the species. These studies were conducted by scientists from federal agencies, universities, private timber companies, and consulting firms, and involved repeated surveys of large areas each year to locate, mark, and reobserve or recapture resident pairs of owls and their offspring. Some studies also included radiotelemetry to examine movements of juvenile owls.

At the request of the United States Secretaries of Agriculture and Interior, a workshop was convened in Fort Collins, Colorado in December 1993 to examine all existing demographic data on the Northern Spotted Owl. The workshop focused exclusively on mark-recapture studies, and was led by Drs. K. P. Burnham, D. R. Anderson and G. C. White. A number of other scientists and analysts familiar with demographic analyses were invited to participate in developing the analytical framework and assisting with data analysis.

Invited participants included all researchers with three or more years of demographic data on Northern Spotted Owls, including researchers from seven studies conducted by federal agencies, two studies conducted by forest products companies, four studies conducted by university scientists, and one study conducted by a consulting company. The two forest products companies declined to present their data for analysis. The consulting firm presented their data for analysis but withdrew their results at the end of the workshop because they were not convinced that their data met the underlying assumptions of the capture-recapture models used in estimating survival probabilities. Thus, results of 11 studies conducted by federal and university scientists were the focus of the final workshop report.

The initial product of the Fort Collins workshop was a summary report prepared and submitted to the U. S. Departments of Agriculture and Interior by the workshop leaders. That report was included as an appendix in agency planning documents (Burnham et al. 1994). Workshop participants felt that a more complete exposition of the workshop proceedings was appropriate, and agreed to prepare individual reports on each of the 11 study areas for publication in a peer-reviewed journal. In addition to the individual study area reports, several additional supporting papers were written, including papers on the history of the issue, general biology of the owl, methods, habitat trends, and management implications. The papers in this volume represent the culmination of this effort.

We would like to thank the editors and reviewers at the *Journal of Wildlife Management* for the very thorough and helpful reviews that they provided on many of the manuscripts in this report. Editor L. M. Smith, and Associate Editors M. J. Conroy and W. R. Clark were instrumental in this regard. We also thank all those who assisted with data analysis at the Fort Collins Workshop, including D. R. Anderson, K. P. Burnham, J. Clobert, J. E. Hines, J. D. Nichols, R. J. Pradel, E. A. Rexstad, T. M. Shenk, G. C. White, and K. R. Wilson. Viktor Bakhtin of the International Crane Foundation provided the cover art.

THE EDITORS

Studies in Avian Biology No. 17:2–5, 1996.

BIOLOGY AND DISTRIBUTION OF THE NORTHERN SPOTTED OWL

R. J. GUTIÉRREZ

INTRODUCTION

The Northern Spotted Owl (*Strix occidentalis caurina*) is one of three subspecies of the Spotted Owl inhabiting western North America (Gutiérrez et al. 1995). The taxonomic separation of these subspecies is supported by genetic (Barrowclough and Gutiérrez 1990, G. Barrowclough, personal communication), morphological (Gutiérrez et al. 1995), and biogeographic information (Barrowclough and Gutiérrez 1990).

The purpose of this chapter is to provide a synopsis of relevant biology of the Northern Spotted Owl particularly with respect to its distribution, habitat use, and life history characteristics. Other literature reviews of Spotted Owl biology that are particularly comprehensive include Campbell et al. (1984), Gutiérrez (1985), Gutiérrez and Carey (1985), Thomas et al. (1990), Verner et al. (1992), and Gutiérrez et al. (1995).

PHYSICAL DESCRIPTION

The Spotted Owl is a medium-sized owl, about 46–48 cm in length and weighs approximately 490–850 g (Dawson 1923, Hamer et al. 1994, Gutiérrez et al. 1995). The Northern Spotted Owl is the largest of the three subspecies (Gutiérrez et al. 1995). It is dark brown with a barred tail and white spots on the head and breast, and has dark brown eyes that are surrounded by prominent facial disks (Bent 1938, Gutiérrez et al. 1995). Three age classes can be distinguished on the basis of plumage characteristics (Forsman 1981, Moen et al. 1991).

The Spotted Owl superficially resembles the Barred Owl (*Strix varia*), a species with which it occasionally hybridizes. Hybrids exhibit characteristics of both species (Hamer et al. 1994).

DISTRIBUTION

GEOGRAPHIC RANGE

The Northern Spotted Owl occurs in the mountains of northwestern California (from Marin Co. north), western Oregon, western Washington, and southwestern British Columbia. The eastern edge of its range generally corresponds with the eastern periphery of the Cascades Range, and with the Central Valley in California (Bent 1938, Gutiérrez et al. 1995).

REGIONAL DISTRIBUTION

The distribution of the Northern Spotted Owl within its known range is relatively contiguous, but is influenced by the natural insularity of habitat patches within geographic provinces, and by natural and man-caused fragmentation of vegetation within and among geographic provinces. For example, few Spotted Owls occur in the western Washington Lowlands where nearly all old forests have been logged and replaced with young forests (USDI 1992a, Gutiérrez 1994a). As a result of the natural and man-caused fragmentation of habitat, Spotted Owls may exhibit a metapopulation structure in some parts of their range (Gutiérrez and Harrison *in press*).

BEHAVIOR

Spotted Owls are territorial. However, the fact that home ranges of adjacent pairs overlap (Forsman et al. 1984, Solis and Gutiérrez 1990) suggests that the area defended is smaller than the areas used for foraging. Territorial defense is primarily effected by hooting calls, barking calls, and/or shrill whistles (Forsman et al. 1984, Fitton 1991). Because they respond readily to imitations of their calls, Spotted Owls are relatively easy to locate (Forsman 1983, Franklin et al. *this volume*).

Northern Spotted Owls are monogamous and usually form long-term pair bonds. "Divorces" occur but are relatively uncommon. There are no known examples of polygyny in this owl, although associations of 3 or more birds have been reported (Forsman et al. 1984, Gutiérrez et al. 1995). Males and females divide nesting duties, with the male providing food to nesting females. The female does all of the incubating and brooding of owlets (Forsman 1976).

Median home range sizes of Northern Spotted Owls range from 5.7–40.2 km² for owl pairs and 3.4–38.2 km² for individual owls (see summary in Gutiérrez et al. 1995). Home range size appears to be correlated with the amount of habitat fragmentation, suitable habitat, and/or primary prey (Carey et al. 1992, Zabel et al. 1995). Spotted Owls maintain smaller home ranges during the breeding season and often dramatically increase their home range size during fall and winter (Forsman 1980, Forsman et al. 1984, Sisco 1990).

HABITAT RELATIONSHIPS

HABITAT USE

Northern Spotted Owls have been detected in many different forest habitats. Forsman et al. (1984) reported owls from the following forest types: Douglas-fir (*Pseudotsuga menziesii*), western hemlock (*Tsuga heterophylla),* grand fir (*Abies grandis*), white fir (*A. concolor*), ponderosa pine (*Pinus ponderosa*), and Shasta red fir (*A. magnifica shastensis*). Owls also have been recorded using redwood (*Sequoia sempervirens*), western red cedar (*Thuja plicata*), mixed conifer-hardwood (Klamath montane), and mixed evergreen forest (Grinnell and Miller 1944, Forsman et al. 1984, LaHaye 1988, Solis and Gutiérrez 1990, Folliard 1993). In essence, most low and mid-elevation conifer or conifer/hardwood forest types within the subspecies' range have been used by the owl if they have the appropriate structure (see below). Some owls have used pure hardwood stands in the southern part of the range if a perennial water source was present.

In California, owls are found from near sea level in coastal forests to a little over 2130 m in the Cascades. The upper elevational limits at which Spotted Owls occur decrease gradually with increasing latitude in Oregon and Washington. In northern Washington and southern British Columbia, few owls occur above 1500 m elevation. In all areas, the upper elevation limits at which owls occur correspond to the transition to subalpine forest, which is characterized by relatively simple structure and severe winter weather.

HABITAT SELECTION

Studies of habitat use indicate that Northern Spotted Owls generally select mature and old-growth forest equal to or more than expected, and early seral stage forest less than expected (Forsman 1980, Forsman et al. 1984, Solis and Gutiérrez 1990, Sisco 1990, Carey et al. 1990, 1992). Individual owls may show variation in the general pattern, with some owls using intermediate-aged stands (50–100 yrs old) in proportion to, or more than, expected. Several landscape level studies indicate that Northern Spotted Owls select habitats that have a significantly higher proportion of mature/old-growth forests around nests and roosts than is randomly available (Ripple et al. 1991, Lemkuhl and Raphael 1993, Hunter et al. 1995).

Ward (1990) found that Spotted Owls foraged in areas that had lower variance in prey densities (prey were more predictable in occurrence) within older forest and near ecotones of old forest and younger brush seral stages. Presumably owls foraging in edge areas might encounter prey that

ventured into the older forest. Carey et al. (1992) and Carey and Peeler (1995) found that owls occupying fragmented landscapes had larger home ranges. When prey communities were dominated by flying squirrels (*Glaucomys sabrinus*), Spotted Owls apparently depleted some local flying squirrel populations (Carey et al. 1992). Carey et al. (1992) suggested that Spotted Owls not only have to forage within many patches but must also "monitor" prey recovery within depleted patches to efficiently use their home ranges. Finally, Zabel et al. (1995) showed that Northern Spotted Owl home ranges are larger where flying squirrels are the predominant prey and, conversely, are smaller where woodrats (*Neotoma* spp.) are the predominant prey.

Habitat structure

Spotted Owls select roosts that have more complex vegetation structure than forests generally available to them (Forsman 1976, Barrows and Barrows 1978, Forsman 1980, Solis 1983, Forsman et al. 1984, Chavez-Léon 1989, Sisco 1990, Solis and Gutiérrez 1990). These habitats are usually multi-layered forests having high canopy closure and large diameter trees in the overstory. In northwestern California, roosts usually are found on the lower third of slopes near streams (Blakesley et al. 1992). Complex vegetation or association with streams may facilitate thermoregulation by maintaining lower ambient stand temperature and providing a variety of perch sites which may allow owls to select cooler microclimates (Forsman 1976, Barrows and Barrows 1978, Barrows 1981, Solis 1983, Forsman et al. 1984).

Northern Spotted Owls nest almost exclusively in trees. Like roosts, nest sites are found in forests having complex structure dominated by large diameter trees (Forsman et al. 1984, LaHaye 1988). Even in forests that have been previously logged, owls select forests having a structure (i.e., larger trees, greater canopy closure) different than forests generally available to them (Folliard 1993, Buchanan et al. 1995). Nests are usually platforms (e.g., old raptor nests, debris accumulations), or cavities in large trees. The proportion of nest types used apparently is related to availability; platforms comprise a higher proportion of nests in disturbed or young forests, whereas nests in tree cavities tend to predominate in old forests (Forsman et al. 1984, LaHaye 1988, Buchanan et al. 1993, Folliard 1993).

Foraging habitat is the most variable of all habitats used by territorial owls (Thomas et al. 1990). Yet foraging habitat is still characterized by the complex structure found at nest and roost sites (Solis and Gutiérrez 1990). Owls will forage in forests with lower canopy closure and smaller trees than forests containing nests or roosts. Habitat structure at Spotted Owl nest sites found in disturbed (i.e., managed) forests is similar to habitat structure found at both foraging and nesting sites in unmanaged (i.e., unlogged forests) (Bart and Earnst 1992, Folliard 1993).

FORAGING BEHAVIOR AND FOOD HABITS

Northern Spotted Owls are perch and pounce predators (Forsman 1976). They are primarily nocturnal hunters but will opportunistically take prey during daylight hours (Laymon 1988, Sovern et al. 1994). On the basis of radio-telemetry observations and prey sampling, Carey and Peeler (1995) suggested that Northern Spotted Owls fit the description of central place foragers.

Spotted Owls eat a variety of prey, the majority of which is small and medium-sized small mammals (Marshall 1942, Forsman 1976, Barrows 1980, Solis 1983, Forsman et al. 1984, Barrows 1987, Carey et al. 1990, Thomas et al. 1990, Ward 1990). Two species dominate the diet: flying squirrels and woodrats. Flying squirrels comprise the bulk of the diet in the northern part of the subspecies' range and woodrats are the dominant prey in the southern part of the range. In addition to mammals, Spotted Owls eat birds, insects, reptiles and amphibians (Solis 1983, Forsman et al. 1984, Thomas et al. 1990).

Barrows (1985, 1987) suggested that nesting pairs of Northern Spotted Owls take more large prey (e.g., woodrats) than non-nesting pairs. However, Ward (1990) did not observe this relationship.

LIFE HISTORY CHARACTERISTICS

FECUNDITY

Although Spotted Owls occasionally breed at 1 year of age, most do not breed until they are ≥2 years old (Miller et al. 1985). Reproduction by Spotted Owls varies greatly among years, with most pairs breeding in good years, and few pairs breeding in poor years (Forsman et al. 1984, Gutiérrez et al. 1995). Annual variation in breeding may be related to weather conditions and fluctuations in prey abundance (e.g., see Zabel et al. *this volume*).

In years when they nest, Spotted Owls raise only one brood. They will on rare occasion renest if a first nest fails (Lewis and Wales 1993, Kroel and Zwank 1992, Forsman et al. *in press*). Most clutches are one or two eggs. In good years some owls raise three young. Although there are three records where California or Mexican Spotted Owls produced broods of four young (see Gutiérrez et al. 1995), Northern Spotted Owls have never been observed to produce more than three

young. The small clutch size, temporal variability in nesting success, and somewhat delayed maturation all contribute to the low fecundity of this species.

Spotted Owl pairs begin courtship activities in late February or March (Forsman 1976, Forsman et al. 1984). Early nesters may lay eggs in March, but the majority of egg laying occurs in April. Nesting phenology apparently is delayed slightly at higher elevations (Forsman et al. 1984), but it is relatively synchronous over the entire range of the subspecies. Most eggs hatch in late April or May, and the majority of young fledge in June. Owlets leave the nest when they are still weak fliers and remain dependent on their parents until late summer or early fall. Once the young disperse, pair members roost together less frequently and begin winter home range expansion (Forsman 1980, Forsman et al. 1984, Sisco 1990).

Some Spotted Owls are not territorial but either remain as residents within the territory of a pair or move among territories. These birds are referred to as "floaters." Floaters have special significance in Spotted Owl populations because they may buffer the territorial population from decline (Franklin 1992). Little is known about floaters other than that they exist. Since they are non-territorial they typically do not respond to hooting as vigorously as territorial birds.

DISPERSAL

Dispersal of juvenile Spotted Owls is obligatory. Dispersal begins in early September (rarely August) and continues into October (Gutiérrez et al. 1985, Miller 1989). The secondary sex ratio (fledged juveniles) estimated by examination of chromosomes is probably 50:50 (see Gutiérrez et al. 1995).

Initial dispersal appears to be in a random direction. However, individual birds once having left their natal territory may have strong, oriented movements (Gutiérrez et al. 1985). Individual dispersal movements can be rapid, and the birds will cross small areas of unsuitable habitat (e.g., grasslands). Some birds may exhibit philopatry but this is rare. Dispersing juveniles may establish a stable first year winter range only to continue dispersal the following spring (Miller 1989).

Primary causes of mortality in both juvenile and adult Spotted Owls are starvation and predation. Predation is most frequently caused by Great Horned Owls (*Bubo virginianus*) and Goshawks (*Accipiter gentilis*) (Forsman et al. 1984, Gutiérrez et al. 1985, Miller 1989). Arboreal hunting mustelids may also prey on eggs, and perhaps females (Gutiérrez et al. 1995). Accidents (e.g., collisions with automobiles or tree limbs) also account for some mortality (Gutiérrez et al. 1985).

Carey et al. (1992) demonstrated that owls occupying areas with more fragmented habitat had larger home ranges than owls found in more contiguous habitat. They hypothesized that these owls would incur a greater energetic cost in hunting a larger home range. A higher energetic cost could negatively affect either reproduction or survival.

The Barred Owl, which is gradually invading the range of the Spotted Owl, may compete with Spotted Owls for space and food (Hamer 1988), thereby reducing survival of Spotted Owls. Although relationships between Barred Owls and Spotted Owls are poorly documented, there is evidence that Barred Owls may, in some cases, usurp the territories of Spotted Owls (Hamer 1988).

SUMMARY

The Northern Spotted Owl is widespread in the Pacific Northwest, occurring in most forested portions of physiographic provinces within its range. It is strictly a forest dwelling species rarely venturing into open habitat unless it is dispersing. Structural features of forests used for roosting, nesting, and foraging are similar. All of these habitats have diverse vegetation structure. However, a broader range of habitats are used for foraging than are used for nesting and roosting.

In addition, both disturbed (e.g., those previously logged or burned) and undisturbed (usually mature/old-growth conifer forests) habitats used by owls show strong structural similarity. In general, Spotted Owls select habitats with large trees and more complex structure than is available to them at a particular locality.

Northern Spotted Owls are monogamous breeders with low fecundity and high survival rates. They are territorial and tend to form long-term pair bonds. Breeding occurs irregularly.

Because of their specificity for certain kinds of habitat, low fecundity, long life span, and apparent negative response to fragmentation and habitat loss (Forsman et al. 1984, Forsman et al. 1988, Carey et al. 1992, Johnson 1992), it should not be surprising that this subspecies was a candidate for population decline following extensive habitat disturbance (Thomas et al. 1990, USDI 1990, 1992). The forests that the owl inhabits also contain extremely valuable timber (Simberloff 1987). This combination of factors has led to the Northern Spotted Owl being one of the most extensively and intensively studied birds in the world.

ACKNOWLEDGMENTS

E. Forsman, M. Raphael and C. de Sobrino reviewed this paper. G. Barrowclough and J. Groth provided information on owl genetics. Funding was provided by the U.S. Forest Service (Contract # 53–91S8-4-FW20).

Key words: behavior, diet, distribution, habitat use, home range, nesting, Northern Spotted Owl, populations, *Strix occidentalis caurina,* reproduction.

Studies in Avian Biology No. 17:6–11, 1996.

HISTORY OF DEMOGRAPHIC STUDIES IN THE MANAGEMENT OF THE NORTHERN SPOTTED OWL

R. J. Gutiérrez, Eric D. Forsman, Alan B. Franklin, and
E. Charles Meslow

INTRODUCTION

The natural history of the Northern Spotted Owl (*Strix occidentalis caurina*) has been well documented because of its association with late seral stage forests in the Pacific Northwest (Gutiérrez et al. 1995). Conservation of the Northern Spotted Owl has been an extremely contentious issue among environmentalists, timber industry groups, land managers, wildlife managers, and scientists because of the great economic value of the trees within its habitat (Forsman and Meslow 1986, Simberloff 1987, Thomas et al. 1990, Thomas et al. 1993a,b, USDI 1992b, Harrison et al. 1993). The controversy began in the early 1970's shortly after the first comprehensive studies of the owl were initiated in Oregon and California (Forsman 1976, Gould 1977). Initially, the primary concern was that logging of mature and old-growth forests was a serious threat to the owl (USDI 1973, Forsman 1976). Harvest of old-growth forests continued on federal lands in the Pacific Northwest at high levels during the 1970's and 1980's despite growing environmental conflict. As the owl's habitat gradually declined, management options decreased, litigation increased, and a plethora of committees, task forces, and work groups attempted to find biologically and socially acceptable solutions to the dilemma (Meslow 1993). The situation became especially acrimonious in 1989, when a series of lawsuits filed by environmental groups essentially halted the sale or harvest of old forests on federal lands within the range of the Northern Spotted Owl (e.g., Seattle Audubon vs Evans 1989, Portland Audubon vs Lujan 1987, Lane County Audubon Society vs Jamison 1991).

The Northern Spotted Owl was federally listed as threatened in 1990 on the basis of three findings by the U.S. Fish and Wildlife Service (USDI 1990): (1) suitable forest habitat was declining throughout its range, (2) populations showed declining trends, and (3) existing regulatory mechanisms were not adequate to protect the owl. Listing of the owl was a particularly sensitive issue because protection measures for federally listed species apply to all lands, regardless of ownership.

In response to the need for owl management strategies, wildlife scientists have made extensive use of empirical data from mark-recapture and telemetry studies to estimate vital rates of Spotted Owls (e.g., Thomas et al. 1990, USDI 1990, Anderson and Burnham 1992). These studies have been used to evaluate population trends and to parameterize theoretical population models that have been used to compare the relative performance of different management strategies. Therefore, we have two objectives in this chapter. First, we provide a synopsis of the influence of these studies on the evolution of owl and forest management plans in the Pacific Northwest to provide context to the demographic studies in the following chapters. Second, we provide a brief review of some of the recent landmark events in the conservation of the owl.

HISTORICAL ROLE OF DEMOGRAPHY IN SPOTTED OWL CONSERVATION

Early conservation efforts for the Northern Spotted Owl were justified primarily on the basis of the strong association between the owl and old forests, and on data suggesting a decline in numbers of sites occupied by owls, concurrent with harvest of old forests (e.g., Forsman et al. 1984). However, during the last decade, the focus of research has shifted from estimating owl numbers and densities to estimating trends in reproduction and survival. This shift in emphasis was appropriate because the link between habitat loss and population trends based on fitness criteria (e.g., survival and reproduction) was considered a more reliable measure of population performance (see Van Horne 1983).

The Northern Spotted Owl issue has been unique among endangered species conservation problems because scientists and wildlife managers knew after almost two decades of research that a relatively large population of Spotted Owls existed in the wild and that, although considerably reduced, the habitat of the owl was still relatively widespread. Thus, the primary questions that scientists were asked to address were "how many Spotted Owls are needed to maintain viable populations?" and "are Spotted Owls really declining as a result of habitat loss?" Answers to these questions required a thorough understanding of owl population dynamics (Dawson et al. 1987).

To provide information on population vital rates, a series of five independent, but closely coordinated, demographic studies were initiated within the range of the owl between 1985–1987 (Anderson and Burnham 1992). Investigators collaborated to ensure that data were collected consistently, with the proximal intention of estimating trends in populations and the ultimate goal of developing a better understanding of factors regulating and affecting Spotted Owl populations. Therefore, the emphasis in these studies was on the demographic processes (especially birth and death rates).

Consistency among the studies was achieved by the shared development of techniques and protocols by researchers for surveys, banding, and determination of reproductive success (see Forsman 1983, Franklin et al. *this volume*). The ability to achieve consistency was due, in part, to the traits of the owl (e. g., territorial, site tenacious, and responsive to imitated vocalizations). Because all researchers whose papers compose this compendium used similar techniques and protocols, results from different studies allowed the use of statistically powerful meta-analyses (Fernandez-Duque and Valeggia 1994) to examine range-wide trends in population parameters (Anderson and Burnham 1992, Burnham et al. 1994b).

In addition to the five original demographic studies, at least ten additional demographic studies of Spotted Owls were initiated between 1989–1992. The 11 studies represented in the following chapters occurred in most of the physiographic provinces within the range of the owl (Figure 1). Between 1983–1993, researchers on the various study areas banded over 7,000 Northern Spotted Owls. Collectively, these studies constitute the largest detailed population dynamics study based on mark-recapture methods of a predatory bird ever conducted.

The Spotted Owl controversy has resulted in a proliferation of mathematical population models designed to investigate the hypothetical responses of owl populations to different kinds of landscape management. Lande (1987, 1988) first explored extinction theory relative to Spotted Owls. Noon and Biles (1990) then used models to examine the sensitivity of the finite rate of population change to estimated vital rates. Territory cluster models, spatially explicit population models, and dispersal models also have been developed to explore conservation strategies for Spotted Owls (e.g., Thomas et al. 1990, Lamberson et al. 1992, Carroll and Lamberson 1993, McKelvey et al. 1993, Boyce et al. 1994, Raphael et al. 1994, Bart 1995).

We emphasize that population models and theory have been used primarily to examine hypothetical population performance under different sets of assumptions about landscapes and

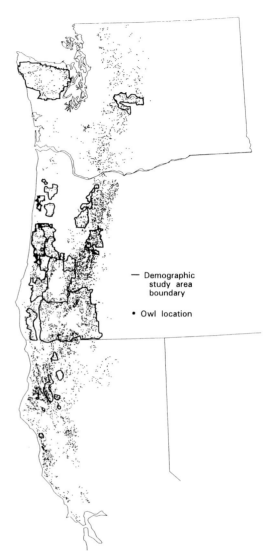

FIGURE 1. Location of known territorial Spotted Owl pairs, single owls, and demographic study areas in the Pacific Northwest.

behavior. They cannot be regarded as definitive analyses of population processes or performance. Nevertheless, demographic information and population models have become "weapons of choice" among competing advocacy groups (see below). The distinction between population modeling and population analysis is blurred in the mind of the public. The first is an abstraction and the latter is an objective assessment of empirical data. Population models are constructed by depicting, mathematically, the characteristics of a population and then examining the hypothetical population behavior under a variety of assumptions. They can be simple or complex depending on the number of parameters used and their purpose. Models can be constructed without knowledge or estimates of the actual parameter values. That is, one can guess at the value or limit of specific parameters. Therefore, population models can be far from reality if the parameters used to qualify the model are incorrect. On the other hand, population analyses, such as those represented by the following chapters, are based on objective evaluation of the life history information of the bird derived by capturing, marking, and resighting the same birds over long periods of time. It is the latter scientific process that currently drives inferences about the status of the Northern Spotted Owl, and is the subject of the chapters in this volume.

USE OF DEMOGRAPHIC DATA IN MANAGEMENT PLANS

THE 1988 FINAL ENVIRONMENTAL IMPACT STATEMENT FOR THE NORTHWEST REGION OF THE U.S. FOREST SERVICE

The first attempt to use demographic information for management was a truncated life table analysis based on preliminary estimates of vital rates derived from mark-recapture studies of banded owls and telemetry studies of juvenile owls (USDA 1988). The risk of population decline was evaluated under a set of alternative management strategies. The efficacy of the proposed management strategy (a series of widely spaced 400-ha habitat islands managed for individual owl pairs) was considered poor based on this analysis. Litigation (Seattle Audubon vs Evans 1989) forced abandonment of this management strategy primarily because the demographic analysis indicated a poor long-term prognosis for the owl population.

THE INTERAGENCY SCIENTIFIC COMMITTEE (ISC)

In 1989 a group of scientists was selected by the affected Federal agencies charged with managing Spotted Owls to develop a scientifically credible conservation plan for Northern Spotted Owls on federal lands (Thomas et al. 1990). This team initially addressed the problem by asking four questions, two of which were related to demography: (1) are Spotted Owl populations declining?, and (2) are there gaps in the distribution of owls resulting from human-caused factors? The ISC concluded that the answer to these questions was "yes." The ISC proposed a conservation strategy that included a system of relatively large habitat conservation areas distributed across the range of the owl. Demographic information was used to estimate theoretically the minimum size of reserves necessary to maintain short-term

(<100 years) population stability as well as to evaluate scenarios of range-wide distributions of owls. Although criticized as inadequate by some scientists and environmental groups (e.g., Harrison et al. 1993), the conservation strategy proposed by the ISC served as the model for a series of subsequent owl and old-growth forest conservation plans. The USDA Forest Service issued a directive to manage in a manner "not inconsistent with" the ISC plan, but litigation forced the agency to broaden the management plan to include all late-successional forest species as well (Seattle Audubon Society vs. Mosley civil case No. C92–479WD).

THE NORTHERN SPOTTED OWL LISTING DECISION

A petition to list the Northern Spotted Owl under the Endangered Species Act was filed with the U.S. Fish and Wildlife Service in 1987. The U.S. Fish and Wildlife Service completed a status review in December 1987 and concluded that listing was not warranted. This decision was challenged in U.S. District Court in 1988 (Northern Spotted Owl and Seattle Audubon Society vs. Hodel, civil case No. C88–573Z). The court ruled that the decision to not list the owl was arbitrary and capricious, and instructed the Service to reexamine the issue (see GAO 1989 for a review). Following a review of the evidence by another status review team and a listing review team (Anderson et al. 1990), the Northern Spotted Owl was listed as "threatened" in 1990 (USDI 1990). Habitat loss, apparent population declines, and failure of existing regulatory mechanisms to protect the owl were the primary reasons cited for listing. Information gathered from demographic studies was used extensively by the teams to evaluate the population status of the owl.

SCIENTIFIC PANEL ON LATE-SUCCESSIONAL FOREST ECOSYSTEMS REPORT TO THE U.S. HOUSE OF REPRESENTATIVES

In 1991, following a request from two committees in the House of Representatives, a team of four scientists was formed to develop a series of alternative strategies for the management of mature and old-growth forests in the Pacific Northwest (Johnson et al. 1991). This team developed 14 different alternatives for the management of old forests, 12 of which were based on a network of large reserves similar to the reserve design proposed by the ISC for Spotted Owls. The size and spacing of the proposed reserves were heavily influenced by the analyses of owl demography conducted by the ISC, and by consideration for Marbled Murrelets (*Brachyramphus marmoratum*) and fish. None of the options proposed by the panel was ever officially adopted. However, these options played a major role in subsequent plans for owls and old forests.

THE NORTHERN SPOTTED OWL RECOVERY PLAN

A Northern Spotted Owl recovery team was formed in 1990. The team was unique among recovery teams because it was appointed by the Secretary of Interior and the majority of the team members were non-scientists (Gutiérrez 1994b). The recovery team used the ISC reserve design as a working model for the design proposed in the recovery plan. However, the recovery team departed from the standard format of identifying numerical targets as de-listing criteria. Rather, the de-listing criteria were based on trends in demographic rates within specific physiographic provinces (USDI 1992b). In other words, population processes were emphasized rather than simple numbers. This departure from tradition was necessary because (1) Spotted Owls were still relatively numerous in most provinces, (2) census information was incomplete, and likely to remain so, (3) logging was still allowed under the plan, and (4) the existing demography studies demonstrated that owl trends could be monitored.

Anderson and Burnham (1992) analyzed the extant demographic data for the recovery team. Their results indicated that Spotted Owl adult female mortality was accelerating over the period during which the demography studies occurred. This result directly led a Federal Court judge to reject the 1992 U.S. Forest Service Spotted Owl EIS.

The Recovery Plan, like the ISC plan, assumed that owl populations would reach a new lower carrying capacity where they would eventually stabilize. Thus, it was likely that owl numbers would continue to decline in the near term or until habitat recovery within designated conservation areas balanced loss of habitat outside of conservation areas. The recovery plan was completed in 1992 but was never formally released by the USDI.

THE ENDANGERED SPECIES COMMITTEE

During the recovery planning process, the Director of the Bureau of Land Management (BLM) requested that a cabinet-level committee be convened to determine the fate of 44 proposed timber sales on BLM lands in western Oregon that had been found by the U.S. Fish and Wildlife Service to "jeopardize" the Northern Spotted Owl. After an evidentiary hearing in January 1992 before an administrative law judge, the committee acted to protect all but 13 of the sales from logging. The primary reasons for the continued protection was the potential negative de-

mographic consequences to the owl population. Of particular concern was the potential loss of habitat connectivity between physiographic provinces. The demographic information derived from the population studies was key to the discussion of possible demographic consequences of the proposed logging. The 13 sales were subsequently withdrawn from logging by the BLM.

THE SCIENTIFIC ANALYSIS TEAM (SAT)

In response to instructions from a federal court judge, the Chief of the Forest Service convened a panel of scientists to assess the viability of species associated with old forests on Forest Service lands within the range of the Northern Spotted Owl. This was the first time that the Forest Service had formally attempted to evaluate proposed plans for the Spotted Owl in a broader ecosystem context. After examining the demographic data on the Spotted Owl, the SAT concluded that ". . . demographic rates or trends observed during a prolonged period of habitat loss will provide little insight as to whether the population will eventually reach a new stable equilibrium when the rate of habitat loss is equaled by the rate of habitat gain . . ." (Thomas et al. 1993a:192). This opinion was in stark contrast to the opinions of some other scientists and environmental advocates who had suggested that the negative trends in demographic data were evidence that proposed agency plans for the owl were inadequate (e.g., Harrison et al. 1993).

THE FOREST ECOSYSTEM MANAGEMENT ASSESSMENT TEAM (FEMAT)

In 1993, the Clinton Administration initiated an effort to resolve the Spotted Owl/old-growth forest impasse by appointing a team of scientists to develop a comprehensive plan for the management of late successional forests on federal lands in the Pacific Northwest (Thomas et al. 1993b). The ten management options proposed by the FEMAT included provisions for various levels of protection for Spotted Owls as well as other late seral stage forest species. The option selected by the Administration (referred to as "Option 9") was similar to several previous plans (Thomas et al. 1990, Johnson et al. 1991, USDI 1992b), with some modifications in reserve design and major changes in recommendations for management of forest lands between the reserve network. Although FEMAT discussed demographic data from capture-recapture studies in their analysis, they concluded that current demographic data alone were not appropriate to assess the outcome of a management plan that would not produce the desired mix of habitats until approximately 100 years after implementation. After release of the FEMAT report, some scientists and environmental activists suggested that the negative trends in population parameters reported by Anderson and Burnham (1992) were sufficient to warrant an immediate cessation of all logging of owl habitat (e.g., Harrison et al. 1993). This view was supported by a group of 14 scientists who wrote a letter to the Secretaries of Interior and Agriculture in September 1993, requesting that implementation of Option 9 be delayed until a full review of all existing demographic information on the Northern Spotted Owl was conducted.

THE 1993 FORT COLLINS WORKSHOP

Several industry groups and timber companies began population studies of Spotted Owls in 1990–1991. These studies paralleled other studies on Federal lands, and resulted in relatively large numbers of owls being located and banded in young and mid-aged (40–70 years) forests in some areas (most notably northwestern California and the east slope of the Cascades in Washington). These findings were interpreted by some as an indication that Spotted Owls were thriving in young forests (e.g., Easterbrook 1994), and motivated a de-listing petition for Spotted Owls in California (California Forestry Association 1993). As a result of this de-listing petition and the previously mentioned September 1993 letter from a group of concerned scientists, the Secretaries of Interior and Agriculture requested in October 1993 that a workshop be immediately convened to update and analyze all demographic data on the Northern Spotted Owl.

All researchers having three or more years of demographic information were invited to attend. Eleven research groups participated. One industry group participated initially, but withdrew their results before the end of the workshop. Two other invited industry groups did not present their data for analysis. The results of the analyses conducted at Fort Collins were provided to the U.S. Forest Service and Bureau of Land Management for inclusion in their planning documents. The results of the individual study area analyses and the meta-analysis of the entire data set form the basis for the individual chapters that follow this review.

THE 1994 U.S. FOREST SERVICE AND BLM FINAL SUPPLEMENTAL ENVIRONMENTAL IMPACT STATEMENT (FEIS)

In February 1994, the USDA Forest Service, USDI Bureau of Land Management, and several other federal agencies released a joint FEIS for the management of late successional forests within the range of the Northern Spotted Owl (USDA and USDI 1994a). A formal presentation of the summary data from the Fort Collins demographic workshop was included in the FEIS (Burnham et al. 1994b). The Record of Decision for the FEIS (USDA and USDI 1994b) was to proceed with implementation of Option 9 (now Alternative 9) on Federal lands, with some adjustments to improve dispersal habitat and to protect additional pairs of owls in some provinces. Despite the negative population trends estimated from the demographic data examined at Fort Collins, it was the opinion of the FEIS Team that the owl population would likely reach equilibrium once the habitat conditions specified in Alternative 9 were attained. A spatially explicit population model (McKelvey et al. 1993), parameterized with demographic data, was used to evaluate the performance of the preferred alternative assuming a range of birth and death rates.

ADVERSARIAL PROCEEDINGS

Demographic information and estimates of habitat loss have been central to litigation and procedural arguments levied by competing advocacy groups (i.e., environmental and industry groups). Demographic trends have been a critical element in this process. Some scientists and environmental activists have relied on demographic trend information and estimates of vital rates derived from demographic studies to suggest that proposed plans do not adequately protect the Spotted Owl (e.g., Harrison et al. 1993, Lande et al. 1994). Other scientists and industry advocates have countered by suggesting that the demographic data may be flawed or that models used to analyze the data may be overly simplistic or inappropriate (e.g., Boyce 1987, Boyce et al. 1994, Bart 1995). In addition, some have tended to emphasize the results of models on demographic processes (e.g., Lande et al. 1994), whereas other groups have emphasized the relatively large size of the owl population (e.g., California Forestry Association 1993). Some scientists associated with the demographic studies of Spotted Owls have assumed a more cautious position, suggesting that there is uncertainty regarding interpretation of the data, and that all of the protagonists should avoid extreme positions (e.g., Thomas et al. 1993a, USDA and USDI 1994a).

SUMMARY

Management of the Northern Spotted Owl is an extremely contentious conservation issue involving many interest groups with divergent views about how the needs of the owl and society should be balanced. It has become a biopolitical cornerstone of large scale conservation policy. Wildlife scientists have played a key role in the development of conservation strategies for the owl and have made extensive use of empirical data from mark-recapture studies for assessing trends in vital rates and for parameterizing theoretical population models. Demographic information, gathered from a series of studies across the range of the owl represents the most detailed population dynamics study of a predatory bird ever undertaken. This information has been used in unique ways and has strongly influenced the conservation of the owl and its habitat. The Spotted Owl issue is unique among endangered species problems because owls were widespread and relatively common over much of their range when demographic studies began. The assessment of birth and death rates to estimate population trends was necessary because estimating changes in owl habitat, or in overall numbers of owls, were insufficient tools to adequately assess population trends. In essence, biologists were asked not only to estimate the status of different owl populations but also to estimate how much logging could continue while local populations declined. Because the owl primarily inhabits old-growth and mature forests on public lands, declining populations have resulted in substantial restrictions in logging on public lands. Decisions to restrict harvest have been considerably influenced by demographic studies of Spotted Owls conducted between 1985–1993. We present a brief history of the role of demographic data in the development of management strategies for the owl.

In addition to the utility of demographic information for the solution of a resource problem, these studies have stimulated theoretical work in such areas as extinction thresholds, population dynamics, dispersal, and reserve design (Lande 1987, 1988; Doak 1989; Thomas et al. 1990; Franklin 1992; Lamberson et al. 1992, 1994). Thus, the demographic studies in the following chapters serve as an example of the effectiveness of coordinated research to problem solving and the advancement of science.

ACKNOWLEDGMENTS

We thank D. Kristan, L. Brennan, C. de Sobrino, M. Raphael, S. DeStefano, and two anonymous reviewers for their comments on the manuscript. Financial support was provided by the USDA Forest Service, USDI Fish and Wildlife Service, USDI Bureau of Land Management, State of California Resources Agency, California Department of Fish and Game, Oregon Department of Fish and Wildlife, and Washington Department of Wildlife and Fish.

Key words: conservation strategies, demography, Northern Spotted Owl, *Strix occidentalis caurina.*

Studies in Avian Biology No. 17:12–20, 1996.

METHODS FOR COLLECTING AND ANALYZING DEMOGRAPHIC DATA ON THE NORTHERN SPOTTED OWL

ALAN B. FRANKLIN, DAVID R. ANDERSON, ERIC D. FORSMAN, KENNETH P. BURNHAM, AND FRANK W. WAGNER

INTRODUCTION

The collection of demographic data reflecting birth and death rates is important for understanding the life-history characteristics and population trends of the Northern Spotted Owl (*Strix occidentalis caurina*). Demographic parameters generally take the form of age-, sex-, and time-specific survival probabilities and fecundity rates. The first step in assessing the validity of inferences derived from such data is demonstration of an appropriate study design, as well as the field and analytical methods used. In addition, the methods used to collect demographic data should be repeatable, logistically feasible, and support the internal validity of the study design. Both study design and methods used to collect demographic data in the field must support the assumptions of models used to analyze those data for valid inferences to be made.

Demographic studies of Northern Spotted Owls reported in this volume are unique in several ways. First, these studies have been able to incorporate capture-recapture modeling approaches to estimate survival probabilities. These types of models have been rarely used with raptors, primarily because of sample size limitations (see Blondel et al. 1990 for reviews on different avian taxa). Second, standardized methods have been incorporated across all studies reported in this volume. This allowed for consistency in data collection and, hence, consistency in interpretation of results across the range of the owl. Third, the spatial extent and spatial replication of demographic studies allowed for broader inferences across the species' range in a meta-analysis (see Burnham et al. *this volume*).

The purpose of this paper is to present common elements of field and analytical methods used to estimate demographic parameters and population trends in Northern Spotted Owls as reported in this volume. We provide general descriptions of study areas, methods of data collection, and analytical methods used to estimate demographic parameters. Specific methods used in individual studies which depart from this general overview are described in the specific chapters pertaining to those studies. We also address important assumptions pertinent to the analytical models used and the allowable scope of inferences. Although confined to demographic studies on the Northern Spotted Owl, we feel this paper will also provide a framework useful for similar research with other raptors. Terminology and symbols used throughout this volume are presented in the Appendix.

STUDY AREAS

This volume includes data from 11 study areas in northern California, Oregon and Washington (Fig. 1). Combined area of these study areas was 45,846 km² (Table 1). All of the study areas were primarily located on public lands administered by the U. S. Forest Service, U. S. Bureau of Land Management, and National Park Service. Inclusion of privately-owned lands in most study areas occurred incidentally as "inholdings" within public lands. However, most study areas on Bureau of Land Management districts included nearly equal mixtures of federal and non-federal lands. Inferences concerning Spotted Owl populations were restricted primarily to federally administered lands within the range of the owl except for the Bureau of Land Management studies (Coos Bay, Eugene BLM, Salem BLM, Roseburg BLM, and South Cascades/Siskiyou; see Fig. 1) which contained large amounts of private land. The 11 study areas encompassed about 27% of the 98,967 km² of federally administered land within the range of the Northern Spotted Owl and about 20% of the 230,690 km² range of the Northern Spotted Owl (USDA and USDI 1994).

Study area selection in all the owl demographic studies was based primarily on logistic considerations and objectives of funding agencies. As a result, study areas were not randomly or systematically distributed across the geographic range of the owl. Most studies were concentrated in the coastal mountains of California, Oregon, and Washington with fewer studies in the Cascade Mountains. We do not know if this uneven distribution of study areas caused bias in the overall evaluation of Spotted Owl populations across their range. However, the overall opinion of the research biologists at the Fort Collins workshop (see Gutiérrez et al. *this volume*) was that the broad representation of study areas from different forest types and management regimes was probably reflective of the overall condition of Spotted Owl populations on federal lands.

Of the 11 study areas, eight included intensively surveyed areas referred to as Density Study Areas (DSAs) (Table 1). DSAs were 204–1011 km² in size and established *a priori* with boundaries based on major topographical features and ownership boundaries. All habitats within DSAs were intensively surveyed for Northern Spotted Owls each year (Franklin et al. 1990), including at least two replicate surveys of each area each year. Minimum size for DSAs was established based on criteria outlined in Franklin et al. (1990) to minimize bias in density estimates due to edge effects. Maximum size for DSAs was dictated by the investigator's ability to survey adequately the entire area given funding and logistical constraints. Outside of the DSAs, no attempt was made to survey entire study areas each year. Rather, surveys focused on specific sites that had a history of occupancy by Spotted Owls. A "site" was defined as an area where Spotted Owls had exhibited territorial behavior in response to surveys on two or more occasions separated by one or more weeks within a given year. Individual sites were surveyed each year regardless of whether they were occupied by Spotted Owls. The use of the two types of survey design (DSAs versus site-specific surveys) reflected a trade-off between gathering additional information on movements and density in the DSAs and increasing sample size and regional scope in the larger study areas.

Two important assumptions regarding study area selection are: (1) study areas are representative of the larger area to which inferences are made, and (2) banded owls within a study area are representative of the population within that area. Whereas the first assumption can be objectively examined by comparison of landscape composition within and outside study area boundaries, the second assumption can not be

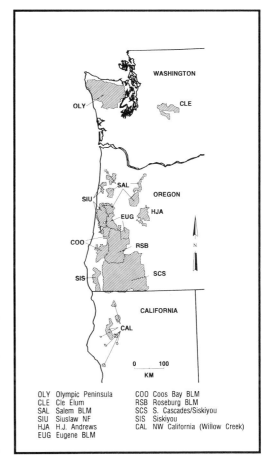

FIGURE 1. Location of 11 study areas used to estimate demographic characteristics of Northern Spotted Owls.

TABLE 1. DESCRIPTION OF THE 11 DEMOGRAPHIC STUDY AREAS FOR THE NORTHERN SPOTTED OWL

Study area (location)	Acronym	Study area size (km²)	DSA size (km²)	Years of banding
Willow Creek (NW California)	CAL	1,784	292	1985–1993
Roseburg (Oregon)	RSB	6,044	310	1985–1993
			326	
S. Cascades & Siskiyou Mts. (Oregon)	SCS	15,216	1,011	1985–1993
			300	
			491	
Salem BLM (Oregon)	SAL	3,249	—	1986–1993
H. J. Andrews (Oregon)	HJA	1,075	300	1987–1993
Olympic Peninsula (Washington)	OLY	8,145	355	1987–1993
Cle Elum (Washington)	CLE	1,763	196	1989–1993
Eugene BLM (Oregon)	EUG	2,082	273	1989–1993
Coos Bay (Oregon)	COO	2,477	—	1990–1993
Siuslaw NF (Oregon)	SIU	2,749	676	1990–1993
Siskiyou NF (Oregon)	SIS	1,262	—	1990–1993

tested. However, there are three lines of evidence which suggest that assumptions 1 and 2 were probably met. First, the 11 demographic studies encompassed over a quarter of the federal lands within the geographic range of the owl and were reasonably well-spaced throughout that range. This suggests that a large portion of the variability present within the owl's range was probably captured. Second, 3,616 territorial individuals (exclusive of 2,443 juveniles) were marked during these studies (Burnham et al. *this volume*) out of a known population of about 6,000 territorial individuals on federal lands in Washington, Oregon, and California (U.S. Dept. Interior 1992). While not all of these marked individuals were alive at the same time, a large portion of the range-wide population was probably marked, especially considering the high survival rates for $\geq$ 1-year old owls (Burnham et al. *this volume*). Third, all research biologists, whose study areas are represented in this volume, agreed that their study areas were not grossly different from habitat amounts and configurations in the matrix surrounding their study areas.

METHODS

FIELD METHODS

The general design of the demographic studies, described in the following chapters, consisted of tracking marked individuals and their associated life history traits over time. Each study area was annually surveyed to locate both marked and unmarked owls. Once owls were located, they were individually marked using unique color bands and numbered U. S. Fish and Wildlife Service (USFWS) bands. Age, sex, and reproductive status of individuals were determined with standardized techniques as detailed below. Thus, for each year, individuals were located, assigned an age-class, identified, and assigned an estimate of their reproductive output.

Surveys

Annual surveys for Spotted Owls were conducted between 1 March and 1 September. Spotted Owls were located using vocal imitations or recorded playback of their calls to elicit responses (Forsman 1983). Both day and night surveys were used to locate owls (Forsman 1983). The primary method for surveying at night was calling for $\geq$ 10 min from a series of stations spaced 0.3–0.5 km along forest roads or trails. "Leapfrog" surveys were also used where two observers alternated walking along continuous transects. Owls were visually located by conducting calling surveys during the day to identify them and determine their reproductive status. Daytime surveys usually focused on areas where owls had previ-

ously responded during nighttime surveys or where owls had been located in previous years. Most daytime surveys were conducted while hiking cross-country.

Survey effort generally increased in the first few years of each study after which it leveled off. A site was assumed unoccupied if Spotted Owls were not detected after 3–6 night surveys, spaced $\geq$ 4 days apart, that completely covered 4–16 km^2 around locations where owls had been previously located during the day. In areas outside of DSAs, the area searched for owls depended on locations of adjacent pairs of owls and topography. Individuals were considered territorial if they exhibited vocal responses to surveys within the same site on $\geq$ 2 separate occasions within the same sampling period.

Determination of sex and age

With the exception of juveniles, the sex of owls >1 year old was distinguished by calls and behavior. Males emit lower-pitched calls than females and do not incubate or brood (Forsman et al. 1984). Juveniles could not be accurately sexed until 1992 when some researchers began determining sexes of juveniles through examination of sex chromosomes in blood samples (Dvořák et al. 1992; see chapters on individual studies).

Spotted owls were aged by plumage characteristics (Forsman 1981, Moen et al. 1991) either visually, using binoculars, or when captured. Four age-classes were used: juvenile (J), 1-year old (S1), 2-year old (S2), and $\geq$3-years old (A). Juveniles were fledged young-of-the-year that were characterized by gray, downy body plumage and retrices with triangular, tufted, white tips through their first summer. One-year old birds possess basic body plumage but are distinguished by tufted white tips on their retrices. Two-year old birds lose the tufts on the tips of the retrices but retain the triangular white tips until the retrices are first molted during the third summer of life. Thereafter, they become indistinguishable from $\geq$3-year old owls that have retrices with rounded and mottled tips.

Capture and marking

Individuals were identified by initial capture, marking, and subsequent recapture or resighting of colored leg bands. Owls were captured with noose poles (Forsman 1983), snare poles, baited mist nets, or by hand. Handling time of captured owls was typically less than 20 minutes. Each owl was marked with a USFWS 7B numbered lock-on aluminum band placed on the tarso-metatarsus. A colored plastic leg band placed on the opposing tarso-metatarsus was used to identify $\geq$1-year old birds in subsequent years without recapture. Some researchers modified the color-band by adding a colored vinyl tab to increase the number of color combinations. Protocols for resighting color-marked individuals generally included blind trials where records of color combinations of owls located at a site in previous years were not examined until after a survey for that site was completed. If identification of color-marks was ambiguous, birds were recaptured and the number from the USFWS band recorded. Juveniles were marked with striped color bands indicating the year when they were captured. Cohort bands were replaced with unique color combinations when juveniles were recaptured in later years. The use of both USFWS and color bands allowed us to evaluate band loss. Only two cases of band loss were confirmed in over 6,000 marked individuals indicating the rate of band loss was very nearly zero. In some studies (see Forsman et al. *this volume,* Reid et al. *this volume,* and Wagner et al. *this volume*), radiotransmitters were used on a portion of the birds captured.

Estimation of reproductive output

We used field estimates of reproductive output (the number of young leaving the nest [fledging] per territorial female) as the basis for estimating fecundity. The average date of fledging (1 June) was considered the birth date. Once located during the day, owls were checked for reproductive activity by feeding them live mice (a procedure referred to as mousing) and observing how they behaved after mice were taken (Forsman 1983). Breeding Spotted Owls usually took such offered prey and carried it to the nest or fledged young. Non-reproductive owls either ate or cached the mice. Non-reproduction was inferred if an individual took ≥ 2 offered mice, and cached the last mouse taken, or a female did not have a well-developed brood patch during April–early May (the normal incubation period). In some cases, we also examined brood patches during the incubation period to determine if females were nesting. Territorial individuals were visited at least twice during the sampling period to determine the number of fledged young or to confirm non-reproduction using either the mousing or brood patch criteria on each visit. These techniques enabled us to characterize the reproductive output of territorial individuals as having 0, 1, 2, or 3 fledged young.

ANALYTICAL METHODS

Estimation of survival

Capture-recapture models were used to estimate age- and sex-specific survival for Northern Spotted Owls from the banding data. These models were statistical constructs used to estimate the parameters of interest from the empirical data. The statistical analysis of capture-recapture or resight sampling data was based on the theory derived by Cormack (1964), Jolly (1965), and Seber (1965) and the simplifications and generalizations published since that time (e.g., Burnham et al. 1987, Clobert et al. 1987, Pollock et al. 1990). Lebreton et al. (1992) provided a comprehensive review of these theories, with examples. The capture history (Burnham et al. 1987: 28) for each owl for each age and sex class provided the basis for parameter estimation and hypothesis testing. The capture history matrix ($\mathbf{X}$, described below in *Parameterization*) is a complete summary of the data. Estimators for all models used various summary statistics from this matrix. Owls were not included in the analysis during the time they carried back-pack transmitters because these types of transmitters may affect survival (Paton et al. 1991, Foster et al. 1992). However, owls fitted with 5-gram tail-mounted transmitters (mostly juveniles) on three study areas were included in the capture-recapture analyses because there was no evidence such small transmitters affected survival (E. Forsman, unpublished data). Owls with tail-mounted transmitters were considered recaptured only if they were located and their identity confirmed during normal calling surveys without the use of radio-telemetry. This ensured that recapture probabilities were not biased by differential detection of radio-marked birds. We assumed a 1:1 sex ratio at fledging for years where juveniles were not sexed. For each cohort of banded juveniles, the individuals subsequently recaptured were sexed and the remaining capture histories (representing individuals never captured) were arbitrarily assigned as males or females such that the total number of males and females was equal (Franklin 1992). The assumption of a 1:1 sex ratio was supported by data on juveniles sexed using chromosomal analysis (see Franklin et al. *this volume*).

Parameterization. The basic model for open mark-recapture populations is the Cormack-Jolly-Seber (CJS) model (Cormack 1964, Jolly 1965, Seber 1965) which considers only time specific survival probabilities (ϕ_i) and recapture probabilities (p_i) for k capture occasions (see Appendix for full summary of notation). These parameters are conditional on an animal being alive at the beginning of occasion i. Survival probabilities are estimated between occasion i and $i+1$ where $i = 1, 2, \ldots, k - 1$. Recapture probabilities are the probability that an animal alive on occasion i is captured (or recaptured) where $i = 2, 3, \ldots, k$ (p_1 is not defined). In the case of the Spotted Owl, "capture" is defined as physical capture of individuals or resighting of their color bands without physical capture. The p_i are nuisance parameters, but must be properly treated or estimators of survival probabilities will be biased. For example, let ϕ_1 be the survival probability between sampling occasions 1 and 2 and ϕ_2 be the survival probability between occasions 2 and 3. Therefore, for $k = 3$ capture occasions, the probability of various capture histories can be parameterized as: $\Pr\{101\} = \phi_1 q_2 \phi_2 p_3$ (where $q_i = 1 - p_i$, the probability of not being captured on occasion i) for individuals captured on the first and third, but not the second, occasion; $\Pr\{111\} = \phi_1 p_2 \phi_2 p_3$, for individuals captured on all three occasions; and $\Pr\{110\} = \phi_1 p_2 \phi_2 q_3$, for individuals captured on the first and second, but not the third, occasion. Assuming the fates of individual animals were independent and that they have the same parameters (ϕ_i and p_i), the data on first recaptures from a single released cohort has a multinomial distribution. Releases from several cohorts are merely a product of these multinomial distributions. The likelihood function follows from this expression and is the basis for statistical inference.

Parameter estimation was based on Fisher's method of maximum likelihood. This method provided estimators of parameters that were asymptotically unbiased, efficient, and normally distributed. Variances and covariances were estimated using quasi-likelihood methods where appropriate (Wedderburn 1974, Cox 1983). These methods allow year- and age-dependent variation to be included in the variance of estimators from models that assume parameters were constant over years or age classes. For example, with the CJS model for a 3-occasion survey, four possible fates were possible for owls marked and released at occasion 1: X_{111}, X_{110}, X_{100}, and X_{101}. Then the likelihood function of the unknown parameters, given the data (X) will be:

$$L(\phi_i, p_i \mid X)$$

$$= C(\phi_1 p_2 \phi_2 p_3)^{X_{111}}(\phi_1 p_2 (1-\phi_3)q_3)^{X_{110}}$$

$$(\phi_1 q_2 \phi_2 p_3)^{X_{101}}((1-\phi_1)q_2(1-\phi_2)q_3)^{X_{100}}$$

where C is the multinomial coefficient, involving the data, but not the parameters.

The analysis of multiple data sets provided extensive model building opportunities beyond the CJS model (Lebreton et al. 1992). Relationships of rates to external variables were modeled in this framework using the logit(θ) transformation which constrains $0 \leq \theta \leq 1$ as

$$\text{logit}(\theta) = \ln\left(\frac{\theta}{1-\theta}\right)$$

where θ represents either ϕ or p. Lebreton et al. (1992) and Hosmer and Lemeshow (1989) presented rationales for use of this logit-link function. Survival probability (ϕ) and recapture probability (p) could then be modeled as a linear logistic function,

$$\text{logit}(\theta_w) = \beta_0 + \beta_1(w)$$

where w is an external or dummy variable. This approach allowed both categorical (e.g., sex, groups) and continuous (e.g., linear time) covariates to be employed in modeling ϕ or p. Lebreton et al. (1992) provided examples of these approaches and more extended theory. We used programs RELEASE (Burnham et al. 1987) and SURGE (Pradel et al. 1990) for analysis of mark-recapture data.

An important consideration with survival probabilities derived from capture-recapture estimators is that $1 - \phi$ = (mortality rate + permanent emigration rate) whereas with true survival (S), $1 - S$ = mortality rate only. In order for $\phi \cong S$, permanent emigration (E) must be negligible. Therefore, $\hat{\phi}$ must be adjusted when E is substantial to reflect true survival probabilities. Some studies (see Burnham et al. *this volume*, Forsman et al. *this volume*, Reid et al. *this volume*, and Wagner et al. *this volume*) used data from radiomarked owls to adjust some estimates of ϕ for E (see Burnham et al. *this volume* for methodology).

Model notation. Model nomenclature (see Appendix) followed Lebreton et al. (1992) and can be summarized as follows. The basic CJS model has time-specificity only, which can be expressed as $\{\phi_t, p_t\}$. This notation indicates a model whose parameters have unrestricted variation solely over time (occasions). If sex (s) or group (g, e.g., where g = study area) effects are added to the model, it can be written as $\{\phi_{s*t}, p_{s*t}\}$ where parameters exhibit unrestricted variation in time within each sex class, or $\{\phi_{g*t}, p_{g*t}\}$ where there is a group effect other than sex. The asterisk (*) indicates interactions (e.g., $s*t$ indicates interactions of sex with time, as well as both main effects). Therefore, a model examining study area effects, sex effects and unrestricted time variation for 1 age-class would be denoted as $\{\phi_{g*s*t}, p_{g*s*t}\}$. Age ($a$) can also be added as a factor and combined with sex, time and group effects in the same manner. The pure age model is denoted as $\{\phi_a, p_a\}$ where parameters vary by age only and, for k occasions, $a = 1, 2, \ldots, k - 1$ ages. Models that include age restricted to classes are denoted as $a1$, $a2$, $a3, \ldots, an$ where n is the number of age-classes used. In models where p_i were age-specific for birds initially banded as juveniles, parameters are subscripted as an' where n' is the number of age-classes over which the restrictions are applied. Additive effects (i.e., no interactions considered) in models are denoted with a '+' instead of a '*'. For example, the subscript $s + t$ indicates that the subscripted parameter varies over time for both sexes but that the difference between the two sexes is constant over time; plots of logit parameter estimates over time for the two sexes would be parallel. Parameters also can be constrained as linear functions of time, denoted as T. The resulting models are similar to the classical analysis of covariance where (1) parameters subscripted as T represents one intercept and one slope estimated for the parameter over time [logit$(\phi_i) = \beta_0 + \beta_1$ (time effects)]; (2) $s + T$ represents different intercepts for each sex with a common slope [logit$(\phi_i) = \beta_0 + \beta_1$ (sex effects) $+ \beta_2$ (time effects)]; and (3) $s*T$ represents different intercepts and slopes for each sex [logit$(\phi_i) = \beta_0 + \beta_1$ (sex effects) $+ \beta_2$ (time effects) $+\beta_3$ (sex effects * time effects)]. The H_0: $\beta = 0$ for estimated slope parameters is tested using a Wald test (Carroll and Ruppert 1988, Hosmer and Lemeshow 1989) of the form:

$$\chi^2 = \frac{\hat{\beta}^2}{\widehat{\text{var}}(\hat{\beta})} \quad \text{with 1 df}$$

Tests of assumptions. Goodness of fit tests (Pollock et al. 1985, Burnham et al. 1987) were used to assess the adequacy and utility of the basic CJS model, $\{\phi_t, p_t\}$. Burnham et al. (1987) outlined the requisite assumptions as: (1) capture, handling, and release do not affect survival; (2) the number released on occasion i is known exactly; (3) there is no band loss, and no bands are misread on capture or resighting; (4) all releases and captures of owls occur in relatively brief time intervals, and recaptured birds are released immediately; (5) any unknown emigration out of a study area is permanent (e.g., owls do not become unavailable for recapture by temporarily leaving the study area); (6) the fate of each individual owl, after any known release, is independent of the fate of any other owl; (7) data sets for the various ages, sexes, and areas are statistically independent; (8) statistical analyses of the sample data are based on an appropriate model; and (9) all owls of an identifiable class (e.g., age, sex) have the same survival and capture probabilities, by study area (i.e., parameters are homogenous within subclasses of individuals). Assumption (1) was tested using TEST 3 of program RELEASE which tests whether previously released individuals have the same future fates as newly released individuals. Assumption (2) and (3) probably were met with the Northern Spotted Owl data (see *Capture and marking* section). Assumption (4) was not strictly met in that the sampling period was relatively long (3–4 months). However, $\hat{\phi}_i$ is unbiased given that the shape of the temporal distribution of releases

(TDR) is constant from year to year and bias in ϕ_i is negligible when the medians of TDR are equal even though the distribution shapes may vary (inferred from Smith and Anderson 1987). This can be tested with Kruskal-Wallis tests (Sokal and Rohlf 1981) and multi-response permutation procedures (Mielke et al. 1981). Assumption (5) was untestable although it can be evaluated qualitatively. We tested assumptions (6), (7) and (9) using TEST 2 and 3 in program RELEASE (Burnham et al. 1987). TEST 3 is sensitive to heterogeneity in ϕ_i and p_i (assumption 9), short-term marking effects (e.g., assumption 1), and failure of assumption (6). TEST 2 also tests assumptions (6) and (1) as well as assumption (7) and for temporary emigration where an individual leaves the study area for at least one year and then returns. Assumption (8) can be properly evaluated through appropriate statistical model selection criteria and procedures, as described below.

Model selection. The most critical problem in the comprehensive analysis of capture-recapture data involving several year, age, and sex classes is selecting an appropriate model to describe the data (Burnham and Anderson 1992, Burnham et al. 1995a). A model should have sufficient structure and parameters to account for significant variability in the data or the resulting estimates will likely be biased. However, if the model has too much structure or too many parameters, then precision is lost unnecessarily. Proper model selection seeks a model that is fully supported by the particular data set and, thus, has enough parameters to avoid bias but not so many that precision is lost (Principle of Parsimony; see Burnham and Anderson 1992).

Model building started with a global model of $\{\phi_{s*a*t}, p_{s*a*t}\}$ for each study area (i.e., separate $\{\phi_{a*t}, p_{a*t}\}$ for each sex). We then used Akaike's Information Criterion, AIC (Akaike 1973, Anderson et al. 1994, Burnham et al. 1994, 1995a, 1995b), to objectively select an appropriate "best" model. This criterion was defined as

$$\text{AIC} = -2\ln(L) + 2K$$

where $\ln(L)$ is the natural logarithm of the likelihood function evaluated at the maximum likelihood estimates and K is the number of estimable parameters from that model. After selection of the best model using AIC, neighboring models of interest can be further investigated using likelihood ratio tests (McCullagh and Nelder 1983) as a further aid in selecting the best model for a particular data set. This procedure tests which of two nested model is best supported by the data using H_O: the model with fewer parameters versus H_A: the model with more parameters. For example, a significant P-value resulting from a test of H_O: model $\{\phi_T\}$ versus H_A: $\{\phi_t\}$ indicates that $\{\phi_T\}$ should be retained as the best model, whereas a non-significant P-value would support retention of $\{\phi_t\}$. In the same manner, likelihood ratio tests can be used to test for specific effects, such as sex, time, and age, using identical models except that one includes the effect of interest and the other does not.

Estimation of fecundity

Age-specific fecundity (b_x) was defined for Northern Spotted Owls as the average number of female fledglings produced by a territorial female of age x (Caughley 1977). Age-specific fecundity was estimated using analysis of variance (ANOVA). Despite the integer nature of the individual data, sample sizes were sufficiently large to justify the assumptions of ANOVA. Data analysis was performed on reproductive output as the response variable using the general linear models (GLM) procedure in SAS (SAS Institute 1990) to test for significant age and time effects and interactions between effects within each study area. After analyses were performed, age-specific fecundity estimates (b_x) were calculated from estimates of mean reproductive output in each age-class by dividing those estimates by 2 to account for an assumed 1:1 sex ratio. In keeping with the 1:1 sex ratio assumption, standard errors of estimates for mean number of young fledged were divided by 2 (Goodman 1960) to estimate $SE(b_x)$.

In counting number of fledged young, we assumed that detection probabilities (analogous to p_i) of broods, and individual young within broods, after two visits was equal to 1.0. Three additional factors may introduce bias into estimates of fecundity. First, reproductively active individuals may have higher detectability than non-reproductively active individuals (e.g., Lundberg 1980). Therefore, fecundity would be biased high because fewer observations of 0 young would be recorded. Second, some fledged young experience mortality after fledging and before some pairs are checked for reproductive activity. In this case, the number of fledged young would be underestimated and, hence, biased downward. Third, some young are not banded immediately after they are counted. This would introduce a positive bias in the recruitment of first-year birds into the population ($b_x\phi_J$) because fledglings that die between the time they are counted and when the site is revisited again to band young are not included in the releases from which juvenile survival is estimated. It is unknown to what extent these competing biases cancel each other.

A cutoff date of 15 July has been proposed to deal with the second potential source of bias (Max et al. 1990). We examined the utility of this cutoff date by testing for differences in reproductive output between 1 June–15 July and 16 July–1 September using data for all years and from all of the 11 studies. Prior to 1 June, pairs checked were either nesting or not reproductively active (i.e., had 0 young). Therefore, we compared only time periods of approximately equal lengths where fledged young were present. We found no significant difference (one-way ANOVA F = 1.18, df = 1, 3247, P = 0.2778) between mean reproductive output before (N = 2824) and after (N = 512) the 15 July cutoff date. In addition, there were no significant interactions between the two groups and years (F = 1.56, df = 8, 3247, P = 0.1327) or the two groups and studies (F = 1.08, df = 9, 3247, P = 0.3775). Therefore, all estimates of reproductive output collected over the sampling period of 1 March through 1 September were used in analyses.

Estimation of population trends

Lambda (λ), the annual rate of population change, was computed from the age-specific survival and fecundity estimates. In general, λ measures both direction in population trend ($\lambda = 1$ indicates a stationary population; $\lambda < 1$, a declining population; and, $\lambda > 1$, an increasing population) and magnitude of population change ($\lambda - 1$) (McDonald and Caswell 1993). For Northern Spotted Owls, we defined the target population to which we made inferences as the territorial, resident females. Although floaters (non-territorial unpaired individuals that do not breed) are known to exist in Spotted Owl populations (Franklin 1992), their influence on the regulation of Spotted Owl populations is unknown. In addition, floaters are undetectable using existing survey methods and, hence, are unmeasurable until they enter the territorial population. Therefore, we restricted our inferences to the territorial portion of the population whose parameters we were able to measure. Thus, λ answers the question, "What is the annual rate of population change for resident, territorial females given that estimated average survival probabilities and fecundity rates stay the same?".

From a management perspective, the research hypothesis of interest is $\lambda < 1$ versus the null that the population is either stationary or increasing ($\lambda \geq 1$), here a 1-tailed test. The form of this test is

$$z = \frac{1 - \hat{\lambda}}{\widehat{SE}(\hat{\lambda})}$$

where $z \approx N(0,1)$.

Leslie (1945, 1948) provides the matrix theory to allow the computation of λ from knowledge of only the age-specific fecundity and survival probabilities (see Lefkovitch 1965, Usher 1972, Caswell 1989, Noon and Biles 1990). We believe use of a simple Leslie matrix model was an appropriately parsimonious approach because it incorporated only those parameters that we could precisely estimate. We used only the female component of the population to estimate λ. The Leslie-Lefkovitch matrix allows $\hat{\lambda}$ to be computed from the characteristic polynomial of this matrix. For the full matrix model which includes all 4 age-classes, this matrix has the form:

$$\begin{bmatrix} \phi_J b_{S1} & \phi_{S1} b_{S2} & \phi_{S2} b_A & \phi_A b_A \\ \phi_J & 0 & 0 & 0 \\ 0 & \phi_{S1} & 0 & 0 \\ 0 & 0 & \phi_{S2} & \phi_A \end{bmatrix} \quad (1)$$

which assumes a birth-pulse population, a postbreeding census, and a time interval of 1 year (Noon and Sauer 1992). The individual studies in this volume included only those age-classes in such matrices for which parameters were estimated. For example, a two age-class matrix was used if parameter modeling procedures indicated the data only supported estimates of survival and fecundity for two age-classes. Lambda can be estimated as the dominant eigenvalue of (1) through matrix eigenanalysis (Caswell 1989) or through numerical search procedures for the unique, positive, real root of the characteristic equation of (1):

$$\lambda^4 - \lambda^3(\phi_A - \phi_J b_{S1}) + \lambda^2 \phi_J (b_{S1}\phi_A - \phi_{S1} b_{S2})$$
$$+ \lambda\phi_J\phi_{S1}(\phi_A b_{S2} - \phi_{S2} b_A) = 0 \quad (2)$$

Maximum likelihood estimates of the survival and fecundity parameters were used in (1) and (2) to estimate λ. Estimation of survival and fecundity estimates depended on the selected model used in estimating those parameters (see chapters on individual studies). For example, if a model with separate estimates for each year (e.g., ϕ_t or ϕ_T for survival estimates) was selected, an average was estimated as the arithmetic mean (see Jolly 1982) and its standard error computed. If a time invariant model was selected (e.g., model ϕ), the single estimate and its standard error was used. Precision of these estimates included any year-to-year and unaccounted for age-specific variability in the parameters as well as proper estimates of sampling variability. The $SE(\lambda)$ was estimated using the delta method (Seber 1982, Alvarez-Buylla and Slatkin 1994), including the sampling covariance terms for survival estimates. Sampling covariances between fecundity and survival estimates were zero because the two variables were statistically independent. The adequacy of the delta method was verified using a parametric bootstrap method (Efron 1982,

Alverez-Buylla and Slatkin 1994) assuming a beta distribution for $\hat{\phi}$ and a log-normal distribution for $\hat{b}$.

Four key assumptions are critical to estimating and interpreting λ estimated from the matrix model (Goodman, 1968, Caswell 1989, Noon and Sauer 1992, McDonald and Caswell 1993). First, we assumed that classifying Northern Spotted Owls into four age-classes was more appropriate than other properties relevant to an individuals fate, such as size or developmental stage. Second, we assumed there was no age-dependency in survival or fecundity in birds that were ≥ 3-year old age-class. Third, use of the matrix model assumes age-specific survival and fecundity rates remain constant over time and are density-independent, and fourth, the population is assumed at a stable age-class distribution where each age-class changes by λ over time. Parsimonious model development dictated the first two assumptions given sample sizes and available data. Concerning the third assumption, there is, in practice, temporal variation in the demographic parameters; our estimates reflect $E(\theta)$ over years for use in the Leslie matrix. Thus, $\hat{\lambda}$ approximates an average estimate over the period of years, even if the estimates of survival and fecundity vary over time. The last assumption becomes largely irrelevant when inferences about λ are limited to projection (what would happen) rather than forecasting (what will happen) (Keyfitz 1972, Caswell 1989:19–20). For the studies in this volume, estimates of λ are properly interpreted as the average annual rate of population change ($E(\lambda)$) for Northern Spotted Owls if conditions during the period of investigation were maintained indefinitely. In other words, the λ estimated from the age-specific survival and fecundity rates would occur if the conditions responsible for shaping the parameter estimates remain unchanged indefinitely. Under this interpretation, the population would eventually reach a stable age distribution. This interpretation differs from one involving forecasting which would state that estimates of λ will apply under future conditions regardless of how they may affect parameter estimates. Alternatively, our estimates of λ can be viewed as integrating environmental effects on survival and fecundity rates into a single index which quantifies the suitability of the environment for a population at a given time and place (McDonald and Caswell 1993).

The estimates of λ referred to the resident population, containing several age classes, and their recruitment. Immigration into the study populations is not estimated by mark-recapture, nor used by the Leslie approach to λ. Estimation of survival probabilities under the mark-recapture framework is conditional on first capture and, therefore, does not measure immigration. In addition, the parameter "immigration" does not appear in the matrix model; only estimates of survival and fecundity are needed.

Estimates of λ could be biased low if the juvenile survival ($\hat{\phi}_J$) estimate used did not approximate S_J because $1 - \hat{\phi}_J$ includes a significant emigration component (see Raphael et al. *this volume*). To estimate this emigration component, we used the other parameter estimates (assuming that they were unbiased with respect to the true parameters), set $\lambda = 1$ (a stationary population), and computed the juvenile probability required to obtain $\lambda = 1$ (denoted as $S_{J|\lambda=1}$). In the same manner, we computed the emigration rate (E) required to have $\hat{\phi}_J = S_{J|\lambda=1}$ as:

$$E_{|\lambda=1} = 1 - \frac{\hat{\phi}}{S_{J|\lambda=1}}$$

In this way, potential biases due to permanent emigration of juveniles from study areas were addressed in terms of a stationary population.

CONCLUSIONS

In analyzing demographic data for Northern Spotted Owls, we used a direct empirical approach in estimating population parameters and trends. This approach included objective, parsimonious model selection procedures to estimate parameters and their standard errors. A parsimonious approach was extended to the use of the Leslie matrix for estimating population trends.

As a simplification of reality (as all models are), the Leslie matrix approach contained only those parameters that we could precisely estimate and that were supported by the available data. Thus, our approach was driven solely by the available data that could be objectively analyzed in an appropriate statistical framework in contrast to other modeling approaches (e.g., Lamberson et al. 1992, McKelvey et al. 1992)

that necessarily assume mechanisms, such as dispersal behavior and birth and death processes, for which we have little or incomplete information. We acknowledge that our approach is not definitive in describing trends in Spotted Owl populations. However, we view our approach as an initial step in an iterative series of more sophisticated approaches. As understanding of the mechanisms and processes governing Spotted Owl populations increases, more sophisticated, data-based modeling procedures can be supported. However, we believe that appropriate parameter estimation procedures and a parsimonious approach to integrating parameter estimates is essential to any approach attempting to estimate trends in Spotted Owl populations.

SUMMARY

We present field and analytical methods used to estimate life history parameters and population trends for Northern Spotted Owls in the Pacific Northwest. Demographic characteristics were examined on 11 study areas distributed through northern California, Oregon, and Washington. Survival probabilities were estimated using mark-recapture estimators with data from annual surveys of individually color-marked owls. Fecundity rates were estimated using direct counts of fledged young. We discuss model selection procedures, tests of assumptions, and potential sources of bias inherent in the estimation techniques. We outline two approaches to examine trends: (1) testing for time-dependency in life history traits; and (2) estimating the annual rate of population change (λ) from demographic parameters and testing λ against the null hypothesis that the population is stationary ($H_0: \lambda = 1$).

ACKNOWLEDGMENTS

We thank W. R. Clark, M. G. Raphael, T. M. Shenk, J. Reid, G. C. White, and two anonymous reviewers for their thoughtful comments on this manuscript. Their input greatly improved its content.

Key words: capture techniques, demographic techniques, fecundity, Leslie matrices, mark-recapture estimators, Northern Spotted Owl, *Strix occidentalis caurina,* survival estimators.

Studies in Avian Biology No. 17:21–30, 1996.

DEMOGRAPHY OF THE NORTHERN SPOTTED OWL ON THE OLYMPIC PENINSULA AND EAST SLOPE OF THE CASCADE RANGE, WASHINGTON

Eric D. Forsman, Stan G. Sovern, D. Erran Seaman, Kevin J. Maurice, Margaret Taylor, and Joseph J. Zisa

INTRODUCTION

Research on the Northern Spotted Owl (*Strix occidentalis caurina*) in Washington State began in the late 1970s, and has included a variety of topics, including response rates in different forest types (Mills et al. 1993), ecological relationships with the Barred Owl (*Strix varia*) (Hamer 1988), home range and habitat use (Hamer 1988, Thomas et al. 1990, North 1993), diet (Richards 1989, Thomas et al. 1990, Sovern et al. 1994), nest site characteristics (Buchannan 1991, Buchannan et al. 1993), prey populations (Carey et al. 1992, Forsman et al. 1994), behavior (Sovern et al. 1994), landscape features around nests (Lemkuhl and Raphael 1993), and distribution (Garcia 1979, Thomas et al. 1990). Although most of these studies emphasized importance of particular types of forest habitat for Spotted Owls, none produced quantitative data on population trends or on underlying parameters that determine population growth rates (e.g., age-specific birth and death rates).

Because information on survival and reproductive rates is critical for assessing the health of any animal population, we investigated age-specific birth and death rates and annual rates of population change of Spotted Owls on two study areas in Washington. Our objective was to provide information that would help clarify the status of the owl in Washington, and that could be used in ancillary studies of Spotted Owl habitat relationships (e.g., Lemkuhl and Raphael 1993).

STUDY AREAS

The two study areas were the Cle Elum Ranger District (1,803 km²) on the east slope of the Cascade Range in central Washington (Fig. 1), and an 8,145 km² area that encompassed most of the Olympic Peninsula in northwestern Washington (Fig. 2). On the Olympic Peninsula the study was initially focused on lands administered by the U.S. Forest Service and Washington Department of Natural Resources, which surrounded the Olympic National Park. The study was expanded to include the Olympic National Park in 1989, after the National Park Service began to survey and band Spotted Owls. The Olympic Peninsula

Study Area was characterized by mountainous terrain and a wet, relatively warm maritime climate. The area was deeply dissected by numerous large river valleys emanating from the Olympic Range at the center of the peninsula. Precipitation occurred mainly as rain, and was particularly heavy on the western slopes of the Olympic Mountains, where it averaged 365 cm/year from 1987–1993 (USDI National Park Service records, Port Angeles, WA). Elevations ranged from sea level to 2,428 m.

The Cle Elum Study Area included the Cle Elum Ranger District on the Wenatchee National Forest, plus inholdings of private land within the district boundary (Fig. 2). This area was also mountainous, but slopes tended to be gentler than on the Olympic Peninsula, and climate was much drier. Mean annual precipitation during 1989–92 was 64 cm (NOAA 1990–1994). Summers were typically warm and dry, and winters were relatively cold with much of the winter precipitation occurring as snow. Elevations ranged from 670–2,084 m.

Vegetation on the Olympic Peninsula was typical of the humid coastal region of western Washington (Franklin and Dyrness 1973, Henderson et al. 1989). Forests of western hemlock (*Tsuga heterophylla*) western redcedar (*Thuja plicata*), Sitka spruce (*Picea sitchensis*), pacific silver fir (*Abies amabilis*) and Douglas-fir (*Pseudotsuga menziesii*) covered most of the area, except on recently harvested areas. Areas above about 1,400 m elevation were mostly covered by non-forest subalpine or alpine vegetation. Because of a long history of clear-cut logging and natural events such as fire and windstorms, most areas administered by the Forest Service and Department of Natural Resources were characterized by a mosaic of shrubs or young trees on cutover areas and mixed-age stands of older trees on unharvested areas. In contrast, most forests within Olympic National Park had never been harvested and were characterized by natural variation in age, species, and structure resulting from wildfire, windstorms, and differences in elevation.

Vegetation on Cle Elum was dominated by mixed conifer stands of Douglas-fir, grand fir (*Abies grandis*), and ponderosa pine (*Pinus pon-*

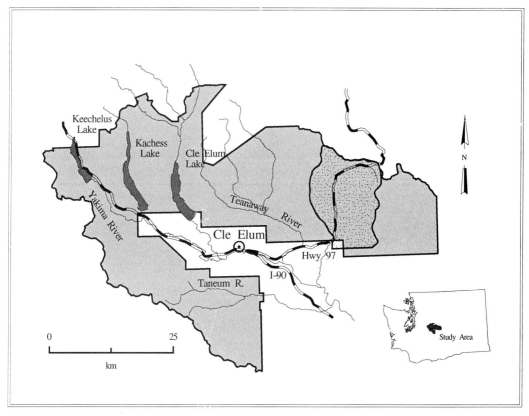

FIGURE 1. Cle Elum Study Area, WA. 1989–1993. Stippled area indicates location of the Density Study Area, a subplot within the larger study area that was completely surveyed each year to estimate numbers of territorial owls.

derosa). Less common species that were frequently associated with these stands included western larch (*Larix occidentalis*), lodgepole pine (*Pinus contorta*), western white pine (*Pinus monticola*) and western hemlock. Although mixed conifer stands predominated in most areas, stands dominated by ponderosa pine and open grassy areas were also common on dry south-facing slopes.

Much of the forest on Cle Elum had been selectively logged or burned one or more times since the early 1900s. Historically, most harvest consisted of partial cutting or selective cutting, in which some overstory trees were removed, leaving much of the stand intact. Small patches of old trees were often left standing. Historic wildfires also played a dominant role in determining species composition and forest structure in Cle Elum. After the initiation of a systematic program of fire suppression in the 1930s, fire-dependent forest types like ponderosa pine generally declined, whereas fire sensitive types like grand fir flourished.

METHODS

The Olympic and Cle Elum studies were started in 1987 and 1989 respectively, and continued through 1993. In both studies we used mark-recapture techniques to estimate survival of banded owls, as described in Franklin et al. *this volume*. Mean annual fecundity (# of female young produced per female owl) was estimated by repeatedly locating pairs of owls during the breeding season and counting the number of young that left the nest (Franklin et al. *this volume*). To find young owls after they left the nest we placed live mice in front of adult owls and then followed them when they captured the mice and carried them to their offspring (Franklin et al. *this volume*).

Both study areas included a subplot that was referred to as a "Density Study Area" (DSA), within which we attempted to monitor annual changes in the number of resident owls (Figs. 1, 2). Survey routes within DSAs were laid out to insure complete coverage of the area, and were surveyed a minimum of 3 times each year during

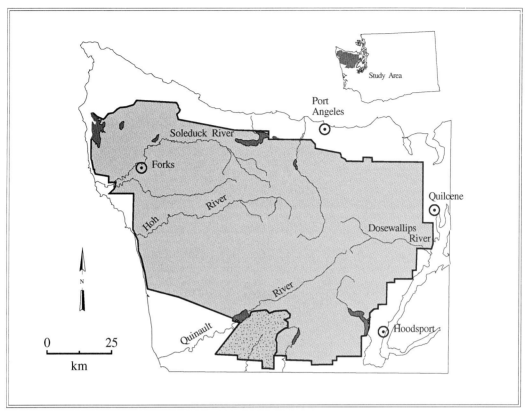

FIGURE 2. Olympic Peninsula Study Area, WA. 1987–1993. Stippled area indicates location of the Density Study Area, a subplot within the larger study area that was completely surveyed each year to estimate numbers of territorial owls.

spring and summer, using techniques described in Forsman (1983) and Franklin et al. *this volume.* Size of DSAs on the Olympic and Cle Elum Study Areas was 355 and 204 km², respectively. In areas outside of DSAs, surveys and banding were conducted on selected areas with a history of owl occupancy, but no attempt was made to survey the entire study area.

Capture-recapture (CR) analyses were conducted on the complete data set for each study area. Survival rates for each sex and age class were calculated from CR data using Cormack-Jolly-Seber open population models in Program SURGE as described in Pollock et al. (1990), Lebreton et al. (1992), Burnham et al. (1995), and Franklin et al. (*this volume*). Akaike's Information Criterion (AIC) (Akaike 1973, Burnham and Anderson 1992, Anderson et al. 1994) was used to identify models that best fit the data. Goodness-of-fit to the statistical assumptions in the CR models was evaluated using tests 1–3 in program RELEASE (Pollock et al. 1985, Burnham et al. 1987).

Juvenile Spotted Owls disperse from their natal territories in their first year, often moving beyond the boundaries of a given study area (i.e., they emigrate). Because emigration is usually indistinguishable from mortality in CR data, juvenile survival estimates from CR analyses may be biased low. To estimate emigration rates of juvenile owls (E_J) we installed 5-gram radio transmitters on the rectrices of a subset of the 1991–1992 juvenile cohorts on both study areas. Emigration was defined as any case in which a radio-marked bird moved into an area not normally searched during our annual calling surveys, survived its first year, and was not detected by our normal calling surveys (Burnham et al. *this volume*). This definition was adopted because: (1) a bird that moves within the original study area is still susceptible to recapture and will be correctly treated by CR models; (2) a bird that leaves the original study area but is captured elsewhere will be reported to the original study area and treated as a recapture; and (3) only birds that emigrate and survive remain in the popu-

TABLE 1. SAMPLE SIZE[a] AND NUMBER OF OWLS
BANDED FOR CAPTURE-RECAPTURE STUDIES OF NORTH-
ERN SPOTTED OWLS ON THE OLYMPIC PENINSULA AND
CLE ELUM STUDY AREAS, WASHINGTON

	Olympic Peninsula	Cle Elum
Years of study	1987–1993	1989–1993
Sample size[a]		
≥3-yr-old males	295	131
≥3-yr-old females	278	96
Number owls banded		
≥3-yr-old males	127	60
≥3-yr-old females	129	56
1- or 2-yr-old males	27	12
1- or 2-yr-old females	15	18
1–2-yr-old, sex undet.	1	
Juveniles	249	186
Total	548	332

[a] Sample size was the sum of the birds captured and released on i occasions ($R_1 + R_2 + ... + R_{k-1}$) in the capture-recapture m-array (Lebreton et al. 1992).

lation; a bird that emigrates and dies has the same effect on the population as one that dies without emigrating. Clearly, the emigration rate defined here will be specific to the study area in which it is estimated.

Estimates of E_J from the radio-marked juveniles were used to adjust estimates of juvenile survival from CR data ($\hat{\phi}_J$) using the formula:

$$\hat{S}_J = \frac{\hat{\phi}_J}{1 - \hat{E}}$$

where $\hat{S}_J$ = the adjusted estimate of survival. We assumed that annual survival probabilities were the same for emigrating and non-emigrating individuals and that tail-mounted radio-transmitters had no effect on emigration rates of juvenile Spotted Owls. Only juveniles that survived at least through March of the year following hatching were used.

The annual rate of population change (λ) was estimated by solving the characteristic equation

resulting from a modified stage-based Leslie matrix (Franklin et al. *this volume*). We made two estimates of λ, one of which was based on the unadjusted survival estimates for juveniles and non-juveniles from the best age-class models, and estimates of fecundity from two age classes (1 and 2-yr-old birds and ≥3-yr-old birds). The second estimate of λ was based on the same parameter estimates as the first, except that we substituted the estimate of juvenile survival that was adjusted for emigration. Estimates of fecundity for 1 and 2-yr-old birds were pooled because of small sample size.

Trends in the total number of territorial birds detected each year within DSAs were assessed using regression analysis in SPSS (Norušis 1990) to test the null hypothesis that there was no change in population size. Years examined were 1988–1993 on the Olympic Peninsula and 1991–1993 on Cle Elum. Data from the first year of study on the Olympic Peninsula DSA (1987) were excluded because some portions of the DSA were not surveyed in that year. A power analysis of the regression (Gerrodette 1987) was conducted using Program TRENDS (T. Gerrodette, personal communication). For all statistical tests, P values ≤ 0.05 were considered significant.

RESULTS

SAMPLE SIZE AND GOODNESS OF FIT

Capture-recapture data were collected from 548 owls on the Olympic Peninsula and 332 owls on Cle Elum (Table 1). Results of TEST 1 in program RELEASE (Burnham et al. 1987) indicated no differences in survival or recapture rates of ≥3-yr-old males and females on either study area (Olympic Peninsula $\chi^2 = 3.50$, df = 11, P = 0.982; Cle Elum $\chi^2 = 6.81$, df = 7, P = 0.530) (Table 2). TEST 1 was not conducted on juveniles because the sex of most juveniles was not known.

For ≥3-yr-old birds, the combined results of TEST 2 and 3 from Program RELEASE revealed no lack of fit for CR data for either males or

TABLE 2. GOODNESS-OF-FIT TEST RESULTS FROM PROGRAM RELEASE (BURNHAM ET AL. 1987) FOR CAPTURE-RECAPTURE DATA FROM ≥3-YR-OLD NORTHERN SPOTTED OWLS ON THE OLYMPIC PENINSULA (OLY) AND CLE ELUM (CLE) STUDY AREAS, WASHINGTON

Study area	Sex	TEST 2 P	TEST 3 P	TEST 2 + 3[a] χ^2	df	P
OLY	Males	0.3937	0.0499	19.89	12	0.0691
	Females	0.2021	0.0008	34.36	13	0.0011
CLE	Males	0.3280	0.7185	5.11	7	0.6466
	Females	0.0612	0.9942	6.03	7	0.5368

[a] TEST 2 tests for statistical independence among age and sex cohorts and individuals (Burnham et al. 1987). TEST 3 tests whether previously released individuals have the same future fates as newly released individuals.

TABLE 3. CAPTURE-RECAPTURE MODELS USED TO ESTIMATE SURVIVAL OF NORTHERN SPOTTED OWLS ON THE OLYMPIC PENINSULA STUDY AREA, WASHINGTON: 1987–1993. MODELS ARE SHOWN IN ORDER OF INCREASING AKAIKE'S INFORMATION CRITERION (AIC) VALUES (AKAIKE 1973). K = THE NUMBER OF ESTIMABLE PARAMETERS

Model[a]	Deviance	K	AIC
≥ 3-yr-old owls			
$\{\phi_s, p_T\}$	786.615	4	794.615
$\{\phi, p_{s+T}\}$	787.540	4	795.540
$\{\phi, p_T\}$	789.584	3	795.585
$\{\phi_{s+T}, p_T\}$	785.622	5	795.622
$\{\phi_s, p_{s+T}\}$	785.822	5	795.822
2-age-class models			
$\{\phi_{a2}, p_{a5+T}\}$	1171.903	8	1187.903
$\{\phi_{a2}, p_{a4+T}\}$	1173.960	7	1187.960
$\{\phi_{a2'+s}, p_{a5+T}\}$	1170.058	9	1188.058
$\{\phi_{a2+s}, p_{a3+T}\}$	1181.509	7	1195.509
$\{\phi_{a2+T}, p_{a3+T}\}$	1181.629	7	1195.629

[a] Model subscripts indicate age (a), sex (s), or time (t, T) effects on survival (ϕ) or recapture (p). An upper case T in a subscript indicates a linear time-effect in the subscripted parameter. Numbers indicate number of age-groups. The subscript a2′ + s indicates 2 age groups with sex effects on non-juveniles, but not on juveniles. An * indicates full age, sex, or time-effects, whereas a + sign indicates a reduced model in which age, sex, or time-effects are additive.

TABLE 4. CAPTURE-RECAPTURE MODELS USED TO ESTIMATE SURVIVAL OF NORTHERN SPOTTED OWLS ON THE CLE ELUM STUDY AREA, WASHINGTON: 1989–1993. MODELS ARE SHOWN IN ORDER OF INCREASING AKAIKE'S INFORMATION CRITERION (AIC) VALUES (AKAIKE 1973). K = NUMBER OF ESTIMABLE PARAMETERS

Model[a]	Deviance	K	AIC
≥ 3-yr-old owls			
$\{\phi_T, p_s\}$	317.177	4	325.177
$\{\phi_T, p_{s+T}\}$	315.181	5	325.181
$\{\phi, p_{s+t}\}$	313.714	6	325.714
$\{\phi, p_s\}$	320.152	3	326.152
$\{\phi_T, p_{s*T}\}$	314.496	6	326.496
2-age-class models			
$\{\phi_{a2+T}, p_{s+T}\}$	533.349	6	545.349
$\{\phi_{a2+T}, p_{a2+s+T}\}$	532.671	7	546.671
$\{\phi_{a2+T}, p_{a2+s}\}$	537.459	6	549.459
$\{\phi_{a2*s}, p_{a2*t}\}$	526.553	12	550.553
$\{\phi_{a2+T}, p_{a3+s}\}$	537.054	7	551.054

[a] Subscripts indicate age (a), sex (s), or time (t, T) effects on survival (ϕ) or recapture (p). Numbers indicate number of age groups. Time effects were either linear (T) or non-linear (t). An * indicates full age, sex, or time-effects. A + sign indicates a reduced model with additive age, sex or time-effects.

females on Cle Elum (Table 2). On the Olympic Peninsula, combined results of TEST 2+3 indicated some lack of fit for both males and females (Table 2). Closer inspection of the data revealed that over 75% of the χ^2 value for TEST 3.SR was contributed by 32 birds banded in 1992. Only six of those individuals were recaptured in 1993. When we excluded the 1992 cohort and ran RELEASE on the first five years of data, Tests 2+3 indicated no lack of fit for males (χ^2 = 16.572, df = 10, P = 0.084), females (χ^2 = 7.715, df = 10, P = 0.657), or for males and females combined (χ^2 = 24.286, df = 20, P = 0.230). The winter of 1992–93 was apparently a particularly difficult one for Spotted Owls on the Olympic Peninsula, because none of the pairs located there in 1993 nested (see FECUNDITY below). This could explain why the adult cohort banded in 1992 had a different future fate than cohorts banded in previous years. Because the sample of birds banded in 1992 was small compared to the total sample for all years, we believe that the resulting lack of fit was not a serious concern in the overall analysis.

CAPTURE-RECAPTURE MODEL SELECTION

For the Olympic Peninsula, the CR model that best fit the data from ≥ 3-yr-old birds was one in which survival (ϕ) differed by sex, and recapture probability (p) varied linearly over time (symbolized as $\{\phi_s, p_T\}$)(Table 3, Fig. 3). For Cle

the model that best fit the data from ≥ 3-yr-old birds was one in which ϕ varied linearly over time, and p varied by sex ($\{\phi_T, p_s\}$)(Table 4, Fig. 4).

The best age-class model for the Olympic Peninsula was $\{\phi_{a2}, p_{a5+T}\}$, indicating that ϕ differed by age (juvenile vs. non-juvenile), but did not differ by sex or year (Table 3, Fig. 3). For Cle Elum the best age-class model was $\{\phi_{a2+T}, p_{s+T}\}$, indicating an age and linear time effect on ϕ, but no sex effect (Table 4, Fig. 4). Thus, age-class models indicated no difference in survival of males and females on either study area. Examination of model output for Cle Elum indicated that the linear time trend on survival was negative (Fig. 4).

On both areas there were one or more alternative models that fit the data nearly as well as the preferred adult models and age-class models (Tables 3, 4). Examination of the alternative models revealed none that seemed more biologically reasonable than the models with lowest AIC values, so all subsequent calculations were based on estimates from the age-class models with the lowest AIC values.

SURVIVAL ESTIMATES FROM
CAPTURE-RECAPTURE MODELS

Estimates of mean annual survival from the best age-class model on the Olympic Peninsula were 0.245 (SE = 0.064) for juveniles and 0.862 (SE = 0.017) for non-juveniles (Fig. 3). On Cle Elum, estimates of survival from the best age-

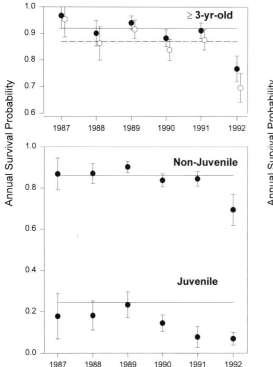

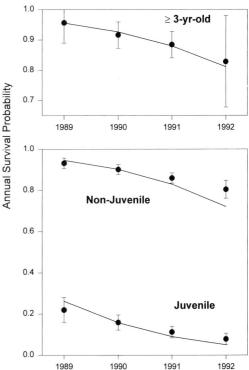

FIGURE 3. Estimates of annual survival for ≥3-yr-old, ≥1-yr-old, and juvenile Northern Spotted Owls on the Olympic Peninsula, WA: 1987–1993. Horizontal lines in top graph represent constant survival estimates for males (solid line, $\bar{\phi}_\delta = 0.920$, SE =0.0201) and females (dashed line, $\bar{\phi}_\circ$ =0.870, SE = 0.0236) from the best adult CR model ($\{\phi_s, p_T\}$). Annual estimates of survival and SEs for ≥3-yr-old males (solid dots) and females (open dots) from a variable time model ($\{\phi_{t+s}, p\}$) are shown for comparison. In the lower graph, horizontal lines indicate constant survival estimates for ≥1-yr-old owls ($\phi_{NJ} = 0.862$, SE = 0.017) and juveniles ($\phi_J = 0.245$, SE = 0.064) from the best age-class model ($\{\phi_{a2}, p_{a5+T}\}$); dots with SEs indicate yearly survival estimates from a variable time model ($\{\phi_{a2+t}, p_{a3+t}\}$).

FIGURE 4. Estimates of annual survival for ≥3-yr-old, ≥1-yr-old, and juvenile Northern Spotted Owls on the Cle Elum Study Area, WA: 1989–1993. Line in top graph represents the nearly linear time trend in survival estimates from the best model for ≥3-yr-old owls (ϕ_T, p_s), with average SE = 0.0351. Annual estimates and associated SEs from a variable time model ($\{\phi_t, p_{s+t}\}$) are shown for comparison. Lines in lower graph represent the nearly linear time trends in survival estimates from the best 2-age-class model (ϕ_{a2+T}, p_{s+T}), with average SEs of 0.0280 and 0.0353 for ≥1-yr-old birds and juveniles, respectively. Annual estimates and associated SEs from a variable time model ($\{\phi_{a2\bullet t}, p_{a2\bullet s}\}$) are shown for comparison.

class model were 0.140 (SE = 0.026) for juveniles and 0.850 (SE = 0.0312) for non-juveniles (Fig. 4). Because standard errors could not be calculated on estimates from models that included a year effect on ϕ, standard errors for survival rates from model $\{\phi_{a2+T}, p_{s+T}\}$ were approximated from the model with the next closest AIC, but no year effect on ϕ (model $\{\phi_{a2}, p_{a2+T}\}$)(Franklin et al. *this volume*).

JUVENILE EMIGRATION RATES

The proportion of radio-marked juveniles that emigrated each year ($\hat{E}_J$) was 0.579 (SE = 0.113)

on the Olympic Peninsula and 0.625 (SE = 0.121) on Cle Elum (Table 5). Logistic regression indicated no year or area effects on emigration rates ($\chi^2 = 2.065$, df = 1, P = 0.151), so the data from both areas were pooled to produce a single estimate of $\hat{E}_J = 21/35 = 0.600$ (SE = 0.083) (Table 5). Based on this estimate of E_J, the adjusted juvenile survival estimate ($\hat{S}_J$) was 0.611 (SE = 0.204) for the Olympic Peninsula and 0.349 (SE = 0.098) for Cle Elum.

FECUNDITY

Fecundity of females that were ≥3 yrs old averaged 0.380 (SE = 0.036) on the Olympic Peninsula and 0.565 (SE = 0.061) on Cle Elum. Sam-

TABLE 5. PROPORTION OF RADIO-MARKED JUVENILE NORTHERN SPOTTED OWLS THAT EMIGRATED FROM THE OLYMPIC PENINSULA AND CLE ELUM STUDY AREAS, WA: 1991 AND 1992 COHORTS.

Area/cohort	n	Proportion emigrating[a] $(\hat{E})$	SE $(\hat{E})$
Olympic Peninsula			
1991	11	0.727	
1992	8	0.375	
1991 & 1992	19	0.579	0.113
Cle Elum			
1991	12	0.583	
1992	4	0.750	
1991 & 1992	16	0.625	0.121
Combined areas			
1991	23	0.652	
1992	12	0.500	
1991 & 1992	35	0.600	0.083

[a] Emigration was defined as a bird that dispersed into an area not normally searched during annual calling surveys, survived until at least 30 March of the year after birth, and was not detected using normal calling surveys (i.e., that would have gone undetected without the use of radio telemetry).

ples for 1- and 2-yr-old birds were too small to calculate separate estimates for each age class, so we used a pooled estimate for those age classes (Olympic Peninsula $\bar{x} = 0.206$, SE = 0.106; Cle Elum $\bar{x} = 0.379$, SE = 0.120).

Fecundity varied among years on both study areas (Olympic Peninsula F = 20.834, df = 6, P < 0.001; Cle Elum F = 20.033, df = 4, P < 0.001) (Figs. 5, 6). Among-year variation in fecundity was due primarily to variation in the proportion of females that attempted to nest, which also varied among years (Olympic Peninsula $\chi^2 = 123.16$, df = 6, P < 0.001; Cle Elum $\chi^2 = 67.074$, df = 4, P < 0.001) (Figs. 5, 6). However, some of the variation in fecundity was also explained by among-year variation in rates of nest failure.

POPULATION RATE OF CHANGE

Survival estimates from the best age-class CR models produced $\hat{\lambda} = 0.947$ (SE = 0.026) for the Olympic Peninsula and $\hat{\lambda} = 0.924$ (SE = 0.032) for Cle Elum. Thus, the point estimates of $\hat{\lambda}$ indicated average annual declines in the territorial population of 5.3% on the peninsula and 7.6% on Cle Elum during the respective study periods. Estimates of λ were less than 1 on both areas (one-tailed test, H_o: $\lambda \geq 1$, Olympic Peninsula z = 2.07, P = 0.019; Cle Elum z = 2.35, P = 0.009). Substituting $\hat{S}_J$ for $\hat{\phi}_J$ in the population growth rate equation produced $\hat{\lambda} = 1.058$ (SE = 0.065) on the Olympic Peninsula and 1.024 (SE = 0.058) on Cle Elum. These estimates of λ were not dif-

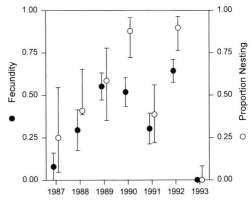

FIGURE 5. Annual fecundity and proportion of ≥ 3-yr-old female Northern Spotted Owls nesting on the Olympic Peninsula Study Area, WA: 1987–1993. (●) with associated SEs indicates fecundity, defined as the number of female young fledged per female owl. (○) with associated 95% confidence intervals indicates proportion of females nesting.

ferent from 1.0 (one-tailed test, H_o: $\lambda \leq 1.0$, Olympic Peninsula z = -0.898, P = 0.815; Cle Elum z = -0.424, P = 0.664). However, power tests indicated that the chance of detecting a difference between the estimated rates of change and $\lambda = 1.0$ was low (10.9% on Cle Elum and 22.6% on the Olympic Peninsula).

CHANGES IN NUMBERS OF OWLS ON DENSITY STUDY AREAS

On the Olympic Peninsula Density Study Area the regression of the annual number of territorial

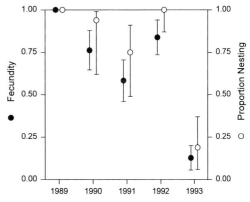

FIGURE 6. Annual fecundity and proportion of ≥ 3-yr-old female Northern Spotted Owls nesting on the Cle Elum Study Area, Washington, 1989–1993. (●) with associated SEs indicates fecundity, defined as the number of female young fledged per female owl. (○) with associated 95% confidence intervals indicates proportion of adult females nesting.

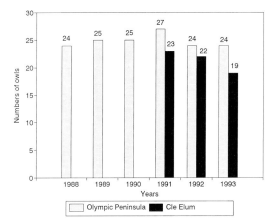

FIGURE 7.   Numbers of territorial Northern Spotted Owls detected during annual surveys on the Olympic Peninsula and Cle Elum Density Study Areas, WA.

owls detected on time (year) indicated no change in numbers from 1988–1993 (H_o: stable population, slope = -0.029, r = -0.04572, P = 0.932, Fig. 7). On the Cle Elum Density Study Area there was a slight (but non-significant) downward trend in the number of owls detected from 1991–1993 (H_o: stationary population, slope = -2.000, r = -0.961, P = 0.179, Fig. 7).

Although no trends were indicated on either study area, the power of the tests used to examine the null hypothesis that the population was stable was only 0.05 for the Olympic Peninsula and 0.06 for Cle Elum. With such low statistical power, it would take a minimum of 10–20 years of monitoring before significant trends could be detected if the annual rate of change was less than 5% per year.

DISCUSSION

SURVIVAL

Capture-recapture models that best fit the data indicated strikingly different patterns in the Olympic and Cle Elum Study Areas. The models that best fit the Cle Elum data indicated decreasing adult survival over time, whereas survival rates on the Olympic Peninsula did not vary among years. These differences were consistent regardless of whether we used models that included all birds divided into two age groups or models that included only birds that were ≥3 yrs old. We do not know why the two study populations should have differed regarding time effects on survival. A variety of possible explanations are possible, including small sample size, slight differences in timing of the two studies, local or temporal differences in climate, differ-

ences in prey populations, or differences in rates of habitat alteration.

In addition to emigration (discussed below) a variety of factors could have biased survival estimates. For example, broods of juveniles were often not banded until after they had been outside the nest for 1–6 weeks. As a result, owlets that left the nest, but died before we located and banded the remaining young were not included in the capture-recapture analysis. This should have caused a positive bias in survival estimates of juveniles, which were estimated from the date that juveniles left the nest. Another factor that may have caused a positive bias in juvenile survival estimates is that the capture interval during the first year of life was typically less than a year, again because many juveniles were not banded until they were out of the nest for some time (Franklin et al. *this volume*). While these positive biases are probably not large, they may at least partially compensate for the negative bias on survival estimates caused by emigration of juveniles.

EMIGRATION RATES

Our estimate of E_J was based on a much smaller data set than was used in the capture-recapture analysis, and only two cohorts were radio-marked for emigration estimates. If the sampled years were anomalous in any way, the results may be misleading. However, in the absence of more complete data, we believe it is reasonable to use the existing information to examine the possible influence of emigration on survival estimates of juvenile owls from capture-recapture studies like ours. This analysis indicates that emigration had a considerable effect on estimates of juvenile survival from CR data, as suggested in Bart (1995) and Burnham et al. (*this volume*).

FECUNDITY

Estimates of fecundity could have been positively biased if non-nesting females were less detectable than nesting females, or negatively biased if some juveniles died after they left the nest but before we estimated brood size. These biases were probably compensatory to some degree, but we had no way to assess them.

Reasons for the considerable annual variation in the proportion of females breeding were unknown, but a number of hypotheses have been proposed for this behavior in owls and other birds of prey, including annual or cyclic variation in prey populations and weather conditions (Pitelka et al. 1955, Southern 1970, Rusch et al. 1972, Adamcik et al. 1978, Newton 1979, Nero 1980, Forsman et al. 1984).

Estimates of adult fecundity on our study areas were higher than for most other study areas

(Burnham et al. *this volume*). Why owls near the northern limits of the range of the species should have higher average fecundity than owls in study areas closer to the center of the range is unclear. We do not believe this was due to biases in sampling procedure, because we used the same techniques on our study areas in Washington that were used on other study areas in Oregon and California. The comparatively higher fecundity on our study areas is particularly interesting in light of evidence that prey biomass on the Olympic Peninsula may be lower than in western Oregon (Carey et al. 1992).

POPULATION GROWTH RATES

Initial estimates of λ, without adjustment of $\hat{\phi}_J$ for emigration, indicated rapidly declining populations of Spotted Owls on both study areas. Estimates of λ based on $\hat{S}_J$ indicated non-declining populations in both study areas. However, we are reluctant to conclude that populations on either of our study areas were stationary, because our adjusted estimate of juvenile survival was based on small samples from only two years, and because there are a variety of other factors that can cause positive and negative biases in estimates of λ, as discussed earlier and in Bart (1995) and Raphael et al. (*this volume*). In addition, power to detect population trends based on only a few years of data is low (Taylor and Gerrodette 1993).

It is unclear how to reduce the effect of juvenile emigration on λ based on banding studies of Spotted Owls. The adjustment we performed relies on the assumption that survival of emigrants is equal to that of non-emigrants. However, if emigrants have a different survival than non-emigrants the adjusted survival rate could be biased either high or low.

In addition, the effect of emigration on $\hat{\lambda}$ for a given study area will depend in part on the rate of immigration, which is unknown. For the purpose of our analysis we assumed that there were no appreciable biases in any other parameter estimates, and addressed only the effects of emigration on juvenile survival estimates. If there is no immigration, then λ based on the CR estimate of ϕ_J will correctly reflect the population trend on the study site. If immigration exactly equals emigration, then λ based on $\hat{\phi}_J$ will underestimate the rate of population change, and λ based on $\hat{S}_J$ will be closer to the actual trend. If immigration is between 0 and the emigration rate, then the actual population trend will be somewhere between those two values of λ. If immigration exceeds emigration, then the actual population growth rate will exceed any of the estimates of λ.

From this discussion it should be clear that adjustments of parameter values to compensate for suspected bias can indicate a potential range for λ, but should not be taken as definitive measures of population trend. It does appear, however, that if there is any immigration at all, then population declines on the Olympic Peninsula and Cle Elum Study Areas are not as drastic as indicated by the unadjusted CR data.

Because adult emigration appears to be infrequent, and is difficult to document, we have ignored it, assuming $\phi_A = S_A$. An analysis of data from 37 radio-marked owls on the Olympic and Cle Elum Study Areas indicated that, although some movement occurred within the study areas, none of the owls left the study area during a two year period of study, with the exception of one bird that underwent temporary emigration (E. Forsman, unpublished data) Nevertheless, estimates of λ are highly sensitive to adult survival rates (Noon and Biles 1990), and a few percent bias in this parameter caused by occasional adult emigration could cause a negative bias of similar magnitude in λ, as suggested by Bart (1995).

CHANGES IN OWL NUMBERS

Regression analysis showed no change in the number of resident territorial owls on either of our Density Study Areas. However, a gradual decline (e.g., 1–5%/year) in the number of resident owls could easily go undetected by this analysis, because the regressions had low statistical power. Additionally, even if the total population were declining, there might be no change in the number of territorial birds during early years of the decline if the territorial birds that died were replaced by floaters (birds without territories). Thus, changes in density of territorial birds might not become apparent for many years, especially if the rate of population decline was small (e.g., 1–2% per year). If the rate of population decline was relatively large (e.g., 5–10% per year), declines in density should become apparent sooner. In either case, our studies are of short duration relative to the time needed to observe such changes.

Because Spotted Owls are relatively long-lived, occur at low densities, and have considerable annual variation in fecundity, it takes many years to get a sufficient sample size for estimation of vital rates and population trends. Our studies were of relatively short duration (Olympic Peninsula = 7 years, Cle Elum = 5 years). Power to detect trends in vital rates and annual rates of population change should improve as more years of data are collected.

SUMMARY

Examination of demographic trends in survival and reproduction is one of the most reliable methods of assessing the health of a population.

To evaluate the performance of Spotted Owl populations in Washington, we examined age-specific birth and death rates and population growth rates on two study areas, the Olympic Peninsula in northwestern Washington, and the Cle Elum Ranger District on the east slope of the Cascade Range. Duration of studies was 1987–1993 on the Olympic Peninsula and 1989–1993 on Cle Elum. The analysis indicated that annual adult survival was declining on Cle Elum. No trends in adult survival were apparent on the Olympic Peninsula. Fecundity of $\geq$3-yr-old females, expressed as the number of female young produced per female owl per year, averaged 0.380 (SE = 0.106) on the Olympic Peninsula and 0.565 (SE = 0.061) on Cle Elum. Fecundity of 1 and 2-yr-old females averaged 0.206 (SE = 0.106) on the Olympic Peninsula and 0.379 (SE = 0.120) on Cle Elum. Fecundity varied among years on both study areas (P < 0.001), primarily due to variation in the proportion of females that attempted to nest. Estimates of non-juvenile survival rates ($\hat{\phi}_{NJ}$) from the best 2-age-class capture-recapture models were 0.862 (SE = 0.017) on the Olympic Peninsula and 0.850 (SE = 0.031) on Cle Elum. Juvenile survival estimates ($\hat{\phi}_J$) from the same models were 0.245 (SE = 0.064) and 0.140 (SE = 0.046) on the Olympic and Cle Elum study areas, respectively. Emigration rates of radio-marked juveniles averaged 0.579 (SE = 0.113) on Cle Elum and 0.625 (SE = 0.121) on the Olympic Peninsula. Adjusting the mark-recapture estimates of $\hat{\phi}_J$ to account for emigration produced an adjusted estimate of juvenile survival ($\hat{S}_J$) of 0.611 (SE = 0.204 on the Olympic Peninsula and 0.349 (SE = 0.098) on Cle Elum. Without the adjustment for juvenile emigration, estimated annual rates of population change ($\hat{\lambda}$) were < 1 on both study areas (Olympic P = 0.019, Cle Elum P = 0.009), with the Olympic Peninsula and Cle Elum populations declining at 5.3 and 7.6% per year, respectively. With the adjustment for juvenile emigration, λ did not differ from 1.0 in either area (Olympic Peninsula P = 0.815, Cle Elum P = 0.664). However, statistical power to detect the estimated rate of change was low. Because small samples were used to estimate average rates of emigration, and because of other factors that could cause positive or negative biases in estimates of λ (Bart 1995), we stress that our analysis should not be interpreted as evidence of a non-declining population. However, the analysis does suggest that estimates of λ based on banding data alone are likely to underestimate λ. Annual counts of owls within two areas that were completely surveyed each year did not indicate a change in owl numbers on either area during the study (P > 0.05), although in both cases the estimated trends were negative. Statistical power of the regression used to test the null hypothesis (H_0: no change in owl numbers over time) was low (0.05–0.06), indicating that the ability to detect trends, even if they were present, was poor.

ACKNOWLEDGMENTS

We thank the many dedicated field biologists who helped locate and band owls, including A. Giese, D. Kelso, R. Lowell, D. Manson, M. Nixon, I. Otto, J. Swingle, M. Townsend, D. Aubuchon, R. Forson, B. R. Casler, C. C. Foster, S. Grayson, C. Johnson, T. Kaminski, J. Lewis, P. J. Loschl, D. McFarlane, D. Rolph, D. Schmidt, S. Smith, C. Tyler, C. Bailey, K. Braun, D. Clarkson, A. Comulada, A. Farris, M. Fasching, H. Herendeen, T. Hoover, G. Hunter, C. Knight, G. Lenhart, W. Meyer, R. Nauman, E. Olexa, A. Parker, T. Parker, S. Pedersen, S. Roberts, D. Root, A. Rubel, R. Schorr, D. Smith, D. Tallmon, and J. Zyskind. Others who provided assistance included J. Anthony, S. P. Horton and P. Whitney of the Washington Department of Natural Resources and H. Allan, D. Hays, A. McMillian, and A. Potter of the Washington Department of Wildlife. B. Moorhead, D. Houston, R. Fredrickson, A. English, and S. Snetsinger were instrumental in development and implementation of the Spotted Owl research program in Olympic National Park. On the Cle Elum Study Area we worked closely with a variety of groups and individuals, including L. Irwin and T. Fleming (National Council For Air and Stream Improvement), D. Herter, L. Melampy, M. Lanphere, M. Rabanal, A. Raedeke, B. Shepard, M. MacDonald, A. Renkert, H. Smith, C. Holloway, C. Eakins, M. Richey, C. Smith, S. Sagor, and G. Riddick (Raedeke and Associates), L. Hicks (Plum Creek Timber Company), and M. Abshire, P. Garvey-Darda, R. Klatt, D. Leversee, L. Neimi, B. Ozuna, S. Stanger, D. Teske, and M. Teske (Cle Elum Ranger District). We greatly appreciate the support of the Forest Service Biologists on whose districts we worked, including J. Cason, M. Jensen, E. Milliman, M. Ostwald, J. Richards, and M. Stall. For assistance with data analysis we thank D. R. Anderson, B. L. Biswell, K. P. Burnham, J. Clobert, A. B. Franklin, J. E. Hines, J. D. Nichols, R. J. Pradel, E. A. Rexstad, T. M. Shenk, G. C. White, and K. R. Wilson. Various drafts of the manuscript were reviewed by M. J. Conroy, S. DeStefano, R. J. Gutiérrez and two anonymous reviewers. Funding was provided by the USDA Forest Service, USDI Bureau of Land Management, USDI National Park Service, and USDI Fish and Wildlife Service.

Key words: capture-recapture, demography, fecundity, Northern Spotted Owl, populations, *Strix occidentalis caurina,* survival, Washington State.

Studies in Avian Biology No. 17:31–36, 1996.

DEMOGRAPHY OF NORTHERN SPOTTED OWLS ON THE SALEM DISTRICT OF THE BUREAU OF LAND MANAGEMENT IN NORTHWESTERN OREGON

D. SCOTT HOPKINS, WAYNE D. LOGAN, AND ERIC D. FORSMAN

INTRODUCTION

Analysis of Northern Spotted Owl (*Strix occidentalis caurina*) populations in northwest Oregon is of particular interest because this area includes portions of the northern end of the Oregon Coast Ranges, an area where historical surveys have generally found low owl densities and poor habitat conditions (Forsman et al. 1977, Forsman 1988, Salem Bureau of Land Management, unpublished data). In one of the few published reports from this area, Forsman (1988) reported finding lower numbers of owls than reported for other regions, and he noted the rate of owls responses during surveys, and presumably owl numbers, had declined between 1976 and 1986.

Since 1974, the Salem District of the Bureau of Land Management (BLM) has conducted surveys for Spotted Owls in both the northern portion of the Coast Ranges and in the northern portion of the Western Cascades in northwest Oregon. Initial survey efforts varied from year-to-year and focused on known locations of Spotted Owl pairs on BLM lands. No attempts were made to mark owls. In 1986, the surveys became more consistent, study area boundaries were expanded, and a banding study was initiated. The primary objective of the study was to provide quantitative information that could be used to assess the condition of the owl population in northwestern Oregon. Data from 1986–1993 on the Salem District were first analyzed at a Spotted Owl Demographic Workshop in Fort Collins, Colorado in December 1993 and were summarized in Burnham et al. (1994b). This paper presents an expanded analysis and discussion of the demographic data collected on Northern Spotted Owls on the Salem District.

STUDY AREA

The Salem Study Area is approximately 3844 km², encompassing most of the BLM lands in the Salem District of the Bureau of Land Management as well as interspersed sections of non-federal land (Fig. 1). The study area includes portions of the Coast Ranges Province and the Western Cascades Province, both of which are located in northwest Oregon (Franklin and Dyrness 1973). The study area is composed of several

separate survey blocks, reflecting the dispersed pattern of BLM land ownership in northwest Oregon (Fig. 1).

The majority of BLM lands in the study area occur in a checkerboard ownership pattern of alternating mi² (259 ha) sections (Fig. 1). Intervening sections are owned primarily by private timber companies and to a lesser extent, by state agencies or the U. S. Forest Service. Of the 159,300 ha of forest lands administered by the BLM within the study area, 57% (90,800 ha) is in the Coast Ranges Province and 43% (68,500 ha) is in the Western Cascades Province. These two provinces are separated by the Willamette Valley, a predominantly agricultural, urban, and residential region.

Forests within the study area are dominated by western hemlock (*Tsuga heterophylla*), Douglas-fir (*Pseudotsuga menziesii*), and western redcedar (*Thuja plicata*). Red alder (*Alnus rubra*) and bigleaf maple (*Acer macrophyllum*) are common hardwoods, and are often intermixed with conifers, or in some cases occur in pure hardwood stands. Sitka spruce (*Picea sitchensis*) occurs in some low-lying areas along the coast. Silver fir (*Abies amabilis*) and noble fir (*Abies procera*) are present in a few areas at elevations >1000 m.

As a result of wildfires, wind storms, and extensive timber cutting, forests in the Coast Ranges are dominated by young conifer forests or conifer/hardwood forests interspersed with recent clear-cuts covered by grasses, brush, and conifer seedlings (Morris 1934, Teensma et al. 1991). Only about 3% of the forested habitats on BLM lands in the Coast Ranges are old-growth conifer stands (≥200 years old); the majority of these stands occur in patches of ≤40 ha (USDI-BLM 1992b).

The portion of the study area in the Western Cascades is also characterized by a mosaic of young forests, recently harvested patches, and older forests. However, less of this region has been harvested, and large blocks of mature forest (80–199 years old), and old-growth forest (≥200 yrs old) are more common than in the Coast Ranges. Old-growth stands currently comprise approximately 14% of the forest habitat on BLM lands in the Western Cascades portion of the study area.

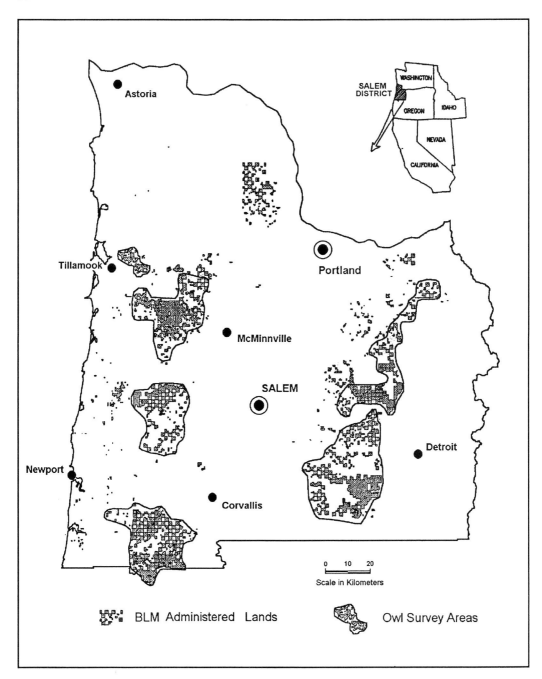

FIGURE 1. Salem District Study Area in northwest Oregon, showing Bureau of Land Management lands, and areas consistently surveyed for Northern Spotted Owls, 1986–1993.

METHODS

Data were collected from pairs or single owls at 123 sites within the study area, including 116 sites on BLM-administered lands and 7 sites on other ownerships. An owl site was defined as a location where Spotted Owls exhibited territorial behavior on at least two occasions ≥2 weeks apart within a given year (Franklin et al. *this volume*). Fifty-four of these owl sites were in the Coast Ranges, and 69 were in the Cascades.

TABLE 1. NUMBERS OF NORTHERN SPOTTED OWLS BY AGE-CLASS AND YEAR CAPTURED, THAT WERE USED IN CAPTURE-RECAPTURE ANALYSIS FOR THE SALEM DISTRICT STUDY AREA IN NORTHWEST OREGON, 1986–1993

Year	≥3 yrs old[a]		1 or 2 yrs old		Juveniles
	M	F	M	F	
1986	13	9	2	0	9
1987	4	7	3	1	13
1988	3	2	2	2	12
1989	8	5	1	0	11
1990	10	11	0	0	14
1991	13	9	1	1	3
1992	17	20	1	1	37
1993	16	5	2	0	2
Totals	74	68	12	5	101

[a] M = male, F = female.

Surveys and banding followed protocols described in Franklin et al. (*this volume*). Survey efforts were consistent at all owl sites, across all survey blocks, and across both physiographic provinces. A capture-recapture data set was compiled from banding and reobservation records of 260 owls from 83 sites where survey efforts over the study period were consistently high (≥ 3 complete visits per season following initial marking of an owl).

Age or group-specific survival was estimated with Cormack-Jolly-Seber open population models in Program SURGE (Lebreton et al. 1992, Franklin et al. *this volume*). Goodness of fit of the data to the assumptions in the global capture-recapture model was examined with Tests 2 and 3 in Program RELEASE (Burnham et al. 1987). Capture-recapture models were constructed for two different data sets, one which included only ≥ 3-yr-old owls, and another that included 2 age groups (juveniles and non-juveniles). The non-juvenile age group included all owls ≥ 1-yr-old. Selection of models that best fit the data was based on Akaike's Information Criterion (AIC, Akaike 1973, Anderson et al. 1994) and likelihood ratio tests (LRT, Burnham et al. 1987).

Age-specific fecundity of territorial females was assessed from 161 records at 58 owl sites where a female was confirmed, and where survey efforts met protocol for determining the number of young produced as described in Franklin et al. (*this volume*). Fecundity was defined as the number of female young fledged per female owl and was estimated by dividing the number of young fledged by two, which assumes that owlets that left the nest had a 50:50 sex ratio (Franklin et al. *this volume*). The finite rate of population growth (λ) was estimated from the age-specific estimates of fecundity and model generated estimates of survival as described in Franklin et al. (*this volume*).

RESULTS

SAMPLE SIZE AND GOODNESS OF FIT

Two hundred eighty-two Spotted Owls were banded during the study. After excluding owls that were radio-marked or that occupied sites that were not consistently surveyed, we used 260 owls in the capture-recapture analysis (142 ≥ 3-yr-old owls, 17 1- and 2-yr-old owls, and 101 juveniles) (Table 1). Most of these owls (74.2%) were from the Western Cascades Range. The small size of the sample from the Coast Ranges precluded separate goodness-of-fit analyses of the Coast Ranges and Cascades Range data. Results of the overall goodness-of-fit tests on non-juveniles (all owls ≥ 1 year old) revealed no lack of fit to the assumptions in the capture-recapture models (Table 2). However, many components of these tests did not have sufficient data, which was not unexpected considering the relatively small sample size. Goodness-of-fit tests of the juvenile data provided no meaningful insights because the number of recaptures was small (N = 15).

MODEL SELECTION

The capture-recapture model that best fit the data from ≥ 3-yr-old owls included a negative linear time trend on survival (Fig. 2) and a sex-

TABLE 2. RESULTS OF GOODNESS-OF-FIT TESTS FROM PROGRAM RELEASE (BURNHAM ET AL. 1987) FOR CAPTURE-RECAPTURE DATA FROM NORTHERN SPOTTED OWLS ON THE SALEM DISTRICT STUDY AREA IN NORTHWEST OREGON, 1986–1993

Age and sex	TEST 2 + 3			TEST 2 P	TEST 3 P
	χ^2	df	P		
≥3-yr-old females	14.121	16	0.590	0.904	0.324
≥3-yr-old males	12.625	14	0.556	0.142	0.837
≥1-yr-old females	14.075	16	0.593	0.843	0.361
≥1-yr-old males	12.511	14	0.565	0.178	0.798

TABLE 3. CAPTURE-RECAPTURE MODELS FOR NORTHERN SPOTTED OWLS ON THE SALEM DISTRICT STUDY AREA IN NORTHWEST OREGON: 1986–1993. MODELS THAT BEST FIT EACH DATA SET ARE INDICATED BY LOWEST AIC VALUES (AKAIKE'S INFORMATION CRITERION, AKAIKE 1973). LIKELIHOOD RATIO TESTS (LRT) INDICATE COMPARISONS BETWEEN THE MODEL WITH THE LOWEST AIC VALUE AND COMPETING MODELS WITHIN 2 AIC UNITS.

Model[a]	K^b	AIC	LRT χ^2	df	P
$\geq$3-yr-old owls					
$\{\phi_T, p_s\}$	4	501.465			
$\{\phi_T, p\}$	3	502.268	2.803	1	0.094
$\{\phi, p_s\}$	3	502.286	2.821	1	0.093
$\{\phi_T, p_{s+T}\}$	5	502.793	0.671	1	0.412
$\{\phi, p_{s+T}\}$	4	504.256			
2-age-class models					
$\{\phi_{a2+T}, p_{a4'+s}\}$	8	721.077			
$\{\phi_{a2}, p_{a4'+s}\}$	7	721.588	2.511	1	0.1130
$\{\phi_{a3+T}, p_{a4'+s}\}$	9	721.974	1.103	1	0.2936
$\{\phi_{a2}, p_{a4'}\}$	6	726.067			
$\{\phi_{a2+T}, p_{a3'+s}\}$	7	728.953			

[a] Subscripts associated with ϕ (survival) and p (capture probability) indicate these parameters have a linear time trend (T), or a variable time trend (t), or a difference between sexes (s), or a difference between two or more age classes (a2, a3, a4), or some additive combination of factors. Models of ϕ and p without subscripts indicate that there were no sex, age or time effects on survival or recapture rates. Age effects on capture probability (denoted as a3' or a4') relate specifically to birds first captured as juveniles, since age of birds first captured as adults was unknown.
[b] Number of estimable parameters in model.

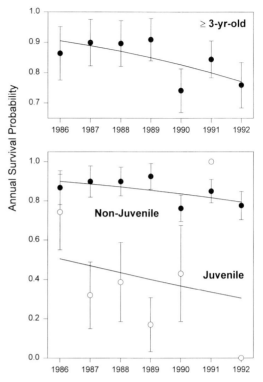

FIGURE 2. Estimates of annual survival for Northern Spotted Owls in the Salem District Study Area in northwest Oregon, 1986–1993. Solid lines represent linear declining survival estimates obtained from the most parsimonious capture-recapture models. Estimates of annual survival (and associated SEs) obtained from models with variable time trends are shown for comparison.

effect on recapture (model $\{\phi_T, p_s\}$, Table 3). Likelihood ratio tests indicated that three other models fit the data nearly as well as the model with the lowest AIC (Table 3).

The model that best fit the 2-age-class data (juveniles and non-juveniles) included an age effect plus a negative linear time trend on survival, and an age and sex effect on recapture (model $\{\phi_{a2+T}, p_{a4'+s}\}$, Table 3, Fig. 2). Likelihood ratio tests indicated that two other models fit the data nearly as well as the selected model (Table 3). All 2-age-class models had age-specific recapture probabilities for juveniles only. This is because the exact age of juveniles at first capture (and all subsequent recaptures) was known. In contrast, the exact age of owls first captured as adults ($\geq$3 year old) was unknown. The best 2-age-class models included 4 age classes on recapture probability (denoted pa4'), suggesting that recapture probabilities gradually improved for owls banded as juveniles, up to age 3 yrs. The age-effect on recapture rates of juveniles appeared to be strongly influenced by the 1986 juvenile cohort, which made up only 9% of all juveniles banded in the 1986–1992 cohorts, but accounted for 33% of all juvenile recaptures.

SURVIVAL ESTIMATES

The estimate of apparent annual survival from the most parsimonious model for $\geq$3-yr-old owls was 0.844 (SE = 0.026). For the best fitting 2-age-class model, estimates of apparent annual survival were 0.851 (SE = 0.022) for non-juveniles and 0.402 (SE = 0.105) for juveniles. Standard errors for estimates of survival from models that included a linear time effect on survival were approximations based on SEs of models with similar AIC values and no time effects on survival.

FECUNDITY ESTIMATES

Estimated mean annual fecundity was 0.3810 for $\geq$3-yr-old owls (SE = 0.036, N = 147). Estimated fecundity for 1- and 2-yr-old females was 0.500 (SE = 0.236, N = 3), but the sample for this estimate was so small that we had little confidence in it. Mean annual fecundity for all females combined, including 11 individuals whose age could not be determined, was 0.370 (SE = 0.034, N = 160). Fecundity of ≥3-yr-old owls varied among years, ranging from a low of 0.021 in 1993 to a high of 0.714 in 1986 (Fig. 3).

RATE OF POPULATION CHANGE

Using survival estimates for juveniles and non-juveniles from the selected age-class model, and separate estimates of adult and subadult fecundity, the estimated rate of population growth ($\hat{\lambda}$) was 1.019 (SE = 0.073), indicating a population that was increasing by 1.9% per year. A one-tailed test of the null hypothesis that $\lambda \leq 1.0$ indicated that λ did not differ from 1.0 (z = 0.26, P = 0.397). This inference to the rate of population change relates primarily to the population of territorial females in the study area, as has been noted by Anderson and Burnham (1992) and Burnham et al. (1994b, *this volume*). A power analysis indicated that there was only an 8.5% chance of detecting a significant trend given the estimated rate of change (i.e., the power of the test was low).

DISCUSSION

Although our estimate of λ was partially based on vital rates calculated from small samples for some age groups (namely, juvenile survival and subadult fecundity), we have no reason to reject the overall inference of a non-declining population from the data presented. This outcome was surprising considering that the northern Oregon Coast Ranges have been consistently identified as having little suitable habitat and few Spotted Owls (Forsman et al. 1977, Forsman 1988, Thomas et al. 1990, USDI FWS 1992, USDA and USDI 1994a). Because our sample was dominated by banded owls from the Western Cascades, a stationary population in that Province may have obscured a declining population in the Coast Ranges. But this explanation seems unlikely considering that a nearby study in the Western Cascades also found a declining population (Miller et al. *this volume*).

Because of the considerable uncertainty regarding possible biases in estimates of birth and death rates of Spotted Owls (Noon and Biles 1990, Anderson and Burnham 1992, Thomas et al. 1993, Burnham et al. 1994b, USDA and USDI 1994a, Franklin et al. 1995, Bart 1995, Raphael et al. *this volume*), we believe estimates of λ should be viewed with caution. However, the negative linear trend in adult survival during the study period is cause for concern, in that we know of no methodological biases that would cause such a trend. Burnham et al. (*this volume*) reported a similar trend on adult female survival from their

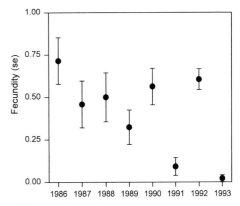

FIGURE 3. Annual fecundity estimates for ≥3-yr-old female Northern Spotted Owls on the Salem District Study Area in northwest Oregon, 1986–1993. Error bars indicate SE. Fecundity was defined as the mean number of female young fledged per female owl detected on the study area.

meta-analysis of data from 12 demographic study areas.

Our sample of recaptured juveniles was small and dominated by a small cohort from 1986. Recognizing that both positive biases (temporary emigration) and negative biases (permanent emigration) could be effecting our estimates of juvenile survival, we believe that our estimate 0.402 for juvenile survival may be biased high as a result of the predominant influence of the 1986 juvenile cohort. The prospect of obtaining a large enough sample of capture-recapture data to adequately assess juvenile survival may be rather unlikely for the Salem Study Area, given the relatively low number of owls present, low reproductive output, and dispersed nature of sampling areas. For this reason, other methods (e.g., radiotelemetry of juveniles) may afford better estimates of juvenile survival than can currently be obtained using capture-recapture methods.

Given larger samples, it would also be more appropriate to evaluate the Salem data in two separate samples, because the data come from two physiographic provinces with markedly different amounts of suitable owl habitat (Raphael et al. *this volume*). A separate analysis of the Coast Ranges data will likely be possible only if we combine our data with data from other studies in the Oregon Coast Ranges, which we hope to do in future analyses.

Estimates of adult survival in the Salem Study Area were near the mean (0.844) reported for 11 study areas in Burnham et al. (1994b). We did not attempt to adjust estimates of juvenile survival to account for permanent emigration as did Burnham et al. (1994b), because no estimates of emigration were available for our study area. It is also likely that some adults occasionally emigrate. To the extent that adults and juveniles emigrated, survived, and went undetected, our estimates of adult and juvenile survival are biased low (Burnham et al. 1994b).

Although a number of biases could effect estimates of fecundity (Bart 1995), we were most concerned about differences in detectability of birds that nested successfully vs. pairs that either did not nest or that failed at nesting. In many cases where we were relatively certain that pairs of owls did not nest or failed at nesting, we could not find the birds enough times to meet the protocol for determination of numbers of young produced (Franklin et al. *this volume*). We were concerned that this could have caused a positive bias in estimates of fecundity, since pairs that nested successfully were usually fairly easy to locate. If we had included cases where we could not relocate pairs enough times to meet survey protocol, but where we were reasonably certain that they had produced no young, our estimate of fecundity for ≥3-yr-old females would have decreased by 1.5%. However, because of other factors that could cause positive or negative bias in estimates of fecundity (Reid et al. *this volume,* Raphael et al. *this volume*), we were reluctant to make adjustments to estimates of fecundity based on an analysis of only one source of possible bias.

Although our analysis indicated a stationary population, we urge caution in interpretation of our results. We are particularly concerned that potential biases affecting the data have not been fully resolved (e.g., Bart 1995, Raphael et al. *this volume*). In addition, our analysis was based on a combined data set from the Coast Ranges and Cascades Mountains Provinces. Thus, while our analysis may represent overall conditions for the entire study area, it may not represent specific conditions within the individual Provinces. Until these concerns are addressed, we believe that management agencies like the BLM would be well-advised to adopt a cautious approach to management of Spotted Owls.

SUMMARY

We estimated age-specific birth and death rates and population growth rates of Spotted Owls based on a sample of banded owls from the Coast Ranges and Western Cascades Ranges in northwest Oregon. Data were collected from 1986–1993. Most (74%) of the banded sample was from the Western Cascades Range Province. Juvenile and non-juvenile survival estimates from the best age-specific capture model were 0.402 ($SE = 0.105$) and 0.851 ($SE = 0.022$), respectively. Fecundity of ≥3-yr-old owls was 0.381 ($SE = 0.036$). The estimated finite rate of population change ($\hat{\lambda}$) was 1.019 ($SE = 0.073$), which did not differ from a stationary population ($P = 0.397$). Although our analysis did not indicate a significant decline in the population during the period of observation, the analysis did indicate that the adult survival rate was declining. Given the declining trend in adult survival and uncertainty regarding bias in demographic estimates we suggest that managers should continue to take a cautious approach regarding management of Spotted Owls in Northwestern Oregon.

ACKNOWLEDGMENTS

For assistance with field surveys and banding we thank S. Bahe, C. J. Beyer, M. Brown, C. A. Cooper, K. J. D'Angiolillo, S. Dowlan, J. S. England, J. N. Irving, D. Larson, L. Larson, M. K. Lohr, A. E. McCaull, R. W. Monthey, R. Pace, G. R. Ross, and L. Scofield. We also thank A. E. McCaull, J. Ponzetti, D. Larson, L. Larson and J. Zeyen-Hall for assistance with data verification and compilation. Special thanks to J. Alegria for statistical assistance. Analytical assistance was provided by D. R. Anderson, K. P. Burnham, J. Clobert, J. E. Hines, J. D. Nichols, R. Pradel, E. Rexstad, T. Shenk, G. C. White, and K. R. Wilson. Reviews by M. J. Conroy, D. W. Holt, T. Stevens, M. G. Raphael, and S. DeStefano improved the manuscript. Any errors in interpretation are our own.

Key words: demography, fecundity, mark-recapture, Northern Spotted owl, Oregon Cascades, Oregon Coast Ranges, population growth, *Strix occidentalis caurina,* survival.

Studies in Avian Biology No. 17:37–46, 1996.

DEMOGRAPHY OF NORTHERN SPOTTED OWLS ON THE H. J. ANDREWS STUDY AREA IN THE CENTRAL CASCADE MOUNTAINS, OREGON

Gary S. Miller, Stephen DeStefano, Keith A. Swindle, and E. Charles Meslow

INTRODUCTION

We initiated intensive monitoring of a Northern Spotted Owl (*Strix occidentalis caurina*) population in the central Cascade Mountains of western Oregon in 1987. Our study was established to collect long-term demographic trend information in order to better understand the current status of the Northern Spotted Owl population in the western Oregon Cascades. In particular, we wanted to determine if concerns about gradual population declines in conjunction with habitat loss were well-founded (Thomas et al. 1990, 1993a; USDI 1990).

The H. J. Andrews Study Area (HJA) was an ideal location to examine these issues. Vegetation on the area is typical of much of the forest and land-use conditions on the west slope of the Cascade range in Oregon. The area also has a long history of Spotted Owl research. The first intensive study of Spotted Owl ecology, including home range size and habitat use, occurred on the HJA area and began in the early 1970s (Forsman 1980, Forsman et al. 1984). Several owl nest sites have been monitored periodically since that time. With this work came some of the first banded Spotted Owls, providing insights into the species' longevity. In addition, the first study of dispersal of juvenile Spotted Owls in Oregon was conducted on the HJA (Miller 1989), along with research on Spotted Owl prey species (Rosenberg 1991) and the influence of habitat fragmentation on owl populations (Johnson 1992).

Our objectives for this long-term monitoring study were to estimate survival based on capture-recapture methods, estimate age-specific fecundity based on direct observations of number of young fledged, and to use this information to calculate rate of population change (λ) for the period 1987–1993. We also compared these results to empirical counts of territorial owls, and discuss owl population dynamics in light of remaining amounts of late seral stage forest on our study area.

STUDY AREA

The 1,474 km² HJA Study Area is located on the west slope of the Cascade Mountain Range in western Oregon, and includes the H. J. Andrews Experimental Forest plus adjacent lands on the Willamette National Forest, and some interspersed private holdings (Fig. 1). The study area is bounded on the east by wilderness and on the west by private lands and lands administered by the Bureau of Land Management. Topography is typical of the Western Cascades Province (Franklin and Dyrness 1973), with mountainous terrain deeply dissected by rivers and streams. Elevations range from 400–1,500m. Climate is maritime, with relatively dry summers and wet winters. Winter precipitation is often in the form of snow at higher elevations.

The study area is within the Western Hemlock (*Tsuga heterophylla*) Zone, the most extensive vegetation zone in western Oregon (Munger 1930, Franklin and Dyrness 1973). Subclimax forests of Douglas-fir (*Pseudotsuga menziesii*), western hemlock, and western redcedar (*Thuja plicata*) dominate most of the area. Although about 52% of the study area has been harvested or is not considered Spotted Owl habitat, extensive stands of older forest are present on much of the area, with most stands being either older than 200 years of age or younger than 40 years of age. Late seral stage forest (≥ 80 yr-old) and younger forest (< 80 yr-old) accounted for 48% and 15%, respectively, of the area of the DSA, and 63% and 16% of the Experimental Forest (Table 1). The remaining land base was comprised of habitats that we believed were not suitable for spotted owls. We did not have estimates for cover types for the GSA.

The study area includes a central, 31,700-ha Density Study Area (DSA), nested within a larger 147,400-ha General Study Area (GSA). The 6,395-ha Experimental Forest is located within the boundaries of the DSA, and makes up 4% of the land area of the GSA (Fig. 1). Hereafter, reference to either GSA or HJA includes the DSA.

METHODS

FIELD METHODS

We monitored Spotted Owl demographic performance and territory occupation from 1987 to 1993. In general, calling surveys to locate Spotted

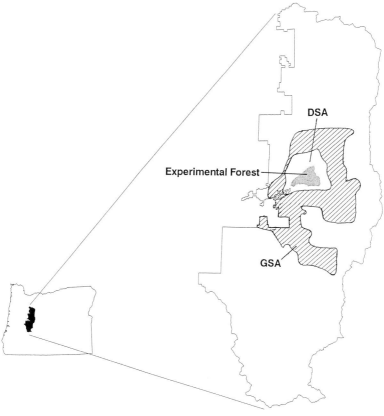

FIGURE 1.   The H. J. Andrews Study Area (HJA) on the Willamette National Forest, west slope of the Cascade Mountain Range, Oregon. The study area included a 31,700-ha Density Study Area (DSA) that was nested within a larger 1,474 km^2 General Study Area (GSA) (diagonal-lined area). The 6,395-ha H. J. Andrews Experimental Forest (dark area) was part of the DSA.

Owls and capture and banding techniques followed Forsman (1983) and Franklin et al. (*this volume*).

Within the DSA, we did complete-coverage surveys, using both night and day calling, to locate owls. Within the GSA, we surveyed for owls in and around areas where we had banded pairs of owls, but we did not attempt to attain complete coverage of the entire area. Surveys were conducted from March–August. Each year, we first searched locations where pairs or single individuals had been located in previous years; historic nest sites and known roost sites were searched first. When there was no response by an owl, adjacent areas were searched. Area searches were initially conducted during the day for those sites with previous information on Spotted Owl use, and at night for those sites with no known history of Spotted Owl use. During day searches, observers walked sites systemati-

cally and used vocal imitations or taped calls to elicit responses from owls (Forsman 1983). In most cases, if owls were present they responded to the observer and could then be located visually at their roost. If day searches were unsuccessful on several occasions at the same site, night calling was initiated in hopes of obtaining a response. Late in the summer, night calling was conducted in the early morning hours, 1–2 hours prior to sunrise, providing the potential to contact owls just before they went to roost. If a response occurred, we had the opportunity to walk into the site as soon as it was light and locate owls on their roosts.

Owls were captured using a noose pole (Forsman 1983). U. S. Fish and Wildlife Service lock-on leg bands and colored plastic leg bands were placed on all owls captured. Owls ≥ 1 yr old were marked with unique color band combinations. Juvenile owls were all marked with the same

TABLE 1. AREA AND PERCENT COVERAGE OF FOUR MAJOR FOREST COVER TYPES ON THE DENSITY STUDY AREA (TOTAL AREA = 31,700 HA) AND EXPERIMENTAL FOREST (TOTAL AREA = 6,395 HA) ON THE H. J. ANDREWS STUDY AREA, WESTERN CASCADE MOUNTAINS, OREGON, 1987–1993. THE EXPERIMENTAL FOREST WAS A SUBSET OF THE DSA AND WAS LOCATED ENTIRELY WITHIN THE BOUNDARIES OF THE DSA. AREA ESTIMATE OF THE DSA INCLUDES THE EXPERIMENTAL FOREST. CLASSIFICATION OF COVER TYPES WAS BASED ON LANDSAT IMAGERY (SEE COHEN ET AL. 1995)

Area	Cover type	Area (ha)	% area
Density Study Area (DSA)	Water	148.2	0.5
	Non-habitat[a]	11,677.1	36.8
	≤80-yr-old forest	4,641.3	14.6
	≥80-yr-old forest	15,282.2	48.1
Experimental Forest	Water	0.4	<0.01
	Non-habitat	1,376.4	21.5
	≤80-yr-old forest	1,004.8	15.7
	≥80-yr-old forest	4,012.9	62.7

[a] Non-habitat included areas not suitable for Northern Spotted Owls, such as non-forested areas (e.g., agricultural fields, natural meadows), open and semi-open hardwood and conifer forest, and lava and rock.

color leg bands. If juveniles were encountered in subsequent years, they were recaptured and rebanded with unique color combinations.

We conducted complete annual counts of non-juvenile (≥1 yr old) territorial owls, which included pairs and resident singles, on the DSA. An owl was defined as a territorial individual if ≥2 visual or auditory detections were recorded, based on an established protocol (Franklin et al. *this volume*). We excluded owls whose territories straddled DSA boundaries or were in relatively inaccessible areas and thus were not surveyed on a consistent basis during each year of the study— we called these "adjusted" counts. For comparative purposes, we also report "unadjusted" counts, where unadjusted refers to inclusion of all owls on the DSA, regardless of whether or not they were included consistently in our annual counts.

We defined annual survey effort as the time spent by all crew members in field activities related to research, including night surveys, daytime follow-ups, and capture and banding. Total survey effort was recorded for the DSA and the GSA. We used linear regression and multiple regression (Ryan et al. 1980, SAS 1990b) to test for trends in density after accounting for differences in survey effort over time. Our ability to detect trends in numbers of owls over time, given our data, was examined with program TRENDS (Gerodette 1987).

We conducted nesting status surveys between 1 April and 1 June each year from 1988–1993. Once a pair was determined to be nesting, the nest site was visited during late May to mid-June to count fledglings. We made ≥2 visits to the site to find and count the number of young fledged, timing the visits so that young were observed as soon as possible after leaving the nest. A mini-

mum of 4 mice were offered to one or both members of the pair during each visit, with visits separated by at least one week, to determine the reproductive status of the adult pair and to assist in locating the young (Forsman 1983, Franklin et al. *this volume*). Annual fecundity was defined as the number of female young produced per female owl, and was based on the number of young leaving the nest (fledging) (Franklin et al. *this volume*). Fecundity was estimated separately for 1–2-yr-old owls and for owls ≥3 yrs old ("adults").

DATA ANALYSIS

We used capture-recapture models to estimate age- and sex-specific survival of color-marked owls (Franklin et al. *this volume*). Capture histories (Burnham et al. 1987:28–36) that spanned the 7-yr period (1987–1993) were developed for each marked owl. Owls were grouped according to sex and age (juveniles were <1 yr old, non-juveniles were ≥1 yr old, adults were ≥3 yrs old).

We used program RELEASE to summarize our capture-release data, to conduct goodness-of-fit tests (GOF) to assess the fit of our data to the Cormack-Jolly-Seber (CJS) model (Pollock et al. 1990, Burnham et al. 1987), and to compare survival rates of adult males and adult females. In RELEASE, GOF tests consist of 2 components, which Burnham et al. (1987:71–77) refer to as TEST 2 and TEST 3. TEST 2 tests several of the requisite assumptions of the CJS model (Franklin et al. *this volume*), but focuses on cohorts of owls (i.e., groups of birds rereleased during the same year). TEST 3 focuses on subcohorts (i.e., individuals with the same capture histories) and tests whether previously released individuals have the same future fates as newly released individ-

TABLE 2. NUMBERS OF NORTHERN SPOTTED OWLS BANDED ON THE H. J. ANDREWS STUDY AREA (HJA) IN THE CENTRAL CASCADES OF WESTERN OREGON DURING 1987–1993

Year	Adult (≥3 yrs) females	Adult (≥3 yrs) males	1–2-yr-old females	1–2-yr-old males	Juveniles
1987	17	20	3	2	12
1988	24	22	3	10	37
1989	26	30	4	7	24
1990	15	11	8	1	29
1991	7	15	3	4	26
1992	17	17	5	3	98
1993	3	8	1	3	0
Totals	109	123	27	30	226

uals. Both TEST 2 and 3 consist of a series of χ^2 contingency tables, the results of which are additive and can be reported as TEST 2 + 3 (Burnham et al. 1987). A P-value that was not significant (>0.1) indicated that there were no differences in estimates of survival and recapture probabilities among cohorts or in the future fates of subcohorts of owls, and thus the data examined fit the CJS model.

Program RELEASE will also compare 2 groups and calculate a survival ratio (ŝ) where $\hat{s} = \hat{\phi}_t / \hat{\phi}_c$, t is treatment effect, and c is control (Burnham et al. 1987:56–71). An s-ratio $\neq$ 1.0 indicates a treatment effect on survival. We compared survival in adult males and adult females, where our "treatment effect" was sex.

We used program SURGE for model building and selection and to produce estimates and variances of survival rates (ϕ) and capture probabilities (p) (Clobert et al. 1987, Lebreton et al. 1992). Model parameterization followed Franklin et al. (this volume) and included considerations for age, sex, and time (years) (see Appendix for notation and subscripts). Model selection philosophy followed the principle of parsimony (Burnham and Anderson 1992) and used Akaike's Information Criteria (AIC) as the basis to select the most appropriate or best model (i.e., the model with the fewest parameters that fit the data and was, in our judgment, biologically realistic) (Akaike 1973, Anderson et al. 1994, Burnham et al. 1995a, Franklin et al. this volume). Models with the lowest AIC value are considered the most appropriate, and those that differed from the best model by an AIC value of ≤2 are presented for comparative purposes. Likelihood ratio tests (McCullough and Nelder 1983) were used to compare models with similar AIC values.

We examined two groups of models based on age of owls: (1) adult and (2) age-class (juvenile-nonjuvenile) models. Not all owls that are 1 or 2 yrs old breed, but our sample of marked owls

in this age range was small. We thus combined data for all owls ≥1 yr old (i.e., nonjuveniles) for the age-class models. We did suspect, however, that adults (i.e., owls ≥3 yrs old) had different survival rates than 1–2-yr-old birds, and so we ran survival models that considered only owls ≥3 yrs old.

We computed lambda (λ), the finite rate of population change, from our age-specific survival and fecundity estimates for the time period 1987–1993 (Franklin et al. this volume). Calculation of λ is based on the matrix theory developed by Leslie (1945, 1948) and Lefkovitch (1965), and is explained more fully by Franklin et al. (this volume). We used the 1-tailed form of the t-test to test the null hypothesis that λ < 1, which would indicate a declining population during 1987–1993 for the resident Spotted Owl population on the HJA Study Area.

Calculations of λ are based on age-specific survival and do not account for permanent emigration. Emigration of marked juvenile owls off of the HJA Study Area undoubtedly occurred, but because the HJA was relatively isolated (i.e., there was only one other demography study nearby), the probability of detecting an owl that moved off the area was low. Therefore, we asked the question, "what would juvenile emigration rate have to be in order for λ to equal 1?" We also asked this same question with regards to juvenile survival, i.e., "what would juvenile survival rate have to be in order for λ to equal 1?" The equation used for answering these questions is given by Franklin et al. (this volume).

We used LANDSAT information to categorize types of habitat within the boundaries of the Experimental Forest and the larger DSA (LANDSAT data on cover types were not available for the entire GSA). Original LANDSAT landform classifications were developed by Cohen et al. (1995). We pooled Cohen et al.'s 12 classifications to 4 cover types, based on their potential suitability as Spotted Owl habitat. These categories were water, non-habitat, closed-canopy forest <80 years old, and forests 80 years or older. Non-habitat included land areas not suitable for owls such as non-forested areas (e.g., agricultural fields, natural meadows), open and semi-open hardwood and conifer forest, and lava and rock. We calculated total land area (ha) and percent coverage for each category.

RESULTS

NUMBER OF OWLS MARKED AND RESIGHTED

During 1987–1993, we color-marked 515 spotted owls, including 226 fledglings, 57 1- or 2-yr-old birds, and 232 adults (≥3 yrs old) (Table 2). Recapture or resighting rates as defined by

TABLE 3. MARK-RECAPTURE DATA DISPLAYED IN *M*-ARRAY FORMAT FOR FEMALE AND MALE NORTHERN SPOTTED OWLS INITIALLY CAPTURED AS JUVENILES (<1 YR OLD), 1- OR 2-YEAR-OLDS, AND ADULTS (≥3 YR OLD) IN THE CENTRAL CASCADE RANGE OF OREGON, 1987–1993. R_i IS THE NUMBER OF ANIMALS MARKED AND RELEASED ON THE ITH OCCASION, M_{IJ} THE NUMBER OF ANIMALS MARKED AND RELEASED ON OCCASION I WHICH WERE RECAPTURED (OR RESIGHTED) ON OCCASION J, AND r_i THE TOTAL NUMBER OF ANIMALS MARKED AND RELEASED ON OCCASION I WHICH WERE LATER RECAPTURED (= ΣM_{IJ}) (BURNHAM ET AL. 1987)

Cohort	i	R_i	m_{ij} for j = 2	3	4	5	6	7	r_i
Juveniles (sexes combined)	1	12	0	2	1	2	0	0	5
	2	37		2	0	2	0	0	4
	3	28			2	3	2	1	8
	4	32				3	1	1	5
	5	36					6	3	9
	6	106						7	7
1–2-yr-old females	1	3	2	0	0	0	0	0	2
	2	5		4	0	0	1	0	5
	3	8			6	0	0	0	6
	4	14				6	2	1	9
	5	9					7	1	8
	6	15						9	9
1–2-yr-old males	1	2	2	0	0	0	0	0	2
	2	12		10	0	0	0	0	10
	3	17			13	0	1	0	14
	4	14				12	0	0	12
	5	16					14	0	14
	6	18						11	11
≥3-yr-old females	1	17	15	1	0	0	0	0	16
	2	39		27	3	1	1	0	32
	3	54			37	6	0	1	44
	4	55				43	4	0	47
	5	57					42	5	47
	6	64						28	28
≥3-yr-old males	1	22	20	0	0	0	0	0	20
	2	40		27	0	0	0	1	28
	3	57			43	3	1	0	47
	4	54				40	3	0	43
	5	58					42	6	48
	6	63						40	40

Burnham et al. (1987:28–36) were 72–80% for owls ≥1 yr old (Table 3). No differences in resighting rates were detected between females and males ($\chi^2 \leq 1.0$, df = 1, P ≥ 0.31). Resighting rate for juveniles (birds <1 yr old), however, was 15%, and was lower than those for other age cohorts ($\chi^2 \geq 142$, df = 1, P < 0.001), probably because juveniles experienced lower rates of survival and higher rates of emigration from our study area than nonjuveniles.

NUMBERS OF TERRITORIAL OWLS ON DSA

Our adjusted counts of number of territorial owls on the DSA were lower than the unadjusted counts for each year during 1988–1993 (1987 was not included because a complete survey of the entire DSA was not conducted that year). This is understandable because the adjusted counts excluded some owls, i.e., those whose territories straddled the DSA boundary or were in relatively inaccessible areas and thus were not consistently included in annual surveys. However, both the unadjusted and adjusted annual estimates of owl numbers within the DSA showed similar trends over time (Fig. 2).

Adjusted counts of owls on the DSA varied by year, but we did not detect an increasing or decreasing trend over time (r = 0.22, slope = 0.06, t = 0.04, df = 4, P = 0.97). The power to detect a trend, either increasing or decreasing, however, was low (1 − β = 0.46) (Gerrodette 1987, Peterman 1990). The proportion of owls detected in the DSA that were banded in a previous year increased from 0.40 in 1988 to a mean of 0.80 (SE = 0.02) per year for the remaining years of the study (1989–1993) (Fig. 3).

DISTRIBUTION OF SURVEY EFFORT

Survey effort for all owl-related research activities on the DSA increased during 1987–1993

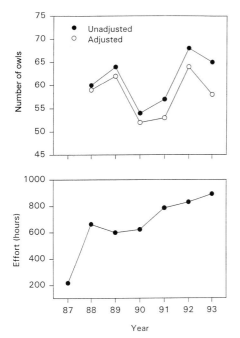

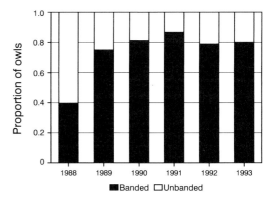

FIGURE 3. Proportion of Northern Spotted Owls detected each year within the 31,700-ha H. J. Andrews Density Study Area that had been banded in previous years, 1988–1993.

FIGURE 2. Trend in numbers of Northern Spotted Owls detected and survey effort for demographic studies on the H. J. Andrews Density Study Area in the central Cascades of western Oregon, 1988–1993. Survey effort was measured as number of hours expended to conduct all field activities related to research on Spotted Owls, including surveys, searches for nests, capture and banding, and observation of banded individuals. The trend in numbers of owls detected was not different from 0 when corrected for survey effort.

(r = 0.88, slope = 90.9, t = 4.12, df = 5, P = 0.009, Fig. 2). A similar, somewhat weaker, trend was observed for the GSA (r = 0.78, slope = 130, t = 2.77, df = 5, P = 0.04). The largest increase in effort occurred between the first and second years (1987–1988) because field work began later in 1987 compared to other years. Effort appeared to approach an asymptote, which is common for long-term field studies (Franklin et al. 1990, *this volume*). After accounting for the increase in survey effort over time, the trend in annual owl counts did not differ from 0 during 1988–1993 (slope = −1.1, t = −0.36, P = 0.74). Numbers of owls varied among years, but there was no obvious increasing or decreasing long-term trend.

FECUNDITY ESTIMATES

Estimated mean annual fecundity was 0.35 (SE = 0.03) for ≥3-yr-old females and 0.15 (SE = 0.10) for 1–2-yr-old owls. Fecundity was consistently higher for adults than younger owls (t = 6.14, df = 63, P < 0.001, N = 377 adults and

30 1–2-yr-old owls). In addition, fecundity and proportion of adult females nesting were high in 1988, 1990, and 1992, and low during alternate years (1987, 1989, 1991, and 1993) (Fig. 4). No successful reproductive activity was detected among the 50 pairs of owls monitored during 1993.

MODEL SELECTION AND ESTIMATES OF SURVIVAL

The combined results for Tests 2 and 3 in Program RELEASE indicated that the data from adult males fit the Cormack-Jolly-Seber model (i.e., no differences in survival rates and recapture probabilities among cohorts [annual releases of marked birds] or in future fates among individual males were detected, $\chi^2 = 16.2$, df = 12, P = 0.18 for Tests 2 + 3). This was not the case for adult females, however, at least at a probability level of 0.10 ($\chi^2 = 19.9$, df = 13, P = 0.10 for Tests 2 + 3). Any problems with lack of fit in the adult female data came from the TEST 3 component of the GOF test, indicating that, in a given year, newly banded and released individuals may have had different future fates than previously banded and released individuals ($\chi^2 = 17.0$, df = 9, P = 0.05 for TEST 3). TEST 2 indicated that fit was adequate for this component of GOF testing (i.e., no differences detected in survival rates and capture probabilities among cohorts, $\chi^2 = 2.8$, df = 4, P = 0.59 for TEST 2). Sample sizes and recapture rates were inadequate to test goodness-of-fit for juveniles and 1–2-yr-old owls. Despite evidence that there may have been some lack of fit to the assumptions in the Cormack-Jolly-Seber models, we proceeded with model testing, assuming that estimates would not be greatly influenced by some lack of fit.

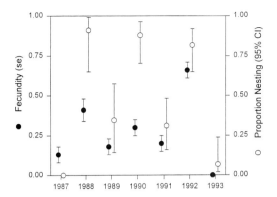

FIGURE 4. Estimated fecundity (± 1 SE) and proportion of females nesting (± 95% CI) for adult female Northern Spotted Owls on the H. J. Andrews Study Area, western Cascade Mountains, Oregon, 1987–1993.

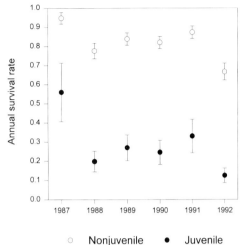

○ Nonjuvenile   ● Juvenile

FIGURE 5. Estimates of survival (±1 SE) for nonjuvenile (≥1 yr old) and juveniles (<1 yr old) Northern Spotted Owls on the H. J. Andrews Study Area, western Cascade Mountains, Oregon, 1987–1993.

Of the 64 adult models examined, the five most parsimonious models (those with the lowest AIC values) all had some form of time variation associated with the capture probabilities, but survival rates appeared constant, with only weak time or sex effects indicated (Table 4). Of the 28 age-class models examined, the model with the lowest AIC value had 11 parameters. This model ($\{\phi_{a2+t}, p_{a3+s}\}$) indicated that survival was a function of two age classes and varied nonlinearly among years, while recapture probability was a function of three age classes and sex. We selected this model as our "best" model, i.e., a biologically reasonable model that followed the principle of parsimony (Franklin et al. *this volume*). The model with the second lowest AIC value (ϕ_{a2+t}, p_{a3+s}) was a 16-parameter model that was not competitive, based on likelihood ratio tests ($\chi^2 = 9.7$, df = 5, P = 0.09, Table 4).

The annual survival estimate for ≥3-yr-old owls from the best adult model ($\{\phi, p_{s+T}\}$) was 0.848 (SE = 0.018). The remaining top competing adult models provided similar survival estimates for adults (Table 5). In models that treated sexes separately, survival was not different between males and females (TEST 1, $\chi^2 = 11.5$, df = 11, P = 0.4). Estimates of survival from the best age-class model (ϕ_{a2+t}, p_{a3+s}) averaged 0.821 (SE = 0.016) for nonjuveniles and 0.288 (SE = 0.052) for juveniles (Table 5).

We plotted estimates of survival for nonjuveniles and juveniles, based on our best age-class model over time (Fig. 5) and tested the null hypothesis that there was not a negative trend in survival. Survival rates did decline during 1987–1993 for both nonjuveniles (r = −0.64, slope = 3.69, df = 5, t = 2.12, P = 0.04 for 1-tailed test) and juveniles (r = −0.64, slope = 4.89, df = 5,

t = 1.78, P = 0.07 for 1-tailed test). In addition, there was a similar pattern in annual variation in survival between nonjuveniles and juveniles (Fig. 5).

POPULATION RATE OF CHANGE

Using the estimates of survival from the best age-class model and our empirical estimates of

TABLE 4. SUMMARY OF CAPTURE-RECAPTURE MODELS EXAMINED FOR ESTIMATING SURVIVAL (ϕ) AND RECAPTURE (P) PROBABILITIES FOR NORTHERN SPOTTED OWLS ON THE H. J. ANDREWS STUDY AREA IN THE CENTRAL CASCADES OF WESTERN OREGON DURING 1987–1993

Model[a]	Number of parameters	Deviance	AIC[b]
Adult models			
$\{\phi, p_{s+T}\}$	4	882.2	890.2
$\{\phi_t, p_{s+T}\}$	9	872.5	890.5
$\{\phi_s, p_{s+T}\}$	5	880.6	890.6
$\{\phi_{s+t}, p_{s+t}\}$	13	864.9	890.9
$\{\phi, p_{s+t}\}$	8	875.0	891.0
Age-class (juvenile-nonjuvenile) models			
$\{\phi_{a2+t}, p_{a3+s}\}$	11	1325.3	1347.3
$\{\phi_{a2+t}, p_{a3+s}\}$	16	1320.9	1352.9
$\{\phi_{a2•t}, p_{a3•s}\}$	18	1320.9	1356.9
$\{\phi_{a2+T}, p_{a3+s}\}$	7	1343.0	1357.0
$\{\phi_{a3+t}, p_{a3+s}\}$	21	1315.8	1357.8

[a] Model subscripts include s for sex, t for time as a categorical variable, and T for time as a continuous (linear) value. A + or • between subscripts signifies additive or multiplicative interactions, respectively, between variables.
[b] Akaike's Information Criterion (Akaike 1973; Franklin et al. *this volume*).

TABLE 5. ESTIMATES OF ANNUAL SURVIVAL (ϕ) FOR NORTHERN SPOTTED OWLS CALCULATED FROM SELECTED CAPTURE-RECAPTURE MODELS, H. J. ANDREWS STUDY AREA IN THE CASCADE MOUNTAINS OF WESTERN OREGON, 1987–1993

Model[a]	Juveniles		Nonjuveniles	
	$\hat{\phi}_J$	SE ($\hat{\phi}_J$)	$\hat{\phi}_A$	SE ($\hat{\phi}_A$)
Adult models ($\geq$ 3-yr-old owls)				
$\{\phi, p_{s+T}\}$			0.848	0.018
$\{\phi_t, p_{s+T}\}$			0.840[b]	0.024[c]
$\{\phi_s, p_{s+T}\}$			♀: 0.872	0.024
			♂: 0.830	0.024
$\{\phi_{s+t}, p_{s+t}\}$			♀: 0.889[b]	0.017[c]
			♂: 0.834[b]	0.017[c]
$\{\phi, p_{s+t}\}$			0.851	0.017
Age-class models (juvenile-nonjuvenile owls)				
$\{\phi_{a2+t}, p_{a3+s}\}$	0.288[b]	0.052[c]	0.821[b]	0.016[c]
$\{\phi_{a2 \cdot t}, p_{a3+s}\}$	0.337[b]	0.052[c]	0.820[b]	0.016[c]
$\{\phi_{a2 \cdot t}, p_{a3 \cdot s}\}$	0.337[b]	0.052[c]	0.820[b]	0.016[c]
$\{\phi_{a2+T}, p_{a3+s}\}$	0.253[b]	0.052[c]	0.822[b]	0.016[c]
$\{\phi_{a3+s}, p_{a3+s}\}$	0.385[b]	0.052[c]	0.255[b,d]	0.052[c]
			0.821[b,e]	0.016[c]

[a] Model subscripts include s for sex, t for time as a categorical variable, and T for time as a continuous (linear) value. A + or • between subscripts signifies additive or multiplicative interactions, respectively, between variables.
[b] Survival estimates averaged over time (years).
[c] Standard error is an approximation based on the nearest (in AIC) model with no time effects on survival probability.
[d] Survival estimate for second-year owls (1-yr-old).
[e] Survival estimate for third-year owls (2-yr-old owls) and adults.

age-specific fecundity, we estimated $\lambda = 0.911$ (SE = 0.012), which was < 1.0 (z = 7.42, P < 0.001). Among the potential biases that may affect calculations of λ (Bart 1995a), we were particularly interested in the influence of juvenile survival or emigration. We, therefore, asked the question, "assuming that λ is really equal to 1.0, and that all other parameters were estimated accurately, how much undetected emigration by juveniles would have to occur, or what would juvenile survival have to be, to attain a λ equal to 1?" Based on additional calculations carried out during the meta-analysis by Burnham et al. (*this volume*), juvenile dispersal (i.e., young of the year surviving and leaving the study area but not being resighted) would have to be 54% or juvenile survival would have had to be 63% for $\lambda = 1.0$.

DISCUSSION

Empirical counts of Northern Spotted Owls on our Density Study Area indicated that the territorial population was relatively stationary during 1987–1993. However, our ability to detect a change in numbers over time was low ($1 - \beta = 0.46$), even for the relatively long period of our study (7 years). We suspect that several more years of count data would be needed in order for us to detect a negative or positive trend in numbers, or to be assured that the territorial population is indeed stationary, based on these kinds of data.

Our calculations of rate of population change ($\lambda = 0.91$, SE = 0.02) suggested that the population of Northern Spotted Owls on the HJA was declining at an annual rate of 9% from 1987 to 1993, which at first seems contradictory to our empirical counts. However, we recommend caution when attempting to relate empirical counts of owls to annual rate of change. Our counts of territorial owls were based on a subsample of the population (DSA only), whereas the estimate of λ was based on owls throughout the entire study area. The rate of tree harvest during the period of this study was less within the DSA than on the rest of the study area, in part due to the influence of the Experimental Forest, which has different management objectives than the rest of the Willamette National Forest and thus lower rates of timber harvest. In addition, the proportion of marked owls on the DSA remained constant at about 80% for each year from 1988–1993. This is an indication that there was at least some turnover (i.e., emigration or mortality of marked owls, which were replaced by unmarked owls) of marked owls on the DSA, because one would suspect that the proportion of marked owls would increase over time rather than remain stable. This premise would be especially true when survey effort is high, as occurred on the HJA area during the last several years of the study.

The juvenile survival rate necessary to make $\lambda = 1.0$ (0.63) was probably higher than what juvenile owls actually experienced on the HJA, but perhaps not unrealistic. Miller (1989) reported an estimated first-year survival rate of 19% with cohort differences from 5–37%, while Forsman et al. (*this volume*) reported juvenile survival, which they adjusted for emigration, of 35% for central Washington and 61% for the Olympic Peninsula.

The juvenile emigration rate necessary to make $\lambda = 1.0$ (0.54) probably was possible for juvenile Spotted Owls banded on the HJA Study Area. This inference is based on the results of two other studies. In 1983, nine juvenile Spotted Owls were radio-marked on the HJA Study Area and followed through dispersal (Miller 1989). All nine of the juveniles left the HJA area and did not return (although radio contact was lost for three of these individuals). In another study, Forsman et al. (*this volume*) found that about 60% of radio-marked juveniles moved off of their study areas in Washington. These data indicate that, for a relatively isolated study area like ours, a juvenile emigration rate of 50–60% is likely. It is therefore possible that a relatively large number of marked juveniles left the HJA Study Area, survived, and went undetected.

Reproductive effort was highly variable on an annual basis, with extremes of virtually no successful reproductive output at all (1993) to very high reproductive output (1992). There was also an interesting pattern of alternatively high and low years of both proportion of females nesting and fecundity. We have not identified a mechanism to explain this pattern and the synchrony among female owls, but suspect food resources may play a role.

Our description of remaining late seral stage forest and other cover types that may be used by owls (i.e., forest <80 yrs old) is cursory at best, but it does provide at least some information on the amounts of these cover types on part of the HJA Study Area. This area contains perhaps some of the best remaining owl habitat in the Pacific Northwest (Thomas et al. 1990). We are convinced that Spotted Owls use, and probably depend, on late seral stage forest for most if not all phases of their life history (breeding, roosting, feeding, protection from predators) (Forsman et al. 1984, Bart and Forsman 1992). In light of this fact, and based on the demographic information provided in this paper, we offer the following conclusions: (1) given our estimate of λ (0.91) and the trend of variable but declining survival rates of nonjuveniles and juveniles over time, we doubt that the Spotted Owl population on the HJA Study Area was stable during 1987–1993; (2) we suspect, however, that the rate of decline was lower than the estimated 9% per year decline suggested by λ because juvenile survival was probably higher than we were able to estimate, given the negative influence that permanent emigration can have on estimations of survival; (3) the remaining tracts of late seral stage forest do, however, provide the potential to maintain a stable population of Spotted Owls on the HJA area, if perhaps at lower than historical levels; and (4) retention of large stands of old growth trees and the use of silvicultural techniques to enhance and promote the maintenance of late seral stage forest would probably help to ensure adequate habitat for Spotted Owls and their prey. The latter point is still a viable option on HJA because harvest of old forests has not been as intensive or extensive as many other parts of the Northern Spotted Owl range (Thomas et al. 1990).

It is also clear to us, given the above discussions of empirical count data, annual variability in reproduction, calculations of survival rates, and juvenile survival and emigration, that determining the status of the Spotted Owl population on the HJA is a difficult task, even with 7 years of data. Intensive monitoring of marked owls on the HJA should be continued, along with increased efforts to document juvenile movements and survival rates. Given the potential life span of a Northern Spotted Owl of perhaps 8–10 yrs (Forsman and Meslow 1986), monitoring and marking should continue for at least 2–4 generations, or about 10–30 additional years.

SUMMARY

We collected demographic trend information on Northern Spotted Owls in the central Cascade Mountains of western Oregon during 1987–1993 in order to better understand the current status of the population and to calculate population rate of change. The H. J. Andrews (HJA) Study Area was an ideal location to examine these issues because the area is typical of much of the forest and land-use conditions on the west slope of the Cascade range in Oregon, and the HJA has a long history of Spotted Owl research, dating back to the early 1970s. We counted numbers of territorial owls, captured and banded 515 owls, collected resightings of marked owls, and determined fecundity (number of female fledglings produced per female) in the field. We then used capture-recapture models to estimate age- and sex-specific survival of color-marked owls and computed lambda (λ), the finite rate of population change, from our age-specific survival and fecundity estimates for the time period 1987–1993. Annual adult and juvenile survival rates were 0.82 (SE = 0.02) and 0.29 (SE = 0.05), respectively, and annual age-specific fecundity was 0.35 (SE = 0.03) female young per adult female and 0.15 (SE = 0.10) per 1- or 2-yr old female. Based on these parameters, we estimated an annual rate of population change (λ) of 0.91 (SE = 0.012), which was significantly <1, indicating that the population of resident adults was declining at a rate of about 9% per year. However, this rate of decline was likely an overestimate because juvenile survival and/or emigration was probably higher than our calculations showed. We conclude that the Spotted Owl population probably declined on the HJA area during 1987–1993, but at a rate lower than indicated by λ.

ACKNOWLEDGMENTS

For assistance with data collection we thank S. W. Adey, S. Albert, M. Brown, J. Buck, T. A. Church, T. L. Cutler, S. M. Desimone, M. Fishman, J. Hall, C. K. Johnson, D. H. Johnson, P. A. Lang, G. A. Lehman, B. Maier, V. Marr, A. V. Miller, T. Odenbaugh, G. Orth, S. Peets, M. Vander Heyden, and F. Weekley. We also thank the staff of the Willamette National Forest, especially the Blue River, McKenzie Bridge, and Sweet Home Ranger Districts, for providing maps and information, assistance in monitoring sites, and logistic support. Housing and office space were provided by the H. J. Andrews Experimental Forest. D. R. Anderson, K. P. Burnham, R. J. Steidl, and G. C. White assisted with data analyses and G. Lienkaemper provided the base map for Fig. 1. This paper benefited greatly from the thoughtful and thorough reviews of R. G. Anthony, M. J. Conroy, E. D. Forsman, R. J. Gutiérrez, D. E. Seaman, J. W. Snyder, R. J. Steidl, and two anonymous reviewers. Funding was provided by the Pacific Northwest Research Station of the U. S. Forest Service.

Key words: demography, fecundity, Northern Spotted Owl, Oregon, *Strix occidentalis,* survival estimation, threatened species.

Studies in Avian Biology No. 17:47–52, 1996.

DEMOGRAPHY OF NORTHERN SPOTTED OWLS ON THE SIUSLAW NATIONAL FOREST, OREGON

Eric D. Forsman, Peter J. Loschl, Raymond K. Forson, and Douglas K. Barrett

INTRODUCTION

Historically, the coastal mountains of northwestern Oregon were covered by forests of Douglas-fir (*Pseudotsuga menziesii*), western hemlock (*Tsuga heterophylla*), and western redcedar (*Thuja plicata*), including extensive areas of trees that were 100–300-years old. Most of these mature or "old-growth" forests were clear-cut or burned between 1860 and 1990. As a result, the Coast Ranges Province is often identified as an area where wildlife that are associated with mature or old-growth forests may be declining in numbers (Forsman et al. 1976, Forsman 1986, Thomas et al. 1990, 1993a, USDI 1992b). Studies within this region have revealed particularly low numbers of Northern Spotted Owls (*Strix occidentalis caurina*), at least within areas where the majority of older forests have been removed by harvest or wildfires (Forsman et al. 1976, Forsman 1986).

In 1990 we initiated a demographic study of Spotted Owls on the Siuslaw National Forest, which is centrally located within the Oregon Coast Ranges Province. The primary objectives of the study were to document trends in birth, death, and population growth rates of Spotted Owls in the Coast Ranges. In addition, we used annual surveys on a portion of the study area to track changes in numbers of territorial Spotted Owls.

STUDY AREA

The 2,749 km² study area included most of the Siuslaw National Forest, as well as intermixed areas of private, municipal and state-owned lands that were located within the National Forest boundary (Fig. 1). The study area was characterized by a moderate maritime climate, with most precipitation falling as rain during October-May. Average annual precipitation was 196 cm from 1990–1993 (U.S. Forest Service, Mapleton Ranger District, unpublished records). Elevations ranged from sea level to 1,352 m.

Forests within the study area were dominated by Douglas-fir, western hemlock, and western redcedar. Deciduous hardwoods such as red alder (*Alnus rubra*), vine maple (*Acer circinatum*) and bigleaf maple (*Acer macrophylum*) also were common on many sites, particularly in riparian zones. As a result of extensive clear-cutting after 1930, the landscape was characterized by a mixture of older forests on uncut areas, dense stands of shrubs and herbs on recently cutover areas, and dense stands of younger trees on older clearcuts.

Prior to implementation of a systematic program of fire control in the 1950s, periodic wildfires burned extensive areas in the Oregon Coast Ranges. On sites where wildfires were relatively cool, many trees survived. Today, these stands typically consist of a mixture of large old, fire-scarred trees with understories of younger trees. On sites subjected to very hot crown fires in the 1800s and early 1900s, forests are typically dominated by relatively even-aged stands of 80 to 140-year-old Douglas-fir.

Vegetation and land management patterns on the Siuslaw Study Area were typical of the Oregon Coast Ranges Province. Little of the area was reserved in Wilderness or Roadless status, and, until the 1990s, the vast majority of the area was managed with timber production as the primary goal. This pattern changed dramatically during the 1990s as harvest on federal lands was sharply curtailed to protect extensive areas of forest for Spotted Owls, Marbled Murrelets (*Brachyramphus marmoratum*), fisheries enhancement, and other ecosystem goals (Thomas et al. 1990, 1993a,b).

METHODS

We use capture-recapture methodology to estimate population parameters, as described in Franklin et al. (*this volume*). Surveys were conducted each year from 1990–1993 between 1 March–1 September to search for and identify owls banded in previous years and to band any new owls detected. All owls detected were banded with a U. S. Fish and Wildlife Service band on one leg and a plastic color band on the other leg. Sex of owls was determined from differences in vocalizations and behavior, and age was determined from plumage characteristics (see Franklin et al. *this volume*).

Estimates of annual survival rates were calculated from capture-recapture data using Cormack-Jolly-Seber open population models in Program SURGE as described in Pollock et al. (1990), Lebreton et al. (1992), Burnham et al. (1995), and Franklin et al. (*this volume*). Akaike's Information Criterion (AIC) was used to identify

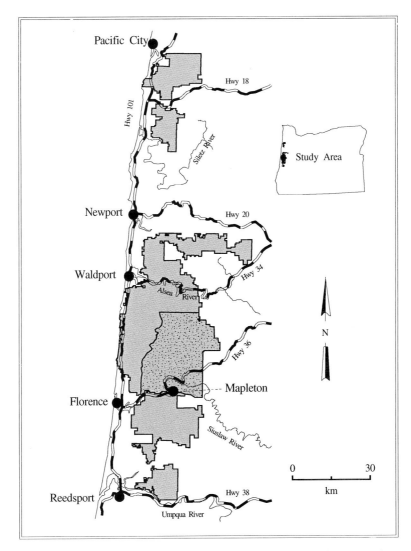

FIGURE 1. Siuslaw National Forest Study Area, Oregon, 1990–1993. Information on survival and fecundity of Northern Spotted Owls was collected from locations scattered throughout the study area. The shaded area with stippling indicates location of a 676 km² Density Study Area, within which we attempted to estimate annual changes in the number of territorial owls.

models that best fit the data (Akaike 1973, Burnham and Anderson 1992, Anderson et al. 1994, Franklin et al. *this volume*). Goodness-of-fit tests (Tests 1–3 in program RELEASE) were used to evaluate how well the data met the assumptions in the capture-recapture models (Pollock et al. 1985, Burnham et al. 1987).

Age-specific fecundity of females was estimated from the sample of all females located each year. Fecundity was defined as the number of female young produced per female, and was calculated by dividing the number of young that left the nest by 2, which assumed a 50:50 sex ratio (Franklin et al. *this volume*). Methods for locat-

ing and counting juveniles after they left the nest are described in Franklin et al. (*this volume*). Among-year variation in fecundity was examined with ANOVA in program SPSS (Norušis 1990).

Estimates of the annual rate of population change (λ) were derived from average estimates of age-specific annual survival and fecundity. We computed λ by solving the characteristic polynomial of a Leslie-Lefkovitch matrix (Noon and Sauer 1992, Franklin et al. *this volume*).

A 676 km² subplot located in the southern half of the study area was designated as a Density Study Area (Fig. 1). This area was completely

TABLE 1. NUMBER OF NORTHERN SPOTTED OWLS BANDED ON THE SIUSLAW NATIONAL FOREST STUDY AREA, OREGON, 1990–1993

	≥3-yr-old birds		1–2-yr-old birds		
Year	Males	Females	Males	Females	Juveniles
1990	37	27	6	2	24
1991	13	13	1	2	3
1992	23	22	2	4	35
1993	4	5	1		10
Total	77	67	10	8	72

TABLE 2. RESULTS OF GOODNESS-OF-FIT TESTS (PROGRAM RELEASE, BURNHAM ET AL. 1987) CONDUCTED ON CAPTURE-RECAPTURE DATA FROM ≥3-YR-OLD NORTHERN SPOTTED OWLS ON THE SIUSLAW NATIONAL FOREST STUDY AREA, OREGON, 1990–1993

Sex	TEST 2 + 3[a]			TEST 2	TEST 3
	χ^2	df	P	P	P
Males	3.83	4	0.430	1.000	0.280
Females	1.15	4	0.886	1.000	0.764

[a] TEST 2 tests whether different cohorts have different future fates. TEST 3 tests whether previously released individuals have the same future fates as newly released individuals (Burnham et al. 1987).

surveyed three times each year during the breeding season (March–August) to estimate the number of territorial owls. Within the remainder of the study area we conducted three or more annual surveys of all areas where we had banded owls in previous years, but we did not do a complete coverage survey of all intervening areas between sites that were historically occupied by owls.

Changes in numbers of territorial owls counted on the Density Study Area were assessed using linear regression to test the null hypothesis H_O: number of territorial owls was stationary or increasing, against the alternative hypothesis H_A: number of territorial owls was declining. A power analysis of the linear regression analysis (Gerrodette 1987) was conducted using Program TRENDS (Gerrodette, personal communication). For all statistical tests, P values ≤0.05 were considered significant.

RESULTS

During 1990–1993 we banded 234 owls on the study area, including 144 birds that were ≥3 yrs old, 18 birds that were 1 or 2 yrs old, and 72 juveniles (Table 1). In addition, the total sample included eight 1- or 2-yr-old birds and 10 ≥3-yr-old birds that immigrated into our study area after they were marked by researchers on adjacent study areas.

GOODNESS-OF-FIT

Examination of capture histories from ≥3-yr-old birds indicated that the data met the assumptions underlying the capture-recapture models (Table 2). Results of TEST 1 in program RELEASE indicated no differences in survival or recapture rates of males and females (χ^2 = 5.843, df = 5, P = 0.322). Numbers of recaptures of juveniles and 1- and 2-yr-old owls were so small that meaningful goodness of fit tests could not be conducted on those age classes.

MODEL SELECTION

Sixty-four models were constructed for owls that were ≥3 years old. The model that fit the data best was one in which there was no sex- or time-effect on survival (model $\{\phi, p_{s+t}\}$)(Table 3). Likelihood ratio tests indicated no difference between the best model and several competing models that included sex-effects or linear time-effects on survival (Table 3).

The model that best fit the data from all age and sex cohorts was a simple model that included no sex-effects or time-effects on survival or recapture and that lumped estimates of survival into 2 age classes (juveniles and ≥1-yr-old birds)(model $\{\phi_{a2}, p_{a2}\}$, Table 3). Likelihood ratio tests indicated no difference between the best model and several competing models (Table 3).

FECUNDITY

The average number of female young produced per female per year was 0.231 (SE = 0.043) for ≥3-yr-old females, and 0.071 (SE = 0.101) for 1- and 2-yr-old birds. Samples of 1- and 2-yr-old birds were too small to estimate fecundity separately for each age class. Mean fecundity of ≥3-yr-old females varied among years (F = 11.04, df = 3, P < 0.001), ranging from a low of 0.037 to a high of 0.457 (Fig. 2). Among-year variation in fecundity was due primarily to variation in the proportion of females that attempted to nest, which also varied among years (χ^2 = 32.407, df = 3, P < 0.001)(Fig. 2).

POPULATION GROWTH RATE

Estimates of survival from the best 2-age-class model were 0.2430 (SE = 0.0924) for juveniles and 0.822 (SE = 0.027) for ≥1-yr-old birds. Based on these estimates and the age-specific estimates of fecundity, the estimated annual rate of population change ($\hat{\lambda}$) was 0.874 (SE = 0.031), suggesting an average annual population decline of 12.6% per year during the period of study.

POPULATION CHANGE ON THE DENSITY STUDY AREA

The number of owls detected on the Density Study Area ranged from 46–58 during the 4 years of survey (Fig. 3). Because there were no time-

TABLE 3. CAPTURE-RECAPTURE MODELS THAT BEST FIT THE DATA FOR NORTHERN SPOTTED OWLS ON THE SIUSLAW NATIONAL FOREST STUDY AREA, 1990–1993. MODELS ARE LISTED IN ORDER OF INCREASING AIC (AKAIKE'S INFORMATION CRITERION) VALUES (AKAIKE 1973) FOR EACH DATA SET. ONE SET OF MODELS INCLUDED ≥ 3-YR-OLD BIRDS ONLY. THE OTHER SET INCLUDED TWO AGE CLASSES (JUVENILES AND ≥ 1-YR-OLD OWLS)

Model[a]	Deviance	K	AIC	χ^2	df	P
≥ 3-yr-old owls						
$\{\phi, p_{s+t}\}$	333.482	5	343.482			
$\{\phi_T, p_{s+T}\}$	333.526	5	343.526			
$\{\phi, p_{s+T}\}$	335.891	4	343.526	2.409	1	0.121
$\{\phi_s, p_{s+t}\}$	331.980	6	343.980	1.502	1	0.220
$\{\phi_T, p_T\}$	336.123	4	344.123	2.641	1	0.104
2-age-class models						
$\{\phi_{a2}, p_{a2}\}$	450.527	4	458.527			
$\{\phi_{a2}, p_{a2+s}\}$	448.738	5	458.738	1.789	1	0.181
$\{\phi_{a2+T}, p_{a2+s}\}$	447.804	6	459.804	2.723	2	0.256
$\{\phi_{a2+T}, p_{2+T}\}$	448.639	6	460.639	1.888	2	0.389
$\{\phi_{a2}, p_{a2 \cdot s}\}$	448.724	6	460.724	1.803	2	0.406

[a] Subscripts indicate age (a), sex (s), or time (t, T) effects on survival (ϕ) or recapture (p). Lower case or capital t's indicate that ϕ or p varied among years, either in a linear fashion (T) or non-linear fashion (t). Numbers indicate number of age-groups estimated by the model. An * indicates full age, sex or time-effects, whereas a + indicates a reduced model in which age, sex or time-effects are additive.

effects on recapture rates in the most parsimonious age-class CR model ($\{\phi_{a2}, p_{a2}\}$), we concluded that annual counts of owls detected on the Density Study Area could be compared without correction for annual differences in detectability of owls. A linear regression indicated no trend in total numbers (slope = -0.600, r = -0.121, P = 0.879), a finding that did not support the null hypothesis that the population was non-stationary. Power of the regression analysis to detect a trend given the observed rate of population change was extremely low (0.05).

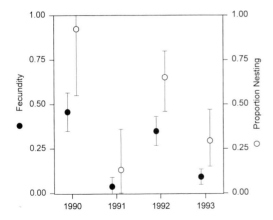

FIGURE 2. Mean annual estimates of fecundity of ≥ 3-yr-old female Northern Spotted Owls on the Siuslaw National Forest Study Area, Oregon, 1990–1993. Proportion of ≥ 3-yr-old females breeding each year is also shown. Fecundity was defined as the number of female young produced per female owl, assuming a 50:50 sex ratio in broods observed.

DISCUSSION

Bias in estimates of survival and fecundity can cause bias in estimates of the annual rate of population change. We believe that our estimates of the annual rate of population change on the Siuslaw Study Area are likely to be biased low because of undetected emigration, particularly by juveniles. However, there are many other factors that can cause positive or negative bias in estimates of survival or fecundity (e.g., see Bart 1995, Raphael et al. *this volume*), and we do not know what the combined effect of these biases is on the estimated rate of population change. However, we should be able to better assess the effects of some of these potential biases as more years of data are accumulated.

After three years of study (4 capture occasions), there was no strong indication of time trends on survival in the study area, and variance in fecundity was so large that no trends in that parameter were obvious either. Another approach that may allow detection of trends in demographic parameters with relatively short-term data sets is the use of meta-analyses on data sets from multiple study areas (Burnham et al. *this volume*).

Because this analysis only covered a period of 3 years (4 capture occasions), there is some question whether the results reflect the actual age-specific differences in survival that may exist in the population. In particular, samples were too small to obtain precise estimates of survival for 1- and 2-yr-old birds. More detailed comparisons of age-specific survival should become possible in future years, as the sample of marked individuals increases.

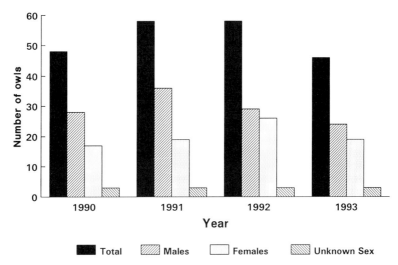

FIGURE 3.   Number of territorial Northern Spotted Owls located per year on the 676 km² Density Study Area on the Siuslaw National Forest, Oregon, 1990–1993. Numbers indicate all territorial owls detected by surveys.

The absence of a significant change in owl numbers on the Density Study Area did not necessarily refute or support the estimate of the annual rate of population change calculated from capture-recapture data. The power of the regression of owl numbers on time was so low (0.05) that the test would not have revealed a gradual decline (or increase) even if it was occurring. Statistical power to detect trends will improve as more years of data are collected. In addition to the problem of statistical power, estimates of owl numbers on the Density Study Area may be confounded in such a way that they do not reflect true population trends. For example, it is possible that in a declining population, observed densities of territorial owls might not change during early years of the decline simply because territorial owls that died could be replaced by floaters (owls without territories)(Franklin 1992). Thus, significant changes in density of territorial owls might not become apparent for many years, especially if the rate of population decline was small (e.g., 1–2% per year). However, if the rate of population decline was as large as suggested by the capture-recapture analysis (12.6% per year), then the population of floaters should be rapidly exhausted, and declines in the territorial population should become apparent within a few years. Also, if the rate of decline was 12.6% per year, then that rate of decline must have started only recently. Otherwise, the population of floaters would have been exhausted long ago, and we would be witnessing a rapid decline in the density of territorial owls. Since a rapid decline in numbers was not apparent on the DSA, we conclude that either the rate of decline suggested by the

capture-recapture analysis is somewhat exaggerated, or the high rate of decline is a relatively recent phenomenon. These relationships should become clearer, as more years of data are accumulated.

SUMMARY

A capture-recapture study was conducted to assess survival, fecundity and population growth rates of Northern Spotted Owls on the Siuslaw National Forest in the Coast Ranges Province of western Oregon from 1990–1993. The most parsimonious capture-recapture model indicated no sex- or time-effects on survival or recapture rates. Age-specific annual survival estimates were 0.2420 (SE = 0.0924) for juveniles and 0.822 (SE = 0.027) for non-juveniles. Fecundity, defined as the number of female young produced per female owl per year, averaged 0.231 (SE = 0.043) for ≥3-yr-old birds and 0.071 (SE = 0.101) for 1- and 2-yr-old birds. Fecundity varied among years, primarily as a result of variability in the proportion of females that nested. The estimated annual rate of population growth ($\hat{\lambda}$) based on age-specific estimates of survival and fecundity was 0.874 (SE = 0.031), suggesting a population decline of 12.6% per year. We suspect that $\hat{\lambda}$ is biased low, primarily because of negative bias in the estimate of juvenile survival due to emigration. However, the extent to which $\hat{\lambda}$ is biased relative to the true rate of population change is unclear, because a variety of other factors could cause positive or negative biases in estimates of vital rates.

In a 676 km²-Density Study Area that was completely searched for owls each year, the number of territorial owls detected did not change significantly from 1990–1993 (slope = -0.600, $r = -0.121$, $P = 0.879$). However, the power of the regression analysis was low (0.05), indicating that more years of data are needed to reliably estimate population trends from the count data. Count data are also subject to a variety of biases that make interpretation difficult.

ACKNOWLEDGMENTS

This study was initiated in cooperation with the Siuslaw National Forest, and was funded by the U. S. Forest Service PNW Research Station and the U. S. Forest Service Pacific Northwest Regional Office. We greatly appreciate the assistance of numerous Forest Service owl callers and District Biologists who helped with owl surveys and banding, especially L. L. Bernhardt, C. E. Bickford, R. J. Davis, D. K. Guthrie, M. L. Ihnat, M. L. Jensen, S. M. Lucas, S. M. Symeonides, N. M. VanGrunsven and H. D. Vogt. Administrative support was provided by personnel at the U. S. Forest Service Mapleton District Office. For assistance with data analysis we thank D. R. Anderson, B. L. Biswell, K. P. Burnham, J. Clobert, J. E. Hines, J. D. Nichols, R. J. Pradel, E. A. Rexstad, T. M. Shenk, G. C. White, K. R. Wilson, and J. L. Zisa. Various drafts of the manuscript were reviewed by M. J. Conroy, J. Haufler, R. W. Mannan, S. DeStefano, and R. J. Gutiérrez. Any errors in interpretation are our own.

Key words: capture-recapture, demography, fecundity, Northern Spotted Owl, Oregon, populations, *Strix occidentalis caurina,* survival.

Studies in Avian Biology No. 17:53–58, 1996.

DEMOGRAPHY OF NORTHERN SPOTTED OWLS ON THE EUGENE DISTRICT OF THE BUREAU OF LAND MANAGEMENT, OREGON

James A. Thrailkill, E. Charles Meslow, John P. Perkins, and Lawrence S. Andrews

INTRODUCTION

Subsequent to a Status Review (Anderson et al. 1990), the Northern Spotted Owl (*Strix occidentalis caurina*) was listed as a federally threatened species. The review team concluded that the Spotted Owl population was at risk in significant portions of its range, primarily due to loss of habitat caused by logging. The review team also identified the central Coast Ranges of Oregon, as an "Area of Special Concern" because this region had been particularly heavily impacted by timber harvest.

In 1989, we initiated a demographic study of Northern Spotted Owls on the western half of the Eugene District of the Bureau of Land Management (BLM), which is located in the central portion of the Oregon Coast Ranges. The primary objective of the study was to provide information on Spotted Owl population trends within the highly modified forest environment that typifies the Oregon Coast Ranges. We also believed that this information would be useful for evaluating the effects of forest management practices on the species (Thomas et al. 1993).

Specific objectives of the study were to estimate age-specific birth, death, and reproductive rates of territorial Spotted Owls. Thomas et al. (1990) argued for the use of demographic parameter estimates to infer the rate and direction of population change for Spotted Owls. We also monitored changes in numbers of territorial owls detected within a smaller portion of the study area.

STUDY AREA

The 1,432 km² study area is located in the central Coast Ranges, 30 km west of Eugene, Oregon (Fig. 1). Contained within the larger surrounding study area is the 425 km² Wolf Creek Density Study Area (DSA). Throughout the study area, intermingled land ownership produces a checkerboard pattern of alternating square mile sections (2.6 km²) that are administered or owned by BLM (44%), the State of Oregon (2%), private industrial timber companies (43%), or "other" landowners (11%) (Fig. 1). Historically, the majority of federal and privately owned lands were managed for timber production, with clear-cut-

ting the dominant harvest method. Topography is characterized by steep mountain slopes with narrow ridges and elevations ranging from 120 to 870 m.

The study area is bounded on the north, west, and south by four other Spotted Owl demographic study areas (Franklin et al. *this volume*), which facilitates the reobservation of dispersing owls. East of the study area is the south terminus of the Willamette Valley, a non-forested agricultural and urban/suburban valley.

Located within the western hemlock (*Tsuga heterophylla*) vegetation zone, the study area is dominated by forests of Douglas-fir (*Pseudotsuga menziesii*) and western hemlock (Franklin and Dyrness 1973). Based on air-photo interpretation, we mapped and calculated that 11% of the study area is covered by old forests in which the dominant overstory trees are >200 years old. Thomas et al. (1990) considered old forest as "superior" Spotted Owl habitat because radio-telemetry studies indicated that Spotted Owls consistently used older forests in excess of availability. On our study area, two percent of old forest habitat is located on privately owned lands, while 98% is on lands managed by BLM.

We classified an additional 13% of the study area as "suitable" habitat (generally mixed-aged forest between 51–199 years old) which meets some or all of the life history needs of the owl. The majority of suitable habitat is also located on BLM lands. Currently, 76% of the study area is covered by young forests (generally < 50 years old) that we consider as "unsuitable" for Spotted Owls because of deficiencies in tree size, canopy closure, and/or stand decadence. Most of the latter stands occur on areas that were cut and replanted.

Forest composition within the DSA was similar to the surrounding study area landscape based on our analysis of available Spotted Owl habitat. Old forest covered 14% of the DSA vs 11% of the surrounding study area.

METHODS

FIELD DATA COLLECTION

Personnel on the Eugene BLM District began a spotted owl monitoring and banding program

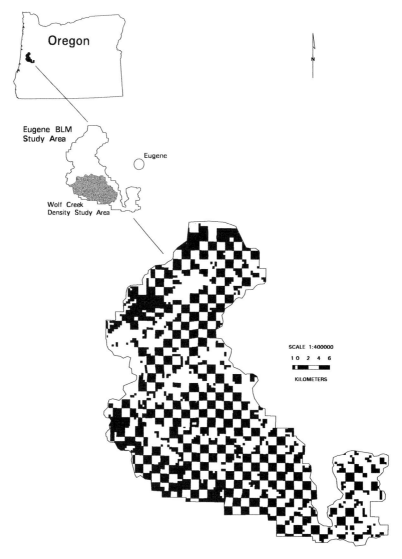

FIGURE 1. Northern Spotted Owl demography study area on the Eugene District of the Bureau of Land Management in the Coast Ranges of western Oregon, 1989–1993. Shaded subplot indicates location of the Wolf Creek Density Study Area (DSA) within the larger study area. Land ownership pattern is indicated by black BLM sections interspersed with white sections of non-federal ownership.

in 1986. Although our study did not formally begin until 1990, we included the cohort of owls banded by district personnel in 1989 (28% of our total sample) in our estimates of survival and fecundity. In 1990 we began annual surveys (April–August) on BLM and privately owned industrial forest lands within the study area with the intent of encountering "new" unbanded owls and reobserving previously banded owls. Field methods used for surveying, locating, determining sex, capturing, reobserving, banding, and determining owl reproductive status followed

Franklin et al. (*this volume*) and Forsman (1983). Four Spotted Owl age-classes were distinguished: juveniles (J), 1-yr-old owls (S1), 2-year-old owls (S2), and ≥3-yr-old owls (A) (Forsman 1981, Moen et al. 1991).

Survey effort on the Wolf Creek Density Study Area was consistent from 1990–1993 and consisted of complete coverage with 6 replicate nighttime surveys each year during the nesting season (March–August). Within the study area (DSA excluded), we surveyed all known (historic) owl territories each year, to confirm and band any owls that were present and to determine their nesting status and numbers of young fledged. We defined an owl territory as a 2.4 km radius centered on an owl nest tree. This distance corresponded to the computed minimum convex polygon annual home range size of an owl pair within the study area (Thomas et al. 1990). The survey was consistent each year and included six replicate nighttime surveys before concluding a territory was unoccupied in a given year.

In addition, we conducted surveys in owl habitat located between owl territories (DSA excluded). The number of replicate surveys in habitat located between territories differed by year (0–3 nighttime surveys in 1990, and 5–6 nighttime surveys in 1991–1993). In 1991, the surveys resulted in an 18% increase in the number of territories that were located and incorporated into our sample. This increase in sample size was due primarily to an increase in the number of field biologists and resulting survey effort, not to an increase in the number of owls on the study area.

DATA ANALYSIS

Chi-square tests were used to assess annual variation in the proportion of pairs nesting during 1990–1993 (calculated by dividing the number of pairs nesting by the total number of pairs checked for reproductive activity before 1 June). Confidence intervals (95%) around mean proportions were calculated following Zar (1984:378–379). Fecundity was estimated for each age-class as the average number of female young produced per female each year. We assumed a 1:1 sex ratio and included all young located during the breeding period in fecundity estimates (Franklin et al. *this volume*). Annual variation in fecundity was analyzed using ANOVA (Zar 1984:162–170).

Goodness-of-fit tests 2 and 3 in program RELEASE were used to determine if the capture-recapture data met the assumptions underlying the global Cormack-Jolly-Seber capture-recapture model (Pollock et al. 1985, Burnham et al. 1987, Franklin et al. *this volume*). TEST 2 examines across recapture occasions for independence and heterogeneity. TEST 3 examines capture histories within release occasions and tests whether previously released individuals have the same future fates as newly released individuals. Survival and recapture rates were estimated from models produced in program SURGE (Lebreton et al. 1992). Notation of capture-recapture models included subscripts that indicated if a particular model included sex effects (s), age effects (a), non-linear time effects (t), or linear time trends (T) (Franklin et al. *this volume*). Akaike's Information Criterion (AIC) (Akaike 1973) was used to identify the most parsimonious model for each data set (Burnham and Anderson 1992, Lebreton et al. 1992, Franklin et al. *this volume*).

TABLE 1. NUMBER OF NORTHERN SPOTTED OWLS BANDED AND USED IN CAPTURE-RECAPTURE ANALYSES ON THE EUGENE BLM STUDY AREA IN THE CENTRAL COAST RANGES OF WESTERN OREGON, 1989–1993

Years	≥3 yrs old		1 or 2 yrs old			Juveniles
	Female	Male	Female	Male	Unknown	
1989	16	21	1	1	2	8
1990	4	5	3	4	1	13
1991	20	16	1	1	0	6
1992	8	3	0	1	0	30
1993	4	4	1	0	0	2
Total	52	49	6	7	3	59

The estimated annual rate of population change ($\hat{\lambda}$) during the period of study was computed from age-class estimates of annual survival (juvenile and nonjuvenile) and the mean estimate of fecundity for all females ≥1 yr old (Franklin et al. *this volume*). Estimates of the rate of population change referred to the resident territorial population, containing several age classes, and their recruitment (Franklin et al. *this volume*).

We used regression analysis to assess annual trends in the number of owls detected in the Wolf Creek Density Study Area. A power analysis was applied to the regression (Gerodette 1987).

RESULTS

CAPTURE-RECAPTURE POPULATION

We banded 176 owls from 1989–1993, including 101 that were ≥3 yrs old, 16 that were 1 or 2 yrs old, and 59 juveniles (Table 1). The sample also included 3 owls that were banded as juveniles on adjacent study areas and subsequently immigrated to our study area.

GOODNESS-OF FIT AND MODEL SELECTION

Goodness-of-fit tests 2 and 3 in program RELEASE indicated no lack of fit for the capture history data from ≥3-yr-old owls (males χ^2 = 0.85, df = 4, P = 0.932; females χ^2 = 3.30, df = 7, P = 0.855), suggesting that Cormack-Jolly-Seber open population models were appropriate for use with those data. For TEST 3, this indicated that owls within a released cohort had similar future expected fates. For TEST 2, this indicated that data for the various age and sex classes were statistically independent. We had so few recaptures of owls banded as juveniles or as 1- or 2-yr-olds that we could not conduct meaningful goodness-of-fit tests for those age groups.

The capture-recapture model that best fit the data from ≥3-yr-old owls had a non-linear time effect on survival, with the additional constraint that survival probabilities were equal in periods 1 and 2 (Table 2). In this model, there was also

TABLE 2. THE "BEST CANDIDATE" CAPTURE-RECAPTURE MODELS FOR NORTHERN SPOTTED OWLS ON THE EUGENE BLM STUDY AREA, OREGON, 1989–1993, AS DETERMINED BY AIC VALUES (AKAIKE 1977, FRANKLIN ET AL. *THIS VOLUME*). ONE ANALYSIS INCLUDED OWLS THAT WERE ≥ 3 YEARS OLD. THE OTHER ANALYSIS INCLUDED TWO AGE GROUPS, JUVENILES AND NONJUVENILES (≥ 1 YR OLD)

Model[a]	Deviance	K[b]	AIC[c]	ϕ[d]
$\geq$3-yr-old owls				
$\{\phi_{t1=t2,t3,t4}, p_{t+s}\}$	235.630	8	251.630	0.860
$\{\phi_T, p_{s+T}\}$	244.739	5	254.739	0.846
$\{\phi, p_{s+T}\}$	253.537	4	261.537	0.854
Two-age-class models				
$\{\phi_{a2+T}, p_{a2+s\cdot T}\}$	363.223	8	379.223	0.853
$\{\phi_{a2\cdot T}, p_{a2+s\cdot T}\}$	362.664	9	380.664	0.855
$\{\phi_{a2+T}, p_{a2+s+T}\}$	368.035	7	382.035	0.848

[a] Parameters are subscripted s for sex, t for time (year) with no linear trend, and T for time as a linear trend. An asterisk (•) indicates interactions. Additive effects in models are denoted with a "+".
[b] K is the number of estimable parameters from the model.
[c] AIC (Akaike's Information Criterion) is used to select objectively an appropriate "best" model.
[d] ϕ = estimate of survival for $\geq$3-yr-old owls or nonjuvenile owls.

a non-linear time effect and a sex effect on recapture probabilities (Table 2).

The most parsimonious model for the two-age class data (juveniles and non-juveniles) included a linear time effect (T) on survival and a sex effect

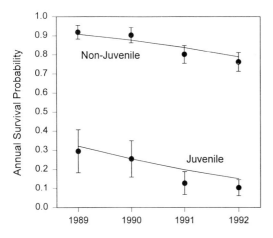

FIGURE 2. Estimates of annual survival probabilities of non-juvenile (≥ 1 yr old) and juvenile Northern Spotted Owls on the Eugene BLM Study Area, 1989–1993. The solid lines indicate nearly linear time trend in annual survival estimates from the selected two-age-class capture-recapture model ($\{\phi_{a2+T}, p_{a2+s\cdot T}\}$). Point estimates and SEs of annual survival from a variable time model ($\{\phi_{a2+t}, p_{a2+s+t}\}$) are shown for comparison with the linear trend model.

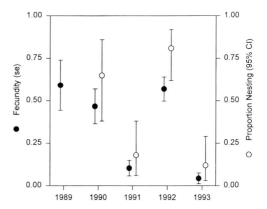

FIGURE 3. Reproductive statistics for female Northern Spotted Owls monitored on the Eugene BLM Study Area, Oregon, 1989–1993. Solid circles with associated SEs indicate mean annual fecundity, defined as the number of female young fledged per female owl. Open circles with associated 95% confidence intervals indicate the proportion of females nesting.

with an interactive linear time effect (s*T) on recapture probabilities (Table 2). A likelihood ratio test indicated that a competing model with the next lowest AIC value (Table 2) did not differ from the most parsimonious model ($\chi^2 = 0.559$, df = 1, P = 0.454).

ESTIMATED SURVIVAL RATES

Mean annual survival estimates from the selected 2-age-class model ($\{\phi_{a2+T}, p_{a2+s\cdot T}\}$) were 0.232 (SE = 0.078) for juveniles and 0.853 (SE = 0.026) for non-juveniles (Fig. 2). Estimated survival rates were similar from several competing models with low AIC values (Table 2).

FECUNDITY

The proportion of pairs nesting varied among years ($\chi^2 = 67.00$, df = 3, P < 0.001), ranging from a high of 0.81 in 1992 to a low of 0.12 in 1993 (Fig. 3). Fecundity averaged 0.290 (SE = 0.036) for $\geq$3-yr-old females, 0.077 (SE = 0.077) for 1- and 2-yr-old females, and 0.272 (SE = 0.033) for all females combined. Successful reproduction by a 1- or 2-yr-old female occurred only one time during this study. Fecundity of all females combined varied among years (F = 28.29, df = 3, P < 0.001), ranging from a high of 0.583 in 1989 to a low of 0.038 in 1993 (Fig. 3).

RATE OF POPULATION CHANGE

The estimated annual rate of population change on the study area was 0.9134 (SE = 0.031), which was < 1.0 (z = 2.76, P = 0.003). This suggested an average annual decline in the territorial population of 8.7% over the study period.

OWL ABUNDANCE

The number of territorial owls detected on the Wolf Creek Density Study Area declined by 17% from 1990 to 1992 but, the decline was not significant ($r^2 = .702$, df = 3, P = 0.118). The power to detect a decline over the interval studied was relatively low (0.47). The number of owls detected ranged from a high of 36 in 1990 to a low of 29 owls in 1992 (1991 = 35, 1993 = 30).

DISCUSSION

JUVENILE SURVIVAL

Banded juveniles that permanently emigrated from the study area, survived, and that were not reobserved, would cause a negative bias in estimates of juvenile survival, which would also result in an underestimate of the annual rate of population change (Burnham et al. *this volume,* Bart 1995). Of the 59 juvenile owls banded on the study area, 78% were not reobserved during the study period. We recaptured 7% of the banded juveniles on our study area while 15% were recaptured on adjacent study areas by other investigators.

If we assume that our estimates of fecundity and non-juvenile survival are accurate, then juvenile survival would have to be 0.603 to achieve $\lambda = 1.0$. A juvenile emigration rate (individuals that leave the study area, survive, and go undetected) of 0.61 would increase the observed juvenile survival rate of 0.23 to 0.603. An average annual juvenile survival rate of 0.603 for this area is possible but, seems biologically unrealistic. If the juvenile survival rate was 0.603, we believe more juveniles would have been reobserved, given the amount of survey area covered by our study and adjacent study areas (Franklin et al. *this volume*). However, one must consider two factors influencing juvenile recapture rates: (1) duration of study, and (2) juvenile dispersal behavior. Juvenile survival may be underestimated in short-term studies (≤ 5 years) like ours simply because not enough years of data have been collected on recaptured owls marked as juveniles (Burnham et al. *this volume*). In addition, non-territorial subadult owls probably move throughout the landscape until they encounter a territorial vacancy or can replace a territory holder. During this time they do not readily vocalize; therefore, probability of recapture is low.

ADULT SURVIVAL

Estimates of survival probabilities derived from the age-specific data (juvenile and nonjuvenile age groups) declined linearly during this study. We do not know if this trend is indicative of some underlying factor such as habitat loss,

or is simply a short-term fluctuation. We know of no methodological bias that should have caused a trend in survival rates of non-juvenile owls.

In most capture-recapture studies of Spotted Owls, it is assumed that permanent emigration of territorial adults is relatively uncommon and that estimates of survival for adult owls are, therefore, reasonably accurate. This assumption seems to be supported by data from radiotelemetry studies in which only one occurrence of permanent emigration was observed in >100 owl years of study (Thomas et al. 1990). However, based on observations during our study, we believe the potential negative bias in survival estimates caused by emigration of non-juvenile owls may be underestimated.

Of 101 territorial owls that were banded on our study area in 1989–1992, 4.0% were confirmed to have relocated to adjacent study areas by 1993. Because these owls were recaptured after they left our study area, their movements were accounted for in the capture-recapture analysis, and did not cause a negative bias in survival estimates. However, it is highly unlikely that we detected all such movements, and this should be cause for concern, as any bias in survival estimates of adult Spotted Owls is likely to have a nearly equal bias on estimates of λ (Noon and Biles 1990, Bart 1995).

Future demographic studies of Spotted Owls should attempt to evaluate potential bias due to permanent emigration of both juvenile and non-juvenile owls (Bart 1995). One approach might be to examine movements of banded birds between or among adjacent study areas that are thoroughly searched for Spotted Owls each year. Another approach would be to use radiotelemetry techniques to monitor the movements of large samples of owls.

FECUNDITY

The high annual variation in the proportion of territorial females that nested on our study area could be due to fluctuations in food supply, weather, habitat alteration, or other factors influencing the reproductive physiology or behavior of the birds. For example, annual variation in breeding by Great Gray Owls (*Strix nebulosa*) and Tawny Owls (*Strix aluco*) fluctuates in response to rodent abundance (Duncan 1992, Southern 1970).

RATE OF POPULATION CHANGE

A major finding from this study was the computed average annual population decline of 8.7%, or 30.5% over the course of the study (1989–1993). We do not disagree that the population of Spotted Owls on our study area is declining, but we do question the magnitude of the decline.

Given the potential biases in juvenile and adult survival rates, estimation of the rate of population change from capture-recapture data will always involve some degree of uncertainty.

Computed vital rates should only be considered in the context of this study area and the period of study. Spotted Owls are long-lived, and vital rates may vary. If the objective is to evaluate long-term trends in Spotted Owl populations in response to management activities, then studies will need to be continued as management plans are implemented, and habitat conditions gradually change. Consideration should also be given to conducting surveys for Spotted Owls in habitat outside of demographic study areas and among different land use allocations to provide an independent sample for comparison with the demographic area results.

CHANGES IN HABITAT AND OWL ABUNDANCE

Approximately 45% of the Density Study Area was comprised of owl habitat in 1984. From 1985–1989, approximately 18% of that habitat was clear-cut. Subsequent to court imposed harvest restrictions on federally owned lands in 1990, an additional 2% of owl habitat was harvested on the study area between 1990–1992. Most of the owl habitat on privately owned land within the study area was harvested prior to 1990.

The 17% decline in numbers of owls detected on the Wolf Creek Density Study Area during 1990–1993 could be a density dependent response, as the population adjusted to the lower carrying capacity subsequent to harvest of suitable habitat. Van Horne (1983) suggested that species densities may reflect conditions in the recent past or temporary present, rather than long-term habitat quality. However, Van Horne (1983) also cautioned against using density alone as an indicator of habitat quality. The combination of declining survival rates and declining abundance lends support to the hypothesis of a non-stationary, declining owl population on our study area. We suggest the population decline is due to the extensive harvest of Spotted Owl habitat in the central Coast Ranges.

SUMMARY

Demographic characteristics of the Northern Spotted Owl were studied on the Eugene District of the Bureau of Land Management in the central Coast Ranges of Oregon from 1989–1993. This region has been identified as an "Area of Special Concern" because past timber harvesting has greatly reduced the amount of Spotted Owl habitat. Survival rates were estimated from capture histories of banded owls, using Cormack-Jolly-Seber open population models. We banded 176 owls, including 101 that were ≥ 3 yrs old, 16 that were 1 or 2 yrs old, and 59 juveniles. The proportion of pairs nesting and fecundity of females varied among years ($P < 0.001$). Estimates of apparent annual survival from the selected capture-recapture model were 0.232 (SE = 0.078) for juveniles and 0.853 (SE = 0.026) for ≥ 3-yr-old owls. The estimated annual rate of population change (0.9134, SE = 0.031) was < 1.0 ($P = 0.003$) over the four years of study, suggesting a population declining at 8.7% per year. We believe the estimated rate of population decline may be somewhat exaggerated because of negative bias in survival estimates resulting from undetected emigration. On a portion of the study area that was thoroughly searched each year, counts of territorial owls decreased by 17% from 1990–1993. We suggest the owl population decline was due to the reduction of Spotted Owl habitat.

ACKNOWLEDGMENTS

The Eugene BLM District initiated funding of this research; M. W. Collopy (National Biological Service, Forest and Rangeland Ecosystem Science Center) administered the contract beginning in 1992. We thank the Eugene BLM biologists and personnel who contributed to this project: J. T. Beall, R. P. Bosch, A. A. D. Center, D. V. Crannell, E. Greenquist, C. J. Jorgensen, G. P. Miller, J. Ruegger, and C. Thomas. The following biologists employed by Oregon State University were responsible for data collection: A. Chung, R. J. Collins, A. S. Connors, M. J. Elliott, C. A. Friesen, D. V. Hamilton, S. Huffman, L. M. Mitchell, W. Rudolph, S. J. Waddington, and S. N. Wray. Assistance in data analysis was provided by D. R. Anderson, K. P. Burnham, G. C. White, E. A. Rexstad, and T. M. Shenk. This study was conducted under the auspices of the Oregon Cooperative Wildlife Research Unit in cooperation with Oregon State University, Oregon Department of Fish and Wildlife, U.S. Fish and Wildlife Service, and the Wildlife Management Institute. Cooperation from the Oregon Department of Forestry and private timber companies was invaluable. We thank an anonymous reviewer, J. B. Lint, W. R. Clark, M. G. Raphael, and E. D. Forsman for comments on earlier drafts.

Key words: Abundance, capture-recapture, demography, fecundity, Eugene Bureau of Land Management, Northern Spotted Owl, Oregon, *Strix occidentalis caurina,* survival.

Studies in Avian Biology No. 17:59–66, 1996.

DEMOGRAPHY OF NORTHERN SPOTTED OWLS ON THE ROSEBURG DISTRICT OF THE BUREAU OF LAND MANAGEMENT, OREGON

JANICE A. REID, ERIC D. FORSMAN, AND JOSEPH B. LINT

INTRODUCTION

Although it is generally thought of as a range management agency, the USDI Bureau of Land Management (BLM) is responsible for managing more than 890,670 ha of federal forest land in western Oregon (Richardson 1980). Historically, timber production was the primary focus on these lands. In recent years, however, the BLM has become increasingly involved in the management of habitat for wildlife and other non-timber resources. One of the primary factors that led to this shift in management focus was concern that species like the Northern Spotted Owl (*Strix occidentalis caurina*) may be adversely effected by the systematic conversion of old forests to intensively managed young forests (Thomas et al. 1990).

When it become apparent that long-term management plans were needed for the Northern Spotted Owl, wildlife biologists in the BLM and U.S. Forest Service became interested in trends in the vital rates of the owl as a possible indicator of the health of the Spotted Owl population, and as a means of documenting long-term changes in the owl population. To assess these trends, we monitored survival and reproductive rates of Spotted Owls from 1985–1993 on the Roseburg District of the BLM, located in the Umpqua River Basin in western Oregon. We also collected information on emigration rates of young owls in order to estimate the effects of emigration on survival estimates from capture-recapture data. Our objective was to provide information that would help managers and scientists better understand the status of the owl population in western Oregon and that could be used as base-line information for formulation of management policy. Herein we describe trends in survival and reproductive rates of Spotted Owls and estimate population trends based on the observed vital rates.

STUDY AREA

The 6,044 km² Roseburg Study Area includes lands administered by the Roseburg District of the BLM and intervening private lands (Fig. 1). With the exception of agricultural and residential areas in the Umpqua valley near Roseburg, the terrain is mountainous. Elevations range from 24–1418 m. A complex network of logging roads is present, providing access to most drainages. Summers are warm and dry and winters are cool and wet. Annual precipitation from 1985–1993 averaged 108 cm, with most precipitation occurring as rain from late fall to early spring (unpublished records, Douglas County Public Works Dept., Roseburg, OR). Temperatures infrequently registered below 0°C or above 38°C.

The Roseburg Study Area includes portions of three different physiographic provinces in western Oregon (Franklin and Dyrness 1973). The Coast Ranges Province northwest of Roseburg and the Western Cascades Province east and southeast of Roseburg are both dominated by forests of Douglas-fir (*Pseudotsuga menziesii*), western hemlock (*Tsuga heterophylla*), and western redcedar (*Thuja plicata*). The Klamath Mountains Province includes the area south of Roseburg, and is characterized by mixed-conifer forests of grand fir (*Abies grandis*), Douglas-fir, sugar pine (*Pinus lambertiana*), incense cedar (*Calocedrus decurrens*), golden chinquapin (*Castanopsis chrysophylla*), live oak (*Quercus* spp.), and pacific madrone (*Arbutus menziesii*) (Franklin and Dyrness 1973).

Land ownership on the study area consists of a "checkerboard" pattern of alternating square mile (2.59 km²) sections of federal and non-federal lands (Richardson 1980). Because of different rates of tree harvest on federal and non-federal lands, age classes of forest within the study area are not uniformly distributed. Forests on most non-federal lands are largely characterized by younger stages of forest growing on cutover areas (mostly <79-yr-old stands). Lands administered by the BLM have not been as extensively harvested as non-federal lands, and include a diverse mix of young forests on cutover areas and older unlogged forests (80–450 years old). By 1992, approximately half (80,020 ha) of the 167,918 ha administered by the Roseburg District was still covered by older forests with dominant trees ≥120 years old (USDI 1992).

Historically, logging on the study area occurred largely in older stands. The primary method of harvest was clear-cutting, followed by replanting with Douglas-fir. This pattern changed somewhat after 1990, when court injunctions curtailed cutting of old forests on lands admin-

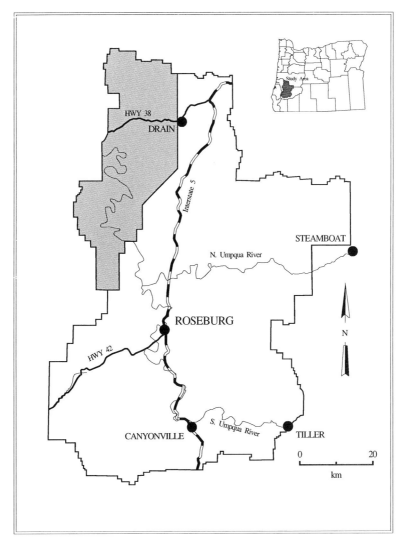

FIGURE 1.   The Roseburg Northern Spotted Owl Demographic Study Area in western Oregon, 1985–1993. The study area included a 1,011 km² Density Study Area subplot (shaded area), within which we attempted to estimate the number of resident owls each year.

istered by BLM in Oregon (Portland Audubon vs. Lujan 1987, Lane County Audubon vs. Jamison 1991). As the cutting of older forests on public lands decreased, harvest of stands of young trees on non-federal lands increased.

The Roseburg Study Area was surrounded on three sides by other Spotted Owl demographic study areas (see Fig. 1 in Franklin et al. *this volume*). This was an ideal situation from the standpoint of a banding study, in that there was a high likelihood that banded owls that emigrated from the Roseburg Study Area would be detected by researchers on adjacent study areas, thus reducing the frequency of undetected emigration.

METHODS

We used mark-recapture techniques to estimate survival of banded owls. Methods used to locate, band, and recapture or resight owls are described in Franklin et al. (*this volume*). Survival rates for each sex and age class were calculated from capture-recapture data using Cormack-Jolly-Seber open population models in Program SURGE as described in Pollock et al. (1990), Lebreton et al. (1992), Franklin et al. (*this volume*), and Burnham et al. (*this volume*). Akaike's Information Criterion (AIC) (Akaike 1973, Anderson et al. 1994) was used to identify models that best fit the data. Goodness-of-fit to the statistical assumptions in capture-recapture models was evaluated using Tests 1–3 in program RELEASE (Pollock et al. 1985, Burnham et al. 1987, Franklin et al. *this volume*).

Juvenile Spotted Owls often disperse beyond the boundaries of a given study area (i.e., they emigrate). Because emigration is usually indistinguishable from mortality in capture-recapture data, juvenile survival estimates from Cormack-Jolly-Seber open population models may be biased low. To estimate emigration rates of juvenile owls (E_J) we placed 5-gram radio transmitters on the rectrices of a subset of the 1991 and 1992 juvenile cohorts and followed the radio-marked owls for 2 years, or until they died or their transmitters failed.

Emigration rates were calculated using individuals that were still alive and whose radio-transmitters were still functioning in the spring following their first year of life (see also Burnham et al. *this volume*). Radio-marked juveniles whose fate could not be determined or that died before 1 April of the year following birth were not included in estimates of emigration. Emigration was defined as any case in which a radio-marked bird moved into an area not normally searched during our annual calling surveys, survived through March of the year following birth, and was not detected by our normal calling surveys (Burnham et al. *this volume*). This definition was adopted for the following reasons: (1) a bird that stays within the original study area is still susceptible to recapture and will be correctly treated by capture-recapture models; (2) a bird that leaves the original study area but is captured elsewhere will be reported to the original study area and treated as a recapture; and (3) only owls that emigrate and survive remain in the population; a bird that emigrates and dies has the same effect on the population as one that dies without emigrating. Clearly, the emigration rate defined here will be specific to the study area in which it is estimated.

Estimates of E_J from the radio-marked juveniles were used to adjust estimates of juvenile survival from capture-recapture data ($\hat{\phi}_J$) using the formula:

$$\hat{S}_J = \hat{\phi}/(1 - \hat{E}_J)$$

where $\hat{S}_J$ = the adjusted estimate of survival. For purposes of this analysis we assumed that annual survival probabilities were the same for emigrating and non-emigrating individuals, that emigration rates during the two years of study were representative of all years, and that tail-mounted transmitters did not influence emigration rates.

Mean annual fecundity (mean number of female young produced per female owl per year) was estimated by locating pairs or single female owls during the day during the breeding season and counting the number of young detected on each visit. Visits to locate and confirm the number of young followed a standardized protocol (Franklin et al. *this volume*). To estimate fecundity we divided the number of young observed by 2, assuming a 50:50 sex ratio. Annual and age-specific variation in fecundity were examined with ANOVA in program SPSS (Norušis 1990).

The annual rate of population change (λ) was estimated by solving the characteristic equation resulting from a modified stage-based Leslie matrix (Franklin et al. *this volume*). One estimate of λ was based on age-specific fecundity estimates and estimates of juvenile and non-juvenile survival from the best age-specific capture-recapture model. A second estimate of λ was based on the same parameter estimates as the first except that it included the estimate of juvenile survival that was adjusted to account for emigration.

To examine changes in numbers of territorial owls over time we conducted complete annual surveys of a 1,011 km² Density Study Area (DSA) within the boundaries of the Roseburg Study Area (Fig. 1). The Density Study Area was located in the Coast Ranges Province in the northwest corner of the Roseburg District. Survey routes in the Density Study Area were designed to insure complete coverage, including calling routes through all historical nest areas as well as calling stations spaced at 0.3–0.5 km intervals along roads throughout the area. We attempted to band all owls detected in the area. Because survey effort and size of the Density Study Area changed from 1987 to 1990, we present estimates of owl numbers in that area only for the period 1990–1993, when effort and coverage were essentially constant. Survey effort outside the Density Study Area focused mainly on areas with a history of occupancy by Spotted Owls.

Trends in the total number of territorial owls detected each year within the DSA were assessed with regression analysis in SPSS (Norušis 1990) to test the null hypothesis of no change in population size. A power analysis of the regression (Gerrodette 1987) was conducted using Program TRENDS (T. Gerrodette, personal communication). For all statistical tests, P values ≤0.05 were considered significant.

RESULTS

We developed capture histories on 476 ≥3-yr-old owls (214 females, 262 males), 117 1- and 2-yr-old owls (58 females, 59 males), and 429 juveniles. Goodness-of-fit tests of the data from ≥3-yr-old owls indicated some lack of fit for TEST 2. This suggested that there may have been

TABLE 1. GOODNESS OF FIT TESTS FROM PROGRAM RELEASE (BURNHAM ET AL. 1987) FOR SPOTTED OWL CAPTURE-RECAPTURE DATA SETS FROM THE ROSEBURG STUDY AREA, OREGON, 1985–1993

Sex/age	TEST 2 + 3[a]			TEST 2 P	TEST 3 P
	χ^2	df	P		
≥3-yr-old males	29.02	19	0.0656	0.0087	0.5393
≥3-yr-old females	26.93	20	0.1374	0.0831	0.3288
All non-juveniles	41.98	20	0.0028	0.0031	0.0742
Juveniles	154.38	21	0.0000	0.6748	0.0000

[a] Test 2 tests whether different cohorts have different future fates. Test 3 tests whether previously released individuals have the same future fates as newly released individuals (Burnham et al. 1987).

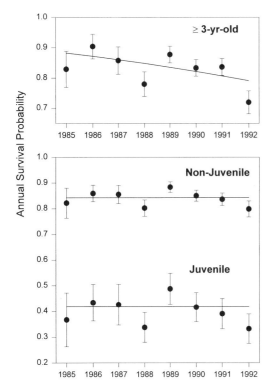

FIGURE 2. Estimates of survival of Northern Spotted Owls, Roseburg, Oregon, 1985–1993. The line in the top graph represents a nearly linear time trend in annual survival estimates for owls banded initially as ≥3-yr-old owls from model $\{\phi_T, p_{s+T}\}$. Point estimates and SEs of annual survival from a variable time model ($\{\phi_t, p_{s+T}\}$) are shown for comparison with the linear trend model. The lower graph depicts nearly linear time trends in annual survival estimates for juveniles and non-juveniles (solid lines), from the most parsimonious age-class model $\{\phi_{a2}, p_{a4'+s}\}$. Point estimates and SEs of annual survival from a variable time model $\{\phi_{a2+t}, p_{a4'+s}\}$ are shown for comparison. Non-juvenile survival estimates included owls first banded as ≥1-yr-old owls, plus that portion of the capture histories of juveniles beginning the year following banding.

some temporary emigration or lack of independence among owl resightings across years (Table 1) (Burnham et al. 1987). TEST 3 indicated no lack of fit for either males or females, or for all non-juvenile owls combined (Table 1). Scrutiny of the data indicated only a few individual owls were responsible for the lack of fit for TEST 2 and did not represent an overall lack of fit. The juvenile data failed TEST 3 ($\chi^2 = 148.623$, df = 13, P < 0.001), but this test was not particularly reliable because the number of recaptures of juveniles was small. Since TEST 3 is sensitive to heterogeneity, the juvenile data may have failed TEST 3 because it was a mix of males and females, or because behavior and movements of juveniles were highly variable.

TEST 1 in program RELEASE indicated no difference in survival of males and females in the ≥3-yr-old age group ($\chi^2 = 23.26$, df = 15, P = 0.079). TEST 1 was not conducted on the juvenile data because we did not determine the sex of many juveniles.

MODEL SELECTION

The most parsimonious capture-recapture model for ≥3-yr-old owls was one in which males and females had the same survival rate and in which survival declined linearly with time (model $\{\phi_T, p_{s+T}\}$, Table 2, Fig. 2). Likelihood ratio tests indicated no difference between the most parsimonious model and several other models, including one that had no annual variation in survival and another that indicated different survival rates for males and females (Table 2).

When four age classes were examined (juveniles, 1-yr-old owls, 2-yr-old owls, ≥3-yr-old owls), the capture-recapture model results indicated no differences in survival between 1- and 2-yr-old owls and ≥3-yr-old owls. As a result, all subsequent modeling was based on models in which owls were lumped into two age-classes (juveniles and non-juveniles). The most parsimonious model from the 2-age-class analysis was one in which juveniles and non-juveniles had different survival rates and survival did not vary

TABLE 2. COMPARISON OF SELECTED CAP-
TURE-RECAPTURE MODELS USED TO EXAMINE SPOTTED
OWL DATA FROM THE ROSEBURG STUDY AREA, OREGON,
1985–1993. ONE SET OF MODELS EXAMINED ONLY OWLS
BANDED AT AGE 3 OR GREATER. THE 2-AGE-CLASS
MODELS INCLUDED TWO AGE CLASSES; JUVENILES
(<1-YR-OLD), AND NON-JUVENILES (≥1-YR-OLD).
MODELS WERE GENERATED IN PROGRAM SURGE (LE-
BRETON ET AL. 1992) AND ARE LISTED IN ORDER OF
INCREASING AIC (AKAIKE'S INFORMATION CRITERION)
VALUES (AKAIKE 1973). K IS THE NUMBER OF ESTIM-
ABLE PARAMETERS. LIKELIHOOD RATIO TEST (LRT)
RESULTS INDICATE WHETHER A PARTICULAR MODEL
WAS SIGNIFICANTLY DIFFERENT THAN THE MODEL WITH
THE LOWEST AIC

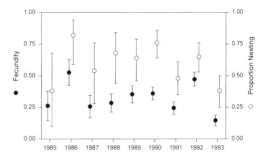

FIGURE 3. Annual fecundity and proportion of ≥3-yr-old female Northern Spotted Owls nesting on the Roseburg Study Area, OR: 1985–1993. Solid circles with associated SEs indicates fecundity, defined as the number of female young fledged per female owl. Open circles with associated 95% confidence intervals indicates proportion of females nesting.

Model[a]	K	AIC	LRT χ^2	LRT df	LRT P
≥3-yr-old models					
$\{\phi_T, p_{s+T}\}$	5	1987.303			
$\{\phi_t, p_{s+T}\}$	11	1987.987	0.68	6	0.995
$\{\phi_T, p_{s\bullet T}\}$	6	1988.821	1.52	1	0.218
$\{\phi, p_{s+t}\}$	10	1988.885	1.58	5	0.904
$\{\phi_{s+T}, p_{s+T}\}$	6	1989.187	1.88	1	0.170
2-age-class models					
$\{\phi_{a2}, p_{a4'+s}\}$	7	3236.954			
$\{\phi_{a2+T}, p_{a4'+s}\}$	8	3238.367	1.41	1	0.235
$\{\phi_{a2\bullet T}, p_{a4'+s}\}$	9	3239.357	2.40	2	0.301
$\{\phi_{a2+t}, p_{a4'+s}\}$	14	3242.974	6.02	7	0.537
$\{\phi_{a2}, p_{a3'+s}\}$	6	3244.732	7.78	1	0.005

[a] Subscripts associated with model parameters indicate if there were categorical age (a), categorical sex (s) or time (t,T) effects on survival (ϕ) or recapture (p). Among-year variation in a parameter is indicated by a t (categorical) or a T (linear) subscript. Numbers indicate number of age-groups estimated by the model. An apostrophe following a number indicates that sex-effects were ignored for juveniles. An • indicates interaction between variables, whereas a + indicates a reduced model in which effects were additive.

with sex or time (model $\{\phi_{a2}, p_{a4'+s}\}$, Table 2, Fig. 2). Likelihood ratio tests indicated no difference between the most parsimonious model and several competing models (Table 2).

SURVIVAL ESTIMATES

Estimated annual survival ($\hat{\phi}$) from the best 2-age-class model was 0.419 (SE = 0.042) for juveniles and 0.843 (SE = 0.010) for non-juveniles. Estimates of non-juvenile survival from the most parsimonious model and the four competing models in Table 2 varied by less than 1%, indicating that model selection had little effect on survival estimates of non-juveniles. Estimates of juvenile survival were more variable than for non-juveniles, differing by as much as 7% among models. The estimate of juvenile survival from the best model was near the upper end of the range of survival estimates produced by the five 2-age-class models in Table 2.

JUVENILE EMIGRATION RATES

The rate of undetected emigration by radio-marked juveniles ($\hat{E}_J$) was 0.077 (SE = 0.052) for the 1991 cohort (2 of 26 owls emigrated), and 0.350 (SE = 0.086) for the 1992 cohort (11 of 31 owls emigrated). The pooled estimate was 0.228 (SE = 0.056; 13 of 57 owls emigrated). Using the pooled estimate of $\hat{E}_J$ to adjust the estimate of juvenile survival from the best 2-age-class model, we calculated an adjusted juvenile survival estimate ($\hat{S}_J$) of 0.542 (SE = 0.066), which was 12.3% higher than the unadjusted estimate.

FECUNDITY

Estimated mean annual fecundity of females was 0.321 (SE = 0.022, N = 697) for ≥3-yr-old owls, 0.144 (SE = 0.062, N = 52) for 2-yr-old owls, and 0.080 (SE = 0.056, N = 44) for 1-yr-old owls. Fecundity differed among years for ≥3-yr-old females (F = 7.572, df = 8, P < 0.001, Fig. 3). Fecundity of 1- and 2-yr-old owls was lower than ≥3-yr-old owls (F = 19.707, df = 1, P < 0.001). For this reason, we used the age-group estimates of fecundity for calculations of the annual rate of population change rather than a combined estimate for all females.

ANNUAL RATE OF POPULATION CHANGE

Based on the age-specific estimates of fecundity and the unadjusted estimates of juvenile and non-juvenile survival from model $\{\phi_{a2}, p_{a4'+s}\}$ we get $\lambda = 0.957$ (SE = 0.015), which is significantly less than 1.0 (z = 2.945, P = 0.002). Substituting the adjusted estimate of juvenile survival ($\hat{S}_J$) for the unadjusted estimate of juvenile survival ($\hat{\phi}_J$) in the population growth rate equation produced $\hat{\lambda} = 0.986$ (SE = 0.020), which is not different

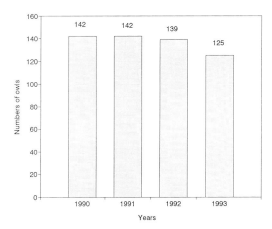

FIGURE 4. Number of territorial Spotted Owls detected on the Roseburg BLM Density Study Area during annual surveys conducted during the breeding season (1 March–31 August), 1990–1993.

from a stationary population ($z = 0.706$, $P = 0.240$). A power analysis of the latter test indicated that there was only a 17.2% chance of detecting a real population decrease of 1.4% per year with the available data.

COUNTS OF OWLS ON THE DENSITY STUDY AREA

Because the best 2-age-class model did not indicate any time effects on recapture probabilities, we assumed that the number of owls counted on the density study area each year could be compared without any correction for year-effects on detection rates. Although fewer owls were detected in 1992 and 1993 than in 1990 and 1991 (Fig. 4), the null hypothesis (no change in numbers of owls) could not be rejected (slope = -5.400, $r = -0.858$, $P = 0.142$). However, the power of the regression analysis (Gerrodette 1987) to detect the observed rate of decline was low (0.27).

DISCUSSION

SURVIVAL

It was not clear why the best model for ≥ 3-yr-old owls included a linear time trend on survival while the best 2-age-class model did not. One possibility was that pooling of 1- and 2-yr-old owls with ≥ 3-yr-old owls in the 2-age-class models produced more variability in the data, obscuring any linear trends. The linear decline in apparent annual survival of ≥ 3-yr-old owls is cause for concern because it could reflect some underlying problem with habitat. However, other explanations for the observed phenomenon should also be considered. For example, it is possible that a decline in survival rates observed

during a relatively short-term study could be a natural oscillation around some equilibrium point.

In our analysis we assumed that the median capture interval for all age cohorts was one year. Deviations from this assumption could cause bias in estimates of survival.

EMIGRATION

Because we did not have estimates of juvenile emigration (E_J) for every year of the study, we had little choice but to assume that pooled data from two radio-marked cohorts represented a reasonable average for all years of the study. This needs further investigation, especially in light of the fact that the estimates of E_J from the two radio-marked cohorts were quite different. However, in the absence of more years of data, we think it is reasonable to examine the potential influence of emigration based on the available data.

It has been suggested that prolonged periods of below average rainfall may have a deleterious effect on Spotted Owls (Noon et al. 1992), thus influencing survival and emigration rates. During the years that we estimated emigration rates, rainfall was comparable to the rest of the study period. From this standpoint, therefore, we did not feel that application of two years of emigration estimates to the entire study period was unreasonable. In fact, based on an analysis from several demographic study areas, an argument could be made that years of below average rainfall may be beneficial to Spotted Owls (E. Seaman, personal communication). Regardless of whether our data accurately estimated the average rate of emigration, they did provide clear evidence that juvenile emigration was relatively high in at least some years, and may have caused juvenile survival (ϕ_J) to be underestimated (Bart 1995, Burnham et al *this volume*).

Estimates of λ are particularly sensitive to non-juvenile survival rates (Noon and Biles 1990). If non-juvenile emigration occurs and is undetected, then non-juvenile survival rates may be underestimated, causing a corresponding underestimate of λ (Bart 1995). Although rates of non-juvenile emigration are generally believed to be low (Burnham et al *this volume*), some non-juvenile emigration does occur, as evidenced by occasional movements of non-juvenile owls from one study area to another (E. Forsman, unpublished data; J. Thrailkill, personal communication). To the extent that such movements occur and go undetected, they may cause non-juvenile survival rates to be underestimated. The Roseburg Study Area is somewhat unique in that it is surrounded on three sides by other demographic study areas where other researchers are banding and monitoring Spotted Owls (see Franklin et al *this volume*). Given this arrangement of study areas, we believe the likelihood of undetected emigration by non-juvenile owls was particularly low for the Roseburg Study Area, but we have no data to prove this conclusively.

FECUNDITY

Causes for the considerable among-year variation in fecundity and proportion of females nesting were unknown. We suspect that variation in prey numbers coupled with long-and-short-term weather phenomena may have been primarily responsible for the observed variation in breeding. Fluctuations in prey populations have been implicated in breeding rates of a number of other owl species, including Great Horned Owls (*Bubo virginianus*; Rusch et al. 1972, Adamcik et al. 1978), Tawny Owls (*Strix aluco*; Southern 1970), Snowy Owls (*Nyctea scandiaca*; Pitelka et al. 1955), and Great Gray Owls (*Strix nebulosa*; Nero 1980).

POPULATION CHANGE

Depending on which estimate of λ was used, the population on the study area appeared to be declining at a rate of 1.4%–4.3% per year. These values might be viewed as a range within which λ could be expected to fall. However, there were other factors that could influence estimates of λ that we were unable to take into account. For example, in our analysis we did not include fecundity estimates from females that were known to be present, but that could not be visually observed well enough to confirm their age or color bands. Although some of these females were known to have nested, most were owls that appeared to be non-nesting or that nested and failed to produce young. Excluding these females tends to overestimate fecundity.

A factor that could have caused us to underestimate fecundity was mortality that occurred after young left the nest, but before brood size was determined (Bart 1995). We were unable to evaluate this bias, but think it was small because the number of young fledged by most pairs was determined within 1–2 weeks after the young left the nest.

CHANGES IN OWL NUMBERS

The lack of a significant change in owl numbers on the Density Study Area did not necessarily confirm or refute the estimates of λ from the capture-recapture analysis. Assuming that a population decline is occurring, there are several factors that could cause changes in the density of territorial owls to lag behind the actual rate of decline in the population. In particular, it is possible that the number of territorial owls might not decline at the same rate as the overall population simply because the territorial population is maintained at a high level through replacement from within a "floater population" of owls without territories (Thomas et al. 1990, Franklin 1992). While this phenomenon might be expected to occur during the initial stages of a decline, it should gradually disappear, perhaps over many years, as the floater population is depleted.

MANAGEMENT IMPLICATIONS

Management of forest lands by the BLM and other landowners within the boundaries of the Roseburg Study Area has led to a reduction of suitable owl habitat during the last 40–50 years (Thomas et al. 1993a, Raphael et al. *this volume*). Even though rates of harvest on BLM lands have declined since 1990, habitat conditions are still changing fairly rapidly in the study area, particularly on private lands, where harvest continues at high levels. In this dynamic environment of changing habitat conditions, it is unlikely that the owl population will reach any sort of equilibrium condition for some time. Present trends in estimates of survival, fecundity, population growth rates, and owl numbers are reflective of past management activities, and do not necessarily indicate what will happen in the long term if there is a continued reduction in cutting of older forests on BLM lands and a commensurate recovery of suitable owl habitat within large areas of federal land that have been targeted for management of late-successional forest ecosystems (Thomas et al. 1990, Thomas et al. 1993b, USDA and USDI 1994).

The absence of strong negative trends in survival and counts of owl numbers on the Roseburg Study Area may indicate that the slowdown in harvest rates on BLM lands already may be having a stabilizing influence on the owl population. However, responses of the population are undoubtedly influenced by a variety of factors in addition to simple changes in habitat amount and distribution (e.g., weather patterns, predation rates, competition with invading species). While it is theoretically possible to address those relationships using experiments that control or account for all the different variables, we believe such experiments will be difficult or impossible to accomplish for a species with life history traits like the Spotted Owl (low population densities, large home ranges, high variation in vital rates, and high mobility). While this represents a challenge for researchers, it also represents a real problem for federal management agencies that are expected to document the effects of their management activities on native plants and animals. We think it is imperative that the public, the courts, and political representatives understand that any management plan adopted for a species like the Spotted Owl is essentially an uncontrolled experiment. To expect that monitoring of such experiments will lead to simple conclusions is unrealistic. Thus, while we believe that management agencies should attempt to monitor the effects of their activities, we do not expect that the time will ever come when decisions regarding management will be judgment free. The challenge for resource managers will be to arrive at a judgments that are considered a reasonable compromise by vying interest groups.

SUMMARY

We conducted a capture-recapture study of Northern Spotted Owls on the Roseburg District of the Bureau of Land Management in western Oregon from 1985–1993. The study was designed to establish baseline estimates of vital rates of Northern Spotted Owls and to examine trends in those vital rates that might be indicative of overall population health. The study area was predominantly forest with alternating sections of federal and non-federal ownership. The sample of marked owls included 593 owls that were ≥ 1-yr-old (272 females, 321 males) and 429 juveniles. Males and females had similar survival rates, and there was little annual variation in survival. Estimated survival rates of juveniles and non-juveniles were 0.419 (SE = 0.042) and 0.843 (SE = 0.010), respectively. Fecundity, defined as the number of young produced per female per year, averaged 0.321 (SE = 0.022) for ≥ 3-yr-old owls, 0.144 (SE = 0.062) for 2-yr-old owls, and 0.080 (SE = 0.056) for 1-yr-old owls. Based on the capture-recapture data, the mean annual rate of change in the resident owl population during the study period (λ) was 0.957 (SE = 0.015), indicating a 4.3% annual decline in the population of resident owls. The estimate of λ was significantly less than 1 (P = 0.002). When $\hat{\phi}_J$ was adjusted for juvenile emigration using information from radio-telemetry studies, $\hat{\lambda}$ was 0.986 (SE = 0.020), which was not different from 1.0 (P = 0.240). However, the power of the test to detect an annual population decline of 1.4% was low. The number of owls detected on a 1,011-km^2 area that was thoroughly surveyed each year did not decline significantly from 1990–1993. We suggest that the negative linear time trend on apparent survival rates of ≥ 3-yr-old owls could reflect a gradual loss of habitat or could simply be a mild oscillation around some equilibrium point.

ACKNOWLEDGMENTS

This study was a cooperative effort between the USDI Bureau of Land Management and the USDA Forest Service PNW Research Station. Funding was provided by USDI Bureau of Land Management, USDI Fish and Wildlife Service, USDI National Biological Service, and the USDA Forest Service PNW Research Laboratory. The study would not have been possible without the combined efforts of a large number of dedicated people, including D. K. Barrett, R. R. Bown, L. J. Brock, J. A. Burns, R. A. Cail, B. R. Casler, A. D. Center, G. S. Center, J. R. DuBrau, N. L. Duncan, R. H. Espinosa, C. C. Foster, R. M. Gadd, J. H. Guetterman, N. A. Hegel, R. B. Horn, M. S. Jackson, D. J. Janson, C. B. Kasner, P. J. Loschl, D. Manson, R. F. Miller, G. W. Mires, L. B. Page, S. L. Pauly, M. K. Pose, R. L. Potts, J. A. Richards, C. Ridgley, M. R. Roan, J. Schlachter, P. A. Shaklee, R. J. Straub, T. T. Teichert, M. Tengesdal, J. W. Witt, D. L. York, and J. J. Zisa. We would like to especially recognize Franklin M. Oliver whose dedication to this project inspired us all. We also thank all the biologists from surrounding study areas who provided invaluable information on emigrants. For assistance with data analysis we thank D. R. Anderson, B. L. Biswell, K. P. Burnham, J. Clobert, A. B. Franklin, J. E. Hines, J. D. Nichols, R. J. Pradel, E. A. Rexstad, T. M. Shenk, G. C. White, and K. R. Wilson. W. R. Clark and two anonymous reviewers provided numerous helpful suggestions on an early draft of the manuscript. Any errors in interpretation are our own.

Key words: capture-recapture, demography, Klamath Province, Northern Spotted Owl, Oregon Cascade Ranges, Oregon Coast Ranges, population growth rates, *Strix occidentalis caurina,* survival.

Studies in Avian Biology No. 17:67–76, 1996.

DEMOGRAPHY OF NORTHERN SPOTTED OWLS IN THE SOUTHERN CASCADES AND SISKIYOU MOUNTAINS, OREGON

FRANK F. WAGNER, E. CHARLES MESLOW, GREGORY M. BENNETT, CHRIS J. LARSON, STEPHEN M. SMALL, AND STEPHEN DESTEFANO

INTRODUCTION

The Northern Spotted Owl (*Strix occidentalis caurina*) occurs widely within the forests of the interior mountains of southwestern Oregon, which are characterized by the regular occurrence of tanoak (*Lithocarpus densiflorus*), white fir (*Abies concolor*), or Shasta red fir (*A. magnifica shastensis*) within forest stand composition. These forests are northern extensions of forest formations of the Sierra Nevada and coastal northern California (Franklin and Dyrness 1973), and are transitional to forests within the Western Hemlock (*Tsuga heterophylla*) and Pacific Silver Fir (*Abies amabilis*) zones of western Oregon and Washington. Habitat for Northern Spotted Owls within these forests occurs as complex mosaics of forest types and age because of complex geologic, soil, and climatic patterns. Additionally, because of past natural fire events and the prevalence of selective logging methods, forest stand development and structure is often uneven-aged (USDA and USDI 1994).

In 1985 we initiated a cooperative effort among Oregon State University, the Bureau of Land Management (BLM), and the U.S. Forest Service to gather demographic data on the Northern Spotted Owl within the southern Cascades and Siskiyou Mountains. Because forest types, natural fire regimes, and timber harvest systems differ from much of the remainder of the Northern Spotted Owl's range, our objective was to obtain estimates of vital rates and population trend that were representative of the region.

For this study, we used capture-recapture and empirical methods to estimate age-specific survival and fecundity rates and rate of population change for the period 1985–1993 for the watersheds of the interior Rogue River basin, upper South Umpqua River, and a portion of the upper Klamath River basin. Because controversy exists in interpreting model-based estimates of population trend when these results differ from trend based on empirical counts of owls (Thomas et al. 1993a, Raphael et al. *this volume*), we report annual count results and trend from bounded density study areas for 1990–1993. We also compare vital rates measured within the density study areas to the study area as a whole. Because un-detected emigration from the study area may negatively bias survival rates, we developed estimates for adult and juvenile emigration rates. Our interest here was to assess our confidence in the direction of the estimated population trend. Additionally, we explored the relationship between precipitation patterns and estimates of annual fecundity.

STUDY AREA

Data collection was initiated on the Southern Cascades and Siskiyou Mountains Study Area in 1985. Initial efforts centered on the Medford District of the BLM but were subsequently expanded during 1987–88 to include the Klamath Resource Area of the Lakeview District, the Rogue River National Forest, the Galice and Illinois Valley Ranger Districts of the Siskiyou National Forest, the Tiller Ranger District of the Umpqua National Forest, and the Klamath Ranger District of the Winema National Forest (Fig. 1). Lands administered by the BLM are typically intermingled with private forest lands, often producing a checkerboard pattern of alternating square mile sections. Timber harvest on private lands has often occurred at an earlier date and more completely than on adjacent Federal lands (USDI 1995). The study area encompasses approximately 15,216 km^2 with about 25% of the area occupied by large non-forested areas, open subalpine forest, and foothill woodlands that do not normally provide habitat for Northern Spotted Owls.

Climate is moderate and maritime influenced. Summers are characteristically hot and dry, and winters are cool and moist (Baldwin 1973), with persistent winter snow cover at elevations >1500 m. Precipitation occurs primarily during October–May with local amounts varying widely in response to topographic effects and rain shadows. Average annual precipitation ranges from 89–175 cm over most of the study area, but reaches 250 cm near the western boundary (Anon. 1982). Data collection for the study coincided with persistent drought conditions. As measured at Medford Oregon, annual precipitation during the study averaged approximately 70% of amounts recorded for the preceding 30 years

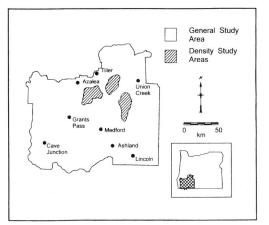

FIGURE 1. The Southern Cascades and Siskiyou Mountains Study Area in southwestern Oregon, 1985–1993. Hatched areas indicate locations of three subareas (Density Study Areas) within which we attempted to estimate the number of resident Northern Spotted Owls each year.

(National Weather Service, Medford Oregon, personal communication).

The study area includes portions of the Mixed-Evergreen, Mixed-Conifer, and True Fir vegetation zones (Franklin and Dyrness 1973). Important plant series (Atzet and Wheeler 1984, Atzet and McCrimmen 1990) for Northern Spotted Owl habitat include the Douglas-fir (*Pseudotsuga menziesii*), White Fir, Tanoak, Shasta Red Fir, and Western Hemlock series.

Prior to fire suppression efforts beginning during the 1920s, forests at moderate to low elevations developed under conditions of relatively frequent fires of low intensity (Agee 1993). This fire history tended to create uneven-aged forests that are now harvested by both selective methods and clear-cutting (USDA and USDI 1994). Intermediate-aged forest stands derived from selective harvest methods predominate over much of the study area, and these stands typically exhibit greater structural complexity than stands which developed under dense even-aged conditions following clear-cutting or high intensity fire. Because of the prevalence of selective timber harvest methods including overstory removal, shelterwoods, and diameter-limit cuts, extensive stands of unharvested mature and old-growth conifer forest are relatively scarce and largely restricted to remaining remote areas. For example, approximately 17% of commercial forestland administered by BLM contained at least 10% stocking of old-growth trees. Of this proportion, only 30% of the acres were unharvested or lightly harvested by selective cutting, and the

remainder was moderately to heavily harvested by selective methods (USDI 1995).

The study area is adjacent to other spotted owl demography study areas to the north and west (Franklin et al. *this volume*). These neighboring study areas facilitate the reobservation of banded owls that subsequently emigrate out of our study area. Additionally, the eastern and southeast boundaries of the study area are near the known range limits of the Northern Spotted Owl. These areas are characterized by open forests of lodgepole pine (*Pinus contorta*), ponderosa pine (*P. ponderosa*), or western juniper (*Juniperus occidentalis*) that may act as filters discouraging emigration by Spotted Owls.

METHODS

FIELD DATA COLLECTION

Methods used for locating, capturing and banding of owls, determining sex and age class, reobservation of marked owls, and determining fecundity are described in Franklin et al. (*this volume*). We used capture-recapture methods to estimate survival rates. During 1985–1993, we uniquely color-marked owls of known age class and sex, and conducted annual surveys to reobserve previously banded owls. We recognized four age classes: fledged juveniles (J), 1-yr-old owls (S1), 2-yr-old owls (S2), and owls ≥3 yrs old (A). We estimated fecundity from direct counts of the number of young fledged by each territorial female owl or by confirming non-reproduction.

Because the study area is large and characterized by diverse forest types, we established four categories of plant-series groupings to facilitate comparison of survival rates within the study area. We examined the area within a 2.4 km radius around individual owl sites by ground reconnaissance, and classified sites dominated by (1) the Douglas-fir series as the Douglas-fir Group, (2) the White Fir series and/or Shasta Red Fir series as the True Fir Group, (3) mosaics of the Douglas-fir series, White Fir series, and the Western Hemlock series as the Mixed Conifer Group, or (4) mosaics of the Douglas-fir series and the Tanoak series as the Douglas-fir/Tanoak Group.

The study area was partitioned into a General Study Area (GSA) and three smaller Density Study Areas (DSAs). We selected the DSAs to be representative of the range of plant series and timber harvest methods occurring within the study area. DSAs were 273 km², 310 km², and 316 km² in size. We used vocal lure surveys to systematically search the DSAs for territorial owls each year from 1990–1993 (Franklin et al. *this volume*). Six replicate surveys during the breeding season (March–August) were required before concluding an area was unoccupied for a given year. Boundaries and calling points for surveys were established *a priori* and remained the same each year. Survey effort was thus constant for all years.

Individual sites with a known history of owl occupancy were surveyed annually within the GSA, but areas between sampled sites were generally not surveyed each year. The number of sites surveyed and the number of marked owls increased annually during the first half of the study before leveling off. Based on a search radius of >1.5 km around owl sites, we estimate that survey coverage exceeded 50% of the available owl habitat within the study area during 1990–1993. Additionally, Federal agencies and private timber companies conducted large scale surveys each year for timber sale evaluations and other monitoring purposes. Resightings of previously banded owls from these efforts were shared with us. Data from the GSA and known sites within the DSAs were collected from 1985–1993 and were combined for estimates of fecundity, survival, and rate of population change.

DATA ANALYSIS

Notation and methods used for analysis of capture-recapture data are described in Franklin et al. (*this volume*). We summarized capture history data and assessed goodness-of-fit to Cormack-Jolly-Seber models with TESTs 2 and 3 in program RELEASE (Burnham et al. 1987). These tests were used to examine capture histories for independence and heterogeneity across and within capture occasions (Burnham et al. 1987, Pollock et al. 1990). Survival and recapture rates were estimated from Cormack-Jolly-Seber models for open populations in program SURGE (Lebreton et al. 1992).

Modeling procedures started with general models that allowed survival (ϕ) and recapture (p) probabilities to vary by sex (s), age (a), nonlinear time (t), linear time (T), or group effects. We then used Akaike's Information Criterion (AIC) (Akaike 1973) to identify the most parsimonious model that adequately fit the data (Burnham and Anderson 1992, Lebreton et al. 1992). Likelihood ratio tests were used to further examine the most parsimonious model and competing models with similar AIC values (Burnham et al. 1987). Modeling included two main efforts: (1) data from owls ≥ 3 yrs old were used in models to examine sex- and time-specific relationships, and (2) multiple age-class models examined age-, sex-, and time-specific effects or interactions.

Age-specific fecundity was estimated as the average number of female fledglings produced per territorial female of known age-class (Caughley

1977). Because fledged young were of unknown sex when observed, we assumed a 1:1 sex ratio.

The annual rate of population change during the time period of the study (λ, Lambda) was computed from age-specific survival and female fecundity estimates by solving the characteristic equation for a stage-based Leslie-Lefkovitch matrix (Noon and Biles 1990, Franklin et al. *this volume*). The calculation of λ used juvenile and non-juvenile (≥ 1-yr-old owls) survival estimates from the best 2-age class model, and fecundity estimates from three age classes (S1, S2, and A) of territorial females.

We tested for differences in survival and recapture probabilities across capture-history data sets for the 4 plant-series groups with TEST 1 of program RELEASE (Burnham et al. 1987). Owls ≥ 1 yr old of both sexes were pooled for this test, and the sample of marked and released owls totaled 555, 462, 640, and 344 respectively for the Douglas-fir, True Fir, Mixed Conifer, and Douglas-fir/Tanoak groups.

We used Chi-square tests to assess annual variation in fecundity of owls ≥ 1 yr old. We compared annual fecundity between owls ≥ 3 yrs old and owls 1–2 yrs old (pooled S1 and S2) with ANOVA. Linear regression was used to compare annual fecundity to the amount of annual precipitation from September through April. We used precipitation amounts recorded at Medford, Oregon (U.S. Dep. Commerce 1994) as an index for the study area as a whole.

To evaluate the trend of owl abundance within DSAs against time, we used linear regression of the natural log of annual counts. We then converted the growth rate, expressed as the slope of the fitted line, to an empirical estimate of the annual rate of population change ($\lambda = r^e$) (Caughley and Sinclair 1994). Because modeling indicated that recapture probabilities within the study area were not significantly affected by annual variation, we used unadjusted annual counts to assess trend. A power analysis of the regression (Gerrodette 1987) was conducted using program TRENDS (T. Gerrodette, personal communication).

We compiled capture-recapture data sets and estimates of annual fecundity for the DSAs and GSA separately. We used TEST 1 of program RELEASE to test for differences in survival and recapture probabilities between the DSAs and GSA. Owls ≥ 1 yr old were pooled and totaled 1422 (GSA) and 289 (DSAs) marked and released owls. We compared fecundity between the GSA and DSAs and among years using ANOVA.

EMIGRATION ESTIMATES

To assess the potential of emigration to negatively bias survival probabilities, we constructed estimates of emigration rates for juveniles and non-juveniles separately. For bias from emigration to occur, owls must leave the study area, live through the first year of emigration, remain undetected, and not return (Anderson et al. 1990). From this definition, we identified 6 components of the overall probability that an owl would emigrate from the study area: (1) the annual probability that a banded owl would leave it's territory and relocate elsewhere (P_1), (2) the probability that an owl would move a distance sufficient to leave the study area (P_{ds}), (3) the probability that an owl would move in a suitable direction to leave the study area (P_{dr}), (4) the probability that an owl would remain alive through the first year of emigration (P_ϕ), (5) the probability that an owl would remain undetected after emigration (P_{nd}), and (6) the probability that an owl would not return after emigrating (P_{nr}). We estimated permanent emigration as the sum of the product of these probabilities for each owl banded within the study area:

$$P(\hat{E}) = \Sigma \; P(\hat{E}_i) = (P_1)(P_{ds})(P_{dr})(P_\phi)(P_{nd})(P_{nr})$$

We estimated P_1 for non-juveniles from radio-marked owls that were observed within the study area (F. Wagner, unpublished data) during 1985–93 for a total of 136 owl-years. We assumed that all non-juveniles would move permanently to new territories at the same rate as radio-marked owls. Territorial relocations were defined as those occurring outside of an estimated home-range area (generally ≥ 2.4 km radius) and persisting for ≥ 1 year. We assumed that all juveniles dispersed from their natal site.

We estimated P_{ds} based on 2 sets of distances: (1) for banded owls that were recaptured as residents after moving to a new territory, the observed straight-line distance between the old and new territories (non-juvenile territorial-relocation distance) or the distance between the natal site and the new territory (juvenile dispersal distance); and (2) for all banded owls, the shortest distance between the location they were banded and the study area boundary in 2-km intervals. For territorial-relocation and juvenile dispersal distances, we derived separate cumulative frequency distributions in 2-km intervals based on the straight-line distances observed for those owls that moved permanently to another territory. We computed P_{ds} as the product of the proportion of owls banded at a given distance from the study area boundary and the probability that an owl would move as far or farther than that distance based on the cumulative frequency distributions. Because male and female juvenile owls exhibit different mean distances of dispersal (Miller 1989), we estimated juvenile emigration separately by sex and assumed a 1:1 sex ratio.

For estimates of P_{dr}, we assumed that territorial relocations and dispersal were random in direction and that these movements occurred with equal probability either towards the study area boundary or towards the interior of the study area.

Because our model-based estimates of survival include some level of bias due to emigration, we estimated P_ϕ with a range of survival probabilities. Hence we attempted to bracket the true survival for juveniles and non-juveniles (S_J and S_{NJ}). The lower limit of this range was set equal to the survival probabilities from the selected age-specific model, and the upper limit was set at what we considered to be optimistic but biologically feasible rates: 0.55 for juveniles, 0.88 for non-juveniles. We assumed that survival was not affected either by the occurrence or distance of a movement.

For P_{nd} and P_{nr}, we assumed that all emigrating owls would neither return to the study area nor be detected outside the study area. These assumptions would cause emigration to be overestimated, especially for dispersing juveniles. Of those owls originally banded on our study area, a significant proportion of the recaptures of dispersing owls has occurred in adjacent study areas. Our calculations may also overestimate potential juvenile emigration because they are based on the shortest distance to the study area boundary rather than the average distance. Alternately, our estimates, which are based on recaptures of banded owls, may underestimate true rates because recapture may vary with distance of dispersal. Therefore we calculated an additional estimate of emigration using the dispersal distances from telemetry-marked owls observed by Miller (1989).

In applying assumptions for this analysis, we attempted to use a realistic but conservative approach that approximated or exceeded true emigration rates. We used our estimates of emigration ($\hat{E}$) to produce less biased survival estimates and to assess our confidence in the direction of the model-based estimate of population trend ($\hat{\lambda}$). We estimated a range of true survival rates, not confounded by emigration, for juveniles ($\hat{S}_J$) and non-juveniles ($\hat{S}_{NJ}$) with the relationship (Burnham et al. *this volume*, Franklin et al. *this volume*):

$$\hat{S} = \frac{\hat{\phi}}{1 - \hat{E}}$$

We compared our results to the S_J and E_J rates necessary to obtain a rate of population change ($\hat{\lambda}$) = 1.0 (Franklin et al. *this volume*). We used $\hat{S}_J$ to interpolate a $\hat{\lambda}$ between the model based $\hat{\lambda}$ and $\lambda = 1$. We tested H_0: $\lambda < 1$ vs. H_a: $\lambda \geq 1$ with a 1-tailed z-test (Franklin et al. *this volume*) using the SE derived from the original model-based estimate $\hat{\lambda}$:

$$z = \frac{1 - \hat{\lambda}}{\text{SE}(\hat{\lambda})}$$

RESULTS

CAPTURE-RECAPTURE DATA

We captured and banded 1,897 owls (Table 1) and captured 23 additional owls that were initially marked on other study areas and subsequently immigrated into our study area. The latter birds, primarily dispersing juveniles, were treated as newly banded owls with their age class determined at the time of first observation following immigration. The sample size of captured and released owls used in capture-recapture analysis was 823 females ≥3 yrs old, 1,032 males ≥3 yrs old, 121 1–2-yr-old females, 142 1–2-yr-old males, and 680 juveniles. These totals include individual birds that were captured (or reobserved) and released multiple times, and are equal to the R totals in the capture-recapture m-array (Burnham et al. 1987)

GOODNESS-OF-FIT

We found no significant lack of fit (TEST 3, program RELEASE) within adult cohorts (females: $\chi^2 = 10.98$, 12 df, P = 0.53; males: $\chi^2 = 10.50$, 12 df, P = 0.57), indicating that owl capture histories within a released cohort had similar survival and recapture probabilities. However, expected future fates differed between cohorts (TEST 2, program RELEASE) released at different occasions (females: $\chi^2 = 29.55$, 5 df, P = < 0.001; males: $\chi^2 = 21.18$, 3 df, P = < 0.001) and for the combined results of TEST 2 and 3 (females: $\chi^2 = 40.54$, 17 df, P = 0.001; males: $\chi^2 = 31.692$, 15 df, P = 0.007). We examined the partitioned test components of TEST 2 and isolated most of the lack of fit to 5 females and 5 males exhibiting temporary emigration. TEST 2 is sensitive to temporary emigration (Burnham et al. 1987), but because the lack of fit was not systematic and stemmed from only a few individuals within relatively large samples, we concluded that the test results did not indicate an overall lack of fit of the data and that Cormack-Jolly-Seber models were appropriate for use.

MODEL SELECTION

The time- and sex-specific model that provided the best fit to the adult data, $\{\phi_T, p_s\}$, showed a negative linear time effect (T) (Fig. 2) on annual survival probabilities (ϕ) with no time effects on recapture probabilities (p). There was a sex effect on recapture rates but not on survival. In com-

TABLE 1. NUMBER OF NORTHERN SPOTTED OWLS BANDED 1985–1993 ON THE SOUTHERN CASCADE AND SISKIYOU MOUNTAINS STUDY AREA, OREGON

| Year | Owls ≥3 yrs old | | Owls 1 & 2 yrs old | | Juveniles |
	Male	Female	Male	Female	
1985	11	11	1	0	5
1986	14	8	2	0	8
1987	17	14	4	2	9
1988	38	33	13	6	50
1989	31	30	6	9	27
1990	122	92	11	13	108
1991	116	100	19	10	137
1992	122	110	16	15	284
1993[a]	85	86	25	25	51
Total	556	484	97	80	680

[a] Owls banded in 1993 are not reflected in capture-recapture analyses because they were not released until the last capture occasion.

mon with the selected model, competing models (Table 2) consistently had a sex effect on recapture rates (males had higher rates than females) and usually included a time effect on annual survival probabilities.

The best fitting age-specific model, $\{\phi_{a2}, p_{a4'+s}\}$, indicated that survival and recapture probabilities varied across age-classes and that recapture rates also differed between males and females. This model indicated no time effects on either survival or recapture probabilities (Fig. 2). Age structure on ϕ was reduced to 2 classes (juveniles and non-juveniles). Comparison with competing models in Table 2 indicated that increasing age structure on recapture probabilities improved AIC values up through 4 age classes, and additive sex effects had a secondary but consistent effect on recapture probabilities.

ESTIMATED SURVIVAL RATES

Estimated survival and recapture rates of owls did not differ among plant-series groups (Test 1: $\chi^2 = 28.14$, 23 df, $P = 0.211$). Therefore, data from the entire study area were combined for estimates of survival and recapture rates.

Estimated annual survival for ≥3-yr-old owls from the selected sex- and time-specific model, $\{\phi_T, p_s\}$, averaged 0.840 (SE = 0.010) (Fig. 2). Because standard errors could not be estimated from models with time effects on ϕ, the standard error was approximated from the closest model in AIC value, $\{\phi, p_s\}$, without a time effect on ϕ.

Estimates of annual survival from the selected age-specific model, $\{\phi_{a2}, p_{a4'+s}\}$, were 0.320 (SE = 0.038) for juveniles ($\hat{\phi}_J$) and 0.824 (SE = 0.009) for non-juveniles ($\hat{\phi}_{NJ}$) (Fig. 2). Estimates of annual survival from the selected model and several competing models varied ≤1% for juveniles and ≤1.4% for non-juveniles. This indicated that

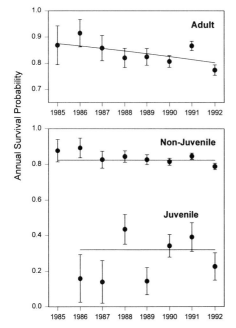

FIGURE 2. Estimates of survival for Northern Spotted Owls on the Southern Cascades and Siskiyou Mountains Study Area, Oregon, 1985–1993. The solid line in the upper graph indicates a nearly linear negative time trend in annual survival for ≥3-yr-old owls from the selected model $\{\phi_T, p_s\}$. Point estimates of annual survival (± 1 SE) from the next most parsimonious model with variable time effects $\{\phi_t, p_s\}$ on ϕ are shown for comparison. Solid lines in the lower graph represent constant survival estimates for non-juveniles (≥1 yr old) and juveniles from the selected age-specific model $\{\phi_{a2}, p_{a4'+s}\}$. Point estimates of annual survival (± 1 SE) from the next most parsimonious model with variable time effects $\{\phi_{a2+t}, p_{a4'+s}\}$ are shown for comparison.

TABLE 2. SUMMARY OF CAPTURE-RECAPTURE MODELS FOR THE NORTHERN SPOTTED OWL ON THE SOUTHERN CASCADES AND SISKIYOU MOUNTAINS STUDY AREA, OREGON, 1985–1993. MODELS ARE LISTED IN ORDER OF INCREASING AIC (AKAIKE'S INFORMATION CRITERION) VALUES (AKAIKE 1973). TIME AND SEX SPECIFIC MODELS INCLUDED ONLY THOSE OWLS INITIALLY MARKED WHEN THEY WERE ≥3 YRS OLD. AGE-SPECIFIC MODELS INCLUDED OWLS INITIALLY MARKED AS TWO AGE CLASSES: NON-JUVENILES (≥1 YR OLD) OR JUVENILES. MODEL SUBSCRIPTS DENOTE AGE CLASSES (E.G., $A2$), SEX (S), LINEAR TIME (T), NON-LINEAR TIME (T), OR ADDITIVE ($+$) EFFECTS

Model	Deviance (-2 ln[L])	K[a]	AIC
Time and sex specific models on owls ≥3 yrs old			
$\{\phi_T, p_s\}$	2292.969	4	2300.969
$\{\phi_t, p_s\}$	2282.350	10	2302.350
$\{\phi, p_s\}$	2296.458	3	2302.458
$\{\phi_{T+s}, p_s\}$	2292.482	5	2302.482
$\{\phi_T, p_{s+T}\}$	2292.663	5	2302.663
Age, sex, and time specific models			
$\{\phi_{a2}, p_{a4'+s}\}$	3441.966	7	3455.966
$\{\phi_{a2}, p_{a4'}\}$	3444.904	6	3456.904
$\{\phi_{a2}, p_{a5'+s}\}$	3441.010	8	3457.010
$\{\phi_{a2 \cdot T}, p_{a4'+s}\}$	3439.020	9	3457.020
$\{\phi_{a2}, p_{a3'+s}\}$	3454.646	6	3466.646

[a] Number of estimable parameters.

survival estimates were not greatly affected by model selection.

FECUNDITY

Annual fecundity of territorial females averaged 0.013 (SE = 0.019) for 1-yr-old owls, 0.145 (SE = 0.056) for 2-yr-old owls, and 0.313 (SE = 0.016) for owls ≥3 yrs old. Estimated annual fecundity for ≥3-yr-old owls (Fig. 3) was higher than for 1 and 2-yr-old owls (F = 40.241, 1 df, P < 0.001). Fecundity of owls ≥1 yr old varied among yrs (χ^2 = 315.48, 24 df, P < 0.001), ranging from 0.075 in 1993 to 0.524 in 1992). Annual variation in mean fecundity rates was negatively correlated with both the amount of precipitation during September–April (r = 0.81, P = 0.004) (Fig. 4), and with mean fecundity from the previous year (r = 0.81, P < 0.001).

RATE OF POPULATION CHANGE

Based on the age-specific estimates of survival from model $\{\phi_{a2}, p_{a4'+s}\}$ and the age-specific estimates of annual fecundity, the estimate of the finite rate of population change ($\hat{\lambda}$) was 0.9105 (SE = 0.0121), which is significantly <1.0 (z = 7.39, P < 0.001). This estimate of λ suggests an average annual decline in the territorial population of 0.0895 during the period of study. Assuming that all other parameters are estimated accurately, values necessary for the true rate of juvenile survival (survival not confounded by emigration) (S_J) or juvenile emigration (E_J) to force $\hat{\lambda}$ = 1.0 were 0.746 and 0.75 (Burnham et al. *this volume*).

CHANGES IN ABUNDANCE WITHIN DENSITY STUDY AREAS

The annual trend in owl abundance within the combined DSAs during 1990–1993 (Table 3) was 0.959. This estimated rate of change did not differ (r = 0.83, P = 0.168) from a stationary rate (λ = 1.0). However, statistical power to detect an average annual decline of 4.1% over three occasions was low (0.31), and a lack of significance would not be unexpected regardless of actual trends.

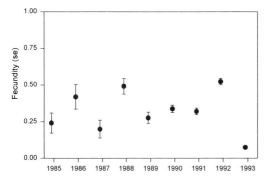

FIGURE 3. Annual variation in fecundity of ≥3-yr-old female Northern Spotted Owls. Annual means and standard errors are expressed as the number of female young fledged per female.

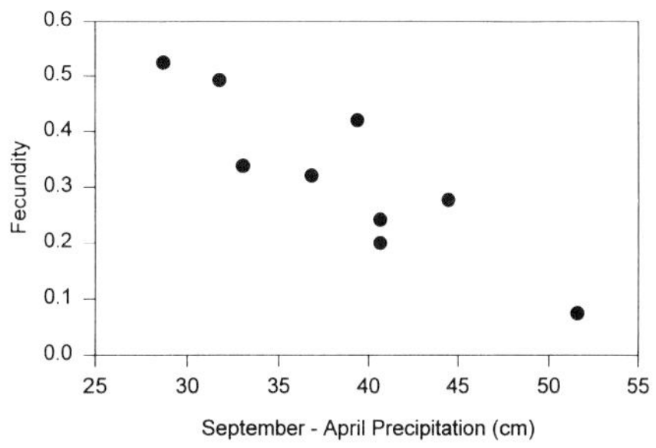

FIGURE 4. Relationship between precipitation during September–April and fecundity of Northern Spotted Owls on the Southern Cascades and Siskiyou Mountains Study Area, Oregon, 1985–1993. Fecundity is the mean number of female young fledged per ≥1-yr-old female.

Most of the decline in owl abundance occurred in the single occasion from 1990 to 1991. Of the 23 owls which occupied sites in 1990 and subsequently were absent without replacement in 1991, 16 owls (69%) were associated with sites that had significant timber harvest within or adjacent to the center of activity. After 1990, most timber harvest within DSAs was administratively directed away from sites occupied by owls.

Estimated annual survival probabilities for 1990–93 were 0.813 (SE = 0.020) within DSAs and 0.843 (SE = 0.016) within the GSA. Neither survival probabilities or recapture probabilities were significantly different (Test 1: χ^2 = 4.97, 5 df, P = 0.419). Mean annual fecundity of ≥1-yr-old females during the same period was lower (F = 20.151, 1 df, P < 0.001) within the DSAs (fecundity = 0.184, SE = 0.024) than in the GSA (fecundity = 0.303, SE = 0.010).

ESTIMATES OF EMIGRATION

The annual rate that non-juvenile owls relocated to new territories was 0.0147 (SE = 0.010). This rate was similar to rates for other samples of radio-marked Northern Spotted Owls in Oregon and northern California (Thomas et al. 1990). The mean territorial-relocation distance observed for recaptured non-juvenile owls was 6.74 km (N = 41, SD = 5.16). Mean dispersal distances observed for recaptured juveniles averaged 17.23 km for males (N = 48, SD = 16.54) and 26.13 km for females (N = 52, SD = 13.82). Given the distribution of banded owls relative to the study area boundary (Fig. 5), the cumulative annual probability that owls would move far enough in a suitable direction to leave the study area was 0.084 for non-juveniles, 0.292 for juvenile males, 0.384 for juvenile females, and 0.338 for pooled juveniles.

Based on these values, the estimated annual rate of emigration ($\hat{E}$) for non-juveniles was 0.001 when P_ϕ was set at 0.88. The annual rate of $\hat{E}$ for juveniles surviving their first year ranged from 0.108 based on P_ϕ set at 0.32 from the 2-age-class model to 0.1859 based on P_ϕ set at 0.55. The juvenile $\hat{E}$ based on $\hat{\phi}_J$ = 0.55 was 25% of the rate needed for λ = 1.0. The corresponding estimate of true survival ($\hat{S}_J$) was 0.394, which is 53% of the rate necessary for λ = 1.0. Using $\hat{S}_J$ = 0.394, we interpolated an adjusted $\hat{\lambda}$ of 0.9577, which is significantly less than λ = 1.0 (z = 3.65, P < .001).

Our observed dispersal distances from banding data were somewhat shorter than dispersal distances observed with radio-marked juveniles in western Oregon (Miller 1989). Substituting telemetry data from Miller (1989) resulted in an $\hat{E}$ of 0.240 when P_ϕ was set at 0.55; and a $\hat{S}_J$ of 0.42. Use of these data gave similar results as

TABLE 3. NUMBER OF NON-JUVENILE NORTHERN SPOTTED OWLS COUNTED ANNUALLY BY AGE AND SEX CLASS WITHIN THE 899 KM² COMBINED DENSITY STUDY AREAS ON THE SOUTHERN CASCADES AND SISKIYOU MOUNTAINS STUDY AREA, OREGON, 1990–1993

	1990	1991	1992	1993
Males ≥3 yrs old[a]	76	68	69	64
Females ≥3 yrs old[a]	60	57	54	53
Males 1–2 yrs old	6	3	2	7
Females 1–2 yrs old	5	2	4	4
Total	147	130	129	128

[a] Includes non-juvenile owls of unknown age.

($P = 0.005$). Based on estimates of survival and fecundity, the estimated rate of population change (λ) was 0.9105 (SE = 0.0121), which was significantly < 1.0 ($P < 0.001$). We calculated estimates of annual non-juvenile (0.001) and juvenile (0.186) emigration to evaluate these as sources of bias in estimating the population change rate. Our estimates of emigration were insufficient to account for the direction and significance of the estimated rate of population change, but a portion of the magnitude of decline may be explained by juvenile emigration. Based on estimated rates of juvenile emigration, we interpolated an adjusted λ of 0.9577, which was significantly less than $\lambda = 1.0$ ($P < .001$). Counts of territorial owls within density study areas (DSAs) did not differ among years during 1990–1993. However, power to detect trends was low. Comparison of vital rates between the DSAs and the remainder of the study area indicated lower fecundity within DSAs ($P < 0.001$), and suggested that the observed owl abundance within the DSAs was dependent on net immigration. We concluded that owl abundance based on empirical counts within DSAs neither supported or contradicted model-based estimates of population trend. Based on the negative population trend estimated over the 9-year period of study and the negative linear time trend on survival rates, we believe a conservative approach to the management of the Northern Spotted Owl and its habitat should be taken within the interior mountains of southwestern Oregon.

ACKNOWLEDGMENTS

A study of this extent and duration is only possible as a cooperative effort. For assistance in coordination and data collection we thank G. Arnold, R. I. Bonn, J. F. Harper, C. Oakley, and R. Schnoes, Medford District, BLM; W. Dean and G. Sitter, Lakeview District, BLM; S. Armentrout, M. Bauer, J. Goode, M. Mamone, M. E. Mayville, D. Schultz, F. Wahl, F. Way, Rogue River National Forest; F. Craig and L. Webb, Siskiyou National Forest; C. Barkhurst, M. Hart, and W. Yamamoto, Umpqua National Forest; P. Buetner, R. Hardy, and E. Olmedo, Winema National Forest; and J. Roth, National Park Service. We are indebted to many individuals who gathered field data, especially B. Adkins, D. Anderson, B. Arrington, F. L. Barnes, S. Barnes, C. Beausoleil, T. L. Berntson, D. Brown, M. D. Broyles, R. Cail, T. Catton, A. Chandler, P. Colvard, M. L. Corbett, R. Crump, R. Cummings, J. Drumm, L. L. Finley, J. A. Fronzuto, K. Gaylord, S. A. Godwin, C. Gruenthal, A. Hamilton, M. Hudson, P. Hughes, M. Humes, M. F. Muchowski, B. Johnson, S. J. Kot, D. Meyer, M. McMillan, C. Milanovitch, M. Neutzmann, T. M. O'Brien, R. T. Owens, C. F. Pegau, S. Phillips, G. Rible, J. Sanborn, B. Seda, R. Singleton, D. Stockdale, L. Stonum, T. S. Stubblefield, N. C. Symeonides, J. L. Vanderhoof, H. Witt, S. Wolff, K. Wright, L. Zerinque and V. Zauskey. K. Olsen and the U.S. Army Corps of Engineers provided logistical support. D. R. Anderson, K. P. Burnham, J. Clobert, J. E. Hines, J. D. Nichols, R. J. Pradel, E. A. Rexstad, T. M. Shenk, R. J. Steidl, G. C. White and K. R. Wilson assisted with data analysis. Funding was provided by the USDI Bureau of Land Management, Medford District and Oregon State Office; the USDA Forest Service, Pacific Northwest Region and Prospect Ranger District, Rogue River National Forest; USDI National Biological Service, Forest and Rangeland Ecosystem Science Center; and the USDI Fish and Wildlife Service. This paper was improved by the thoughtful reviews of W. R. Clark, E. D. Forsman, M. G. Raphael, and an anonymous reviewer.

Key words: capture-recapture, demography, emigration, fecundity, Northern Spotted Owl, population rate of change, Siskiyou Mountains, southern Cascades, southwestern Oregon, *Strix occidentalis caurina,* survival.

Studies in Avian Biology No. 17:77–82, 1996.

DEMOGRAPHY OF NORTHERN SPOTTED OWLS IN SOUTHWESTERN OREGON

CYNTHIA J. ZABEL, SUSAN E. SALMONS, AND MARK BROWN

INTRODUCTION

Northern Spotted Owls (*Strix occidentalis caurina*) are associated with lower elevation, commercially valuable, late-successional coniferous forests in the Pacific Northwest. Meta-analyses of demographic parameters indicate that Northern Spotted Owl populations are declining throughout their range (Anderson and Burnham 1992, Burnham et al. *this volume*). Recent research has attempted to determine whether management activities have affected the viability of Spotted Owl populations, and results have led to development of conservation plans for the species (Dawson et al. 1987, Thomas et al. 1990, Murphy and Noon 1992, USDI 1992, Thomas et al. 1993b).

In the Recovery Plan for the Northern Spotted Owl (USDI 1992b) threats to the species were identified as small population sizes, declining populations, limited amounts of habitat, continued loss and fragmentation of habitat, geographically isolated populations, and predation and competition from other avian species. Weather and fire are natural processes that also may affect reproductive success of Spotted Owls. Weather may be a factor in the high annual variability in fecundity of Spotted Owls, as has been suggested for other predatory bird species (Newton, 1979, 1986). However, these factors have not been addressed in previous studies of Spotted Owls.

Our objectives were to estimate survival, fecundity, and annual rates of population change (λ) for resident, territorial female Spotted Owls at two study areas in the coastal mountains of southwestern Oregon. We tested if the amount of rainfall was correlated with reproduction of Spotted Owls. While surveying for Spotted Owls, we documented the increased presence of Barred Owls (*Strix varia*), a potential competitor of Spotted Owls.

STUDY AREAS

COOS BAY STUDY AREA

The 2,477 km² Coos Bay Study Area included most of the Coos Bay BLM District as well as some adjacent private lands. Most of the Coos Bay Study Area was within the Oregon Coast Ranges Province, which is characterized by high rainfall and steep, mountainous terrain with deep soils. Elevations range from just above sea level to 900 m. The study area was surrounded by five other Spotted Owl demographic study areas and the Pacific Ocean (Franklin et al. *this volume*). Land ownership is intermingled public and private lands forming a checkerboard landscape of alternating square-mile sections. Large amounts of forest have been harvested within the past 20–30 years, especially on private lands. This has resulted in a highly fragmented landscape with obvious structural boundaries between different-aged stands.

Forests in this area are in the western hemlock (*Tsuga heterophylla*) Zone (Franklin and Dyrness 1973). Douglas-fir (*Pseudotsuga menziesii*) dominates the canopy. Western hemlock and western redcedar (*Thuja plicata*) form secondary components of the overstory in most stands. The southern portion of the Coos Bay Study Area extended into the Klamath Province, which is drier with shallower soils (Franklin and Dyrness 1973). In the latter province, Douglas-fir is the dominant species, but western hemlock becomes uncommon and Port-Orford-cedar (*Chamaecyparis lawsoniana*) is common.

SISKIYOU STUDY AREA

The 1,262 km² Siskiyou Study Area included most of the Chetco and Gold Beach Ranger Districts on the Siskiyou National Forest, and small amounts of adjacent state and private land. This study area was within the coastal region of the Siskiyou Mountains, the most northern range in the Klamath Province. The Siskiyou mountains are steep and elevations range from sea level to 1060 m. Soils are often moderately shallow and unstable, with inclusions of ultra-mafic serpentine soils that are unproductive and not capable of producing closed canopy forests used by Spotted Owls.

Vegetation within the Siskiyou Study Area is in the Mixed-Evergreen Zone (Franklin and Dyrness 1973), and is dominated by Douglas-fir forests with Port-Orford-cedar a common secondary component. On most sites the overstory is relatively open with a dense mid-canopy of tanoak (*Lithocarpus densiflorus*) and other broadleaved evergreen trees, and a dense shrub layer dominated by evergreen huckleberry (*Vaccinium ovatum*). The northern tip of the California Coast Province, where coastal redwood (*Sequoia sempervirens*) dominates the overstory, extends into

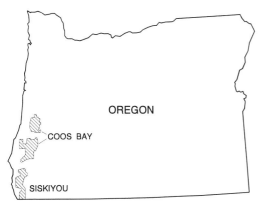

FIGURE 1. Coos Bay and Siskiyou Study Areas in southwestern Oregon, 1990–1993.

TABLE 1. GOODNESS-OF-FIT TEST RESULTS FOR CAPTURE-RECAPTURE DATA ON ≥3-YEAR-OLD SPOTTED OWLS IN THE COOS BAY AND SISKIYOU STUDY AREAS, OREGON, 1990–1993. RESULTS ARE FOR TESTS 1–3 IN PROGRAM RELEASE (BURNHAM ET AL. 1987)

Test	Coos Bay			Siskiyou		
	χ^2	df	P	χ^2	df	P
TEST 1	5.97	5	0.31	1.22	4	0.88
TEST 2 + 3						
Males	2.98	4	0.56	0.50	3	0.92
Females	6.47	3	0.09	0.23	3	0.97
Total	9.45	7	0.22	0.72	6	0.99

the southern edge of the study area. Serpentine areas are characterized by open forests (<40% canopy closure) of Jeffrey pine (*Pinus jeffreyi*), Douglas-fir, incense-cedar (*Calocedrus decurrens*), and knobcone pine (*P. attenuata*) with dense shrub layers of evergreen huckleberry and manzanita (*Arctostaphylos* spp.).

METHODS

The Coos Bay and Siskiyou demography studies were initiated in March 1990. In the Siskiyou Study Area, efforts were concentrated in Chetco Ranger District for most of the first season, but subsequently expanded late in 1990 to include the Gold Beach Ranger District.

Methods used to determine reproduction and survival of Spotted Owls followed those described by Franklin et al. (*this volume*). Programs RELEASE (Burnham et al. 1987) and SURGE (Pradel et al. 1990) were used for analyses of capture-recapture data. Choice of the best capture-recapture model to estimate survival for each study area was based on Akaike's Information Criterion (AIC), as described in Franklin et al. (*this volume*). We tested 64 models on data from owls that were ≥3 yrs old. Numerous age class models were tested on the data from all owls.

Fecundity was defined as the number of female young fledged per female (Franklin et al. *this volume*) for which we determined reproductive success by 15 July. Means and variances for fecundity were calculated using formulae for a discrete frequency distribution. Confidence limits were calculated using a relationship between the F distribution and the binomial distribution (Zar 1984). Mann-Whitney U tests were used for comparisons among age groups. Due to small sample sizes, a nonparametric Kruskall-Wallis ANOVA (Zar 1984) was used to test for annual differences in fecundity.

Weather data, provided by the state of Oregon climatologist's office, were averaged across five weather stations on the Coos Bay Study Area and three weather stations on the Siskiyou Study Area. We used linear regression to compare fecundity to the total amount of precipitation within the breeding season (1 March–30 June). To compare amounts of precipitation that occurred during our studies to a long term average, we calculated 30-year averages from monthly rainfall records published by the National Oceanic and Atmospheric Administration. *t*-tests were used to compare differences between observed rainfall (from 1990–1993) and 30-year averages, using data from 1 March to 30 June.

RESULTS

NUMBER OF OWLS BANDED

We banded 376 owls on the Coos Bay Study Area and 110 owls on the Siskiyou Study Area. At Coos Bay this included 191 owls ≥3 yrs old (93 females and 98 males), 49 1- and 2-yr-old owls (26 females and 23 males), and 136 juveniles. The sample also included nine owls ≥3 yrs old and 13 1- or 2-yr-old owls that were marked by researchers on adjacent study areas and subsequently immigrated into our study area. Owls banded at Siskiyou included 69 ≥3-yr-old owls (31 females and 38 males), 10 1- or 2-yr-old owls (5 females and 5 males), and 31 juveniles. The sample also included one immigrant from another study area.

GOODNESS-OF-FIT TESTS

Goodness-of-fit tests generated with program RELEASE (Burnham et al. 1987) indicated no lack of fit to the assumptions in the capture-recapture models for the ≥3-yr-old age group on either study area (Table 1). TEST 1 results indicated that overall survival and recapture probabilities did not differ between males and females at either study area (Table 1). However, for Coos

TABLE 2. Capture-recapture Models Used to Estimate Survival of Spotted Owls on the Coos Bay Study Area, Oregon. Models for ≥ 3-year-old Owls and 2-age-classes (Juveniles and Non-juveniles) Are Presented. Models Shown Are Those with the Lowest AIC (Akaike 1973) Values. Results of Likelihood-ratio Tests Between Each Model and the Best Model Are Indicated. K = Number of Parameters in Model; D_S-D_G = (Deviance of Simple Model) − (Deviance of More General Model) = Likelihood-ratio Test Result; df = $(K_G - K_S)$

Model	K	AIC	D_S-D_G	df	P
Time and sex specific models on ≥ 3-year-old owls					
$\{\phi_t, p_{s+t}\}$	6	390.027			
$\{\phi_t, p_s\}$	5	390.037	2.010	1	0.18
$\{\phi_t, p_{s+T}\}$	6	390.221		0	
$\{\phi_t, p_{s \cdot T}\}$	7	390.728	1.299	1	0.23
$\{\phi_{s \cdot T}, p_{s \cdot T}\}$	8	390.849	3.178	2	0.22
2-age-class models					
$\{\phi_{2a+t}, p_{2a+s}\}$	7	599.444			
$\{\phi_{2a+t}, p_{2a \cdot s}\}$	8	600.154	1.290	1	0.26
$\{\phi_{2a \cdot t}, p_{2a+s}\}$	9	602.999	0.445	2	0.80
$\{\phi_{2a+t}, p_{2a+s+t}\}$	9	603.091	0.353	2	0.84
$\{\phi_{2a \cdot t}, p_{2a \cdot s}\}$	10	603.798	1.646	3	0.68

TABLE 3. Capture-recapture Models Used to Estimate Survival of Spotted Owls on the Siskiyou Study Area, Oregon. Models Shown Are Those with the Lowest AIC (Akaike 1973) Values. Results of Likelihood-ratio Tests Between Each Model and the Best Model Are Indicated. K = Number of Parameters in Model; D_S-D_G = (Deviance of Simple Model) − (Deviance of More General Model) = Likelihood-ratio Test Result; df = $(K_G - K_S)$

Model	K	AIC	D_S-D_G	df	P
Time and sex specific models on ≥ 3-year-old owls					
$\{\phi, p_T\}$	3	180.814			
$\{\phi_T, p_T\}$	4	181.127	1.687	1	0.22
$\{\phi, p_{s+T}\}$	4	181.490	1.324	1	0.25
$\{\phi, p_t\}$	4	181.836	0.978	1	0.36
$\{\phi_s, p_T\}$	4	181.859	0.955	1	0.37
Time and sex specific models on ≥ 1-yr-old owls					
$\{\phi_T, p_T\}$	4	207.854			
$\{\phi, p_T\}$	3	207.909	2.055	1	0.17
$\{\phi_{s+T}, p_T\}$	5	209.439	0.415	1	0.53
$\{\phi_T, p_t\}$	5	209.848	0.006	1	0.94
$\{\phi_t, p_t\}$	5	209.848	0.006	1	0.94

Bay, component 1.T2 (which tests differences between groups by year; Burnham et al. 1987:128) indicated that recapture probabilities differed significantly between males and females in 1991 ($\chi^2 = 3.89$, P < 0.05). This was consistent with results from the model selection process in Program SURGE indicating that the best model for Coos Bay had sex-specific recapture probabilities.

MODEL SELECTION—COOS BAY

Because we had small numbers of owls banded as 1- or 2-yr-olds, we could not justify using models with 1- or 2-yr-old owls as a separate age class. Therefore, we compared one set of models for ≥ 3-yr-old owls, and another set of 2-age class models that included juveniles and non-juveniles (≥ 1-yr-old). The most parsimonious model for ≥ 3-yr-old owls indicated that survival varied among years, and that recapture rates varied with sex and year (Table 2). Likelihood ratio tests indicated several other models did not differ from the model with the lowest AIC value (Table 2). Males had a higher recapture probabilities than females. The most parsimonious 2-age-class model indicated that survival differed between juveniles and non-juveniles and among years (Table 2).

MODEL SELECTION—SISKIYOU

Thirty one juveniles were banded at the Siskiyou Study Area, but none were recaptured. Be-

cause a juvenile survival estimate of zero could distort survival models, we used only models that examined ≥ 3-yr-old owls and ≥ 1-yr-old owls. Likelihood-ratio tests indicated no difference between the five best models at Siskiyou, regardless of whether we included only ≥ 3-yr-old owls, or all non-juvenile owls (Table 3). The most parsimonious model for ≥ 3-yr-old owls indicated survival was independent of time and sex, and recapture probability was decreasing linearly with time (Table 3). When all owls ≥ 1-yr-old were included in the analysis, the best model included a linear time trend on survival and recapture (Table 3).

DEMOGRAPHIC PARAMETER ESTIMATES

Estimates of apparent annual survival (Fig. 2) from the best 2-age-class model at Coos Bay ($\{\phi_{2a+t}, p_{2a+s}\}$) (notation follows Lebreton et al. 1992) were 0.86 (SE = 0.02) for non-juveniles and 0.22 (SE = 0.045) for juveniles. Standard errors for mean survival estimates from this time-dependent model were approximated from the best time-independent model since SEs could not be calculated directly from models with time-dependent survival. The survival estimate for ≥ 3-yr-old owls from the most parsimonious model at Siskiyou ($\{\phi, p_T\}$) was 0.83 (SE = 0.045) (Fig. 2).

Fecundity varied among years at both study areas (H = 65.4, 3 df, P = 0.0001 at Coos Bay; H = 13.0, 3 df, P = 0.005 at Siskiyou) (Fig. 3). On average, 1- and 2-yr-old owls at Coos Bay had significantly lower fecundity ($\bar{X} = 0.16$, SE =

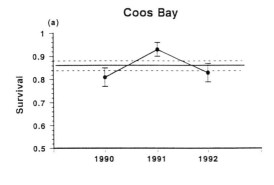

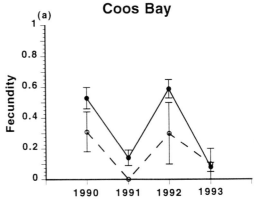

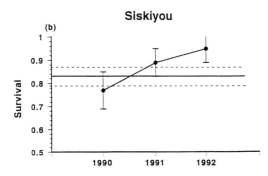

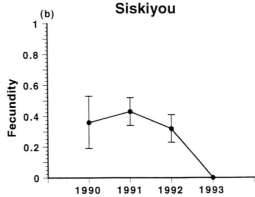

FIGURE 2. Estimates of survival for Northern Spotted Owls at Coos Bay and Siskiyou Study Areas, Oregon, 1990–1993. Point estimates (± 1 SE) are from the most parsimonious time-dependent capture-recapture models. Solid, horizontal lines indicate constant survival estimates from the best time-independent models (dashed lines indicate 1 SE).

FIGURE 3. Estimates of fecundity (± 1 SE) for Northern Spotted Owls at Coos Bay and Siskiyou Study Areas, Oregon, 1990–1993. Solid circles represent data for ≥ 3-yr-old owls. Open circles represent 1- and 2-yr-old owls. No 1- or 2-yr-old owls nested at Siskiyou during these years.

0.06) than ≥ 3-yr-old owls ($\bar{X} = 0.33$, SE $= 0.03$) ($Z = 2.0$, $P = 0.05$). At Siskiyou, no 1- or 2-yr old owls nested at sites we surveyed; mean adult fecundity was 0.30 (SE $= 0.05$).

The estimated finite rate of annual population change for ≥ 3-yr-old females at Coos Bay was 0.93 (SE $= 0.02$), which was significantly < 1.0 ($t = 3.25$, $P = 0.0006$). In the Siskiyou data, λ reduces to simply survival of non-juvenile owls (0.83), because a juvenile survival rate of zero cancels all other terms (see Noon and Biles 1990: 21). Also, no standard error could be computed for λ in the Siskiyou data because the juvenile survival estimate was $\phi_J = 0$.

PRECIPITATION AND FECUNDITY

Fecundity was negatively correlated with total precipitation during the nesting season at both study areas ($r = -0.93$, 3 df, $P = 0.04$ for Coos Bay; $r = -0.92$, 3 df, $P = 0.04$ for Siskiyou)(Fig. 4). The index of precipitation explained 86% and

85% of the variance in fecundity from the respective study areas. Precipitation during the nesting season was 24% below the 30-year average in 1990 ($t = -5.0$, $P = 0.02$), normal in 1991 ($t = 1.9$, $P = 0.16$) and 1992 ($t = -1.9$, $P = 0.16$), and 92% above normal in 1993 ($t = 4.4$, $P = 0.02$).

BARRED OWLS

We made no deliberate attempt to survey for Barred Owls at either study area. However, during regular surveys for Spotted Owls, Barred Owls sometimes responded. The number of sites where Barred Owls were detected at Coos Bay was 1 in 1990, 0 in 1991, 12 in 1992, and 11 in 1993. Because our survey effort (number of people doing surveys and length of field season) and technique were essentially constant from 1990–1993, we assumed this reflected a real increase in number of Barred Owls. On the Siskiyou Study Area, three Barred Owls were detected from 1990–1993.

DISCUSSION

Four years of data from the Coos Bay and Siskiyou Study Areas provide only first estimates of survival, fecundity, and rates of population change for Spotted Owls at these sites; however, our estimates of adult survival and fecundity were similar to those from other studies of longer duration (Burnham et al. *this volume*). The estimate of population change for Coos Bay during 1990–1993 indicated that this population was declining at a rate of 7% per year. Having no estimate for juvenile survival in the Siskiyou data made estimating λ problematic. However, if we assume our non-juvenile survival and fecundity estimates were accurate, the juvenile survival rate would have to be 0.61 in order for this population to be stationary (i.e., $\lambda = 1.0$) (Burnham et al. *this volume*). This is 1.5 times larger than the highest juvenile survival rate reported for 11 Spotted Owl demography study areas. Similarly, for the Coos Bay population to be stationary, the juvenile survival rate would need to be 0.49. This is also higher than any reported estimate from other Spotted Owl demography studies (Burnham et al. *this volume*), but not higher than estimates derived from radio telemetry data (Forsman et al. *this volume,* Reid et al. *this volume*).

Potential sources of bias in λ have been discussed (Bart 1995, Burnham et al. *this volume,* Raphael et al. *this volume*). Factors other than juvenile survival estimates that may have exaggerated the rate of decline were particularly a problem for the Siskiyou data. The Siskiyou Study Area was isolated from any other demography study, increasing the likelihood that emigrating owls were undetected. It was long and narrow, which may exacerbate emigration biases (Raphael et al. *this volume*). Survey effort on the Siskiyou Study Area declined after two years when the budget was reduced by 65%. Therefore, no new sites were surveyed, and banded juveniles that survived were not likely to be reobserved. Finally, both the Siskiyou and Coos Bay studies were of short duration. All of these factors could effect estimates of survival and lead to greater uncertainty about the true rate of population change.

Reproduction varied greatly between 1990 and 1993 at both study areas. Similar variation in reproduction was reported in other studies (e.g., see Forsman et al. *this volume,* Reid et al. *this volume,* Thrailkill et al. *this volume*). The negative correlation between fecundity and precipitation indicated that weather affected variability in reproduction of Spotted Owls at our study areas. Reproduction was lowest in 1993, the only year during our study when rainfall during the nesting season was significantly greater than average. Similar associations between precipitation

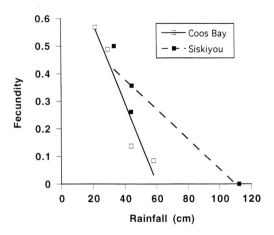

FIGURE 4. Correlation between precipitation during the breeding season (1 March–30 June) and fecundity of Northern Spotted Owls at the Coos Bay and Siskiyou Study Areas, Oregon, 1990–1993.

and fecundity were found just east of the Siskiyou Study Area (Wagner et al. *this volume*). Heavy rainfall has adversely affected breeding success in many other predatory bird species, including Buzzards (*Buteo buteo*) and Goshawks (*Accipiter gentilis*) (Kostrzewa and Kostrzewa 1990), Kestrels (*Falco sparverius*) (Newton 1979), Peregrine Falcons (*Falco peregrinus*) (Mearns and Newton 1988, Olsen and Olsen 1989a, 1989b) and Sparrowhawks (*Accipiter nisus*) (Newton et al. 1993). Rain may lower the hunting success of birds and increase their energy requirements, thus reducing their ability to reproduce successfully (Newton 1979, 1986).

For a long-lived species such as the Spotted Owl, reproductive activity over the short-term may have little effect on rates of change in population size; populations can probably persist through periods of low fecundity (Noon and Biles 1990). The rate of change in Spotted Owl populations is most affected by variation in adult survival (Lande 1988, Noon and Biles 1990, Anderson and Burnham 1992). Major causes of known mortality among Spotted Owls are starvation and avian predation (Miller 1989, Foster et al. 1992, Paton et al. 1992). It has been suggested that the larger Barred Owl may be displacing Spotted Owls in some areas (Taylor and Forsman 1976, USDA 1988, Dunbar et al. 1991). Barred Owls are distributed throughout the Oregon Coast Ranges and were recorded at 46 sites from 1980–1991 (USDI 1992b). The increase in Barred Owl detections at Coos Bay from 1990–1993 indicates that they could be a threat to Spotted Owls there.

Threats to Spotted Owl populations in the Oregon Coast Ranges were reported to be greater than those in any other Oregon Province (USDI 1992b). Loss of habitat and poor habitat connectivity for dispersal were identified as special concerns within the Oregon Coast Ranges and Klamath Province. Less than 40% of the forests remaining at the Coos Bay and Siskiyou study areas are suitable nesting, roosting, and foraging habitat for Spotted Owls (Raphael et al. *this volume*). Bart and Forsman (1992) reported that areas with <40% suitable owl habitat supported lower densities of Spotted Owls, and pairs had lower reproduction than in areas with >60% suitable owl habitat. Home range sizes, an indication of owl density, were significantly larger at Siskiyou than at two other study areas within the Klamath Province in northwestern California (Zabel et al. 1995). Comparing adult fecundity of Spotted Owls among the 11 study areas, the Siskiyou ranked third lowest and Coos Bay fifth lowest (Burnham et al. *this volume*). Lack of suitable habitat may be contributing to the apparently declining populations of Spotted Owls at Coos Bay and Siskiyou.

Demographic studies such as ours require many years of data before population trends can accurately be detected. The Siskiyou and Coos Bay studies were terminated after four years due to lack of funding. Problems in interpreting results from these studies have been discussed. It is not cost effective to initiate short term or poorly funded demographic studies. We recommend that demographic studies not be initiated without a long term commitment to fund them adequately.

SUMMARY

Northern Spotted Owls in the Oregon Coast Ranges were identified as being at particular risk due to loss of habitat and poor connectivity of remaining habitat (USDI 1992b). We estimated survival, fecundity, and annual rate of population change (λ) from 1990–1993 for Spotted Owls on the Coos Bay District of the Bureau of Land Management and the Siskiyou National Forest, Oregon. For the Coos Bay Study Area, the estimated survival rates from the best model (ϕ_{a2+t}, p_{a2+s}) were 0.86 (SE = 0.02) for non-juveniles and 0.22 (SE = 0.045) for juveniles; mean fecundity was 0.33 (SE = 0.03) for adults and 0.16 (SE = 0.06) for subadults. These estimates indicated that the population was declining at an annual rate of 7% (P = 0.0006). For the Siskiyou Study Area, non-juvenile survival from the best model ($\{\phi, p_T\}$) was estimated at 0.83 (SE = 0.045), with juvenile survival of 0; mean adult fecundity was 0.30 (SE = 0.05). These estimates indicated that this population was declining at a rate of 17% annually (SE undefined). However, due to several sources of potential bias, λ was probably underestimated and we were uncertain of the true rate of population change. There was a significant negative correlation (P = 0.04) between fecundity and precipitation during the nesting season at both study areas. Detections of Barred Owls increased from 1990–1993 at one of the study areas. These vital rate estimates were consistent with those from other demographic studies, but they are only preliminary estimates due to the short duration of these studies. We recommend that demographic studies be initiated only when adequate funding is secured for long term studies.

ACKNOWLEDGMENTS

Funding for these studies was provided by the Coos Bay District of the Bureau of Land Management (BLM), the Siskiyou National Forest, and the National Biological Service Forest and Rangeland Ecosystem Science Center, Corvallis, OR. L. Mangan, L. Webb, and M. W. Collopy were instrumental in keeping these studies funded and providing assistance during all phases of work. Field crew members at Coos Bay were C. Bemis, J. Bright, M. J. Christensen, M. Dodd, D. Garcia, C. M. Hale, J. Heaney, K. Kritz, B. R. Marechal, L. A. Needles, J. Pratt, D. Price, P. Shaklee, S. E. Sutton, and E. A. Vorisek; at Siskiyou they were B. Dill, M. Freitas, J. Maret, G. R. Orth, D. Ross, C. M. Schlobohm, J. D. Seeger, J. R. Spitler, K. Suryan, R. Suryan, and T. Weist. The following Forest Service and BLM biologists contributed time and help: D. Austin, K. Baty, B. Christensen, F. Craig, R. Culbertson, C. Dillingham, J. Guetterman, J. Heaney, B. Hudson, K. Kritz, S. Langenstein, R. Miller, and R. Sadak. G. Taylor from the Oregon Climatologist's Office provided weather data. T. Hines assisted in analyzing the Coos Bay data. For assistance with data analysis we thank D. R. Anderson, B. L. Biswell, K. P. Burnham, J. Clobert, A. B. Franklin, J. E. Hines, J. D. Nichols, R. J. Pradel, E. A. Rexstad, T. M. Shenk, G. C. White, and K. R. Wilson. Comments from W. Clark, E. D. Forsman, W. Laudenslayer, M. G. Raphael, J. Verner, J. R. Waters, and two anonymous reviewers improved the manuscript.

Key words: Barred Owl, California, demography, fecundity, lambda, Northern Spotted Owl, Oregon, precipitation, *Strix occidentalis caurina, Strix varia,* survival rates.

Studies in Avian Biology No. 17:83–91, 1996.

DEMOGRAPHIC CHARACTERISTICS AND TRENDS OF NORTHERN SPOTTED OWL POPULATIONS IN NORTHWESTERN CALIFORNIA

ALAN B. FRANKLIN, R. J. GUTIÉRREZ, BARRY R. NOON, AND JAMES P. WARD, JR.

INTRODUCTION

In California, research on the distribution and numbers of Northern Spotted Owls (*Strix occidentalis caurina*) began in the early 1970's (Gould 1977). Early indications that the owl population could be declining in California received little attention until the early 1980's when focused ecological research on the owl began in northwestern California (Gutiérrez et al. 1984). Debate over trends in Northern Spotted Owl populations in California recently culminated in a petition to remove the owl in California from the federal list of threatened and endangered species (California Forestry Association 1993). Much of this recent debate has centered around predictive modeling approaches which lacked supporting empirical data (Harrison et al. 1993). In 1985, we began a long-term study on the population ecology of the Northern Spotted Owl in northwestern California (Franklin et al. 1990). Our study followed five years of previous studies in the same region that established baseline information on Spotted Owl habitat and dispersal ecology (Gutiérrez et al. 1985, LaHaye 1988, Sisco 1990, Solis and Gutiérrez 1990). Objectives of our long-term demographic research have been to document life history characteristics of Northern Spotted Owls, monitor long-term population trends on public lands in northwestern California, and to relate estimates of fitness with measures of habitat structure and composition.

In this paper, we present estimates of age- and sex-specific survival probabilities, fecundity rates, and trends in those estimates over a 9-year period. In addition, we test the null hypothesis that the population of Spotted Owls in northwest California was stationary or increasing against the alternative that the population was declining during the period of our study. Throughout this paper, we use the term *stationary* when referring to constant population size over time and *stable* when referring to constant demographic parameters over time (Seber 1982:400).

STUDY AREA

We studied Spotted Owls within a 10,000-km² area of northwest California (Fig. 1) that included portions of the Six Rivers, Klamath and Shasta-Trinity National Forests and isolated parcels administered by the Bureau of Land Management. The area was located in the Klamath physiographic province where Mixed Evergreen, Klamath Montane, Oregon Oak and Tan Oak vegetation types predominate (Küchler 1977). Elevations ranged from 200 to 1,700 m. Within this area, we established a 292-km² study area, near Willow Creek, Humboldt Co., California, which was systematically surveyed each year to estimate density of Spotted Owls (Franklin et al. 1990, Ward et al. 1991). This Willow Creek study area contained 49 Spotted Owl sites. We also selected 12 satellite areas, each 10–30 km² in size and each containing 2–5 Spotted Owl sites. These satellite areas contained a total of 41 Spotted Owl sites and were selected to increase sample size over a wider geographic area. We conducted surveys for Spotted Owls from 1985–1993 on the Willow Creek study area and 1987–1993 on the satellite areas.

Two additional demographic studies began in 1990 west of our study area on lands owned by Simpson Timber Company (L. Diller, personal communication) and Louisiana-Pacific Corporation (M. Pious, personal communication). A large portion of the area surrounding our study area was surveyed each year for Spotted Owls by the U.S. Forest Service, Bureau of Land Management and private land-holders. These adjacent demographic studies and surveys were useful for detecting movements of banded birds outside areas we surveyed.

METHODS

Spotted owl sites within the study areas were surveyed on multiple occasions between April and August each year to locate and mark resident owls, and to assess reproductive output. The Willow Creek study area was entirely surveyed at least twice each year. Field methods used for surveying, capturing, marking, and estimating reproductive output are detailed in Franklin et al. (*this volume*). Individuals were uniquely identified, through capture, recapture, or resighting of color bands. In this paper, we defined "capture" either as initial capture of unmarked individuals or as recapture or resighting of previously marked individuals. Marked individuals were used to estimate survival probabilities while measures of reproductive output were used to estimate fe-

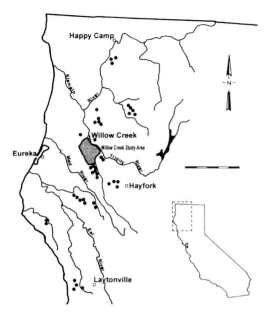

FIGURE 1. Locations of the Willow Creek study area (shaded area) and satellite sites occupied by Northern Spotted Owls for ≥ 1 year (dots) in northwestern California.

cundity (see Franklin et al. *this volume*). We recognized four age-classes of birds when estimating survival and fecundity: juvenile (J), 1-year old (S1), 2-year old (S2) and ≥3-year old (A) (see Franklin et al., *this volume*).

ESTIMATING DEMOGRAPHIC PARAMETERS

We examined mark-recapture data for goodness-of-fit to a global model using TEST 2 and TEST 3 in program RELEASE (Burnham et al. 1987:71–77). Goodness-of-fit for reduced models was assessed by computing likelihood ratio tests between global and reduced models and then adding the χ^2 values and degrees of freedom from these tests to the values obtained from the goodness-of-fit tests for the global models (Lebreton et al. 1992). To examine the assumption that captures occurred in a brief sampling period, we tested for differences in median capture dates between years (Smith and Anderson 1987) using Kruskal-Wallis tests (Sokal and Rohlf 1981). We initially tested for differences in median capture dates between years for ≥1-year old owls and juveniles separately, to determine if pooling across years within each age-class was appropriate, and then tested for differences between ≥1-year olds and juveniles. Nonparametric multiple comparisons were used to test all possible pairs of years with α adjusted by the number of tests performed (Dixon et al. 1990). Smith and Anderson (1987)

provided a formula for adjusting survival rates to a 12-month interval if intervals between capture occasions did not equal 1 year:

$$\tilde{\phi} = \hat{\phi}^{12/x}$$

where $\tilde{\phi}$ was the adjusted survival estimate, $\hat{\phi}$ the unadjusted mark-recapture survival estimate and x is the difference in months between medians.

We modeled survival probabilities using model nomenclature, selection and testing procedures outlined in Franklin et al. (*this volume*). Akaike's Information Criterion (AIC) was used primarily in model selection; models with lowest AIC were selected as the best models explaining the mark-recapture data. Models within 1 unit of AIC were considered to be competing models and were examined more closely with likelihood ratio tests (Lebreton et al. 1992) that tested H_O: reduced models best fit the data, versus H_A: the more complex model best fit the data. We examined trends in survival using two sets of capture-history matrices. The first set consisted of owls which were initially captured when they were ≥3-years old, separated by sexes. The second data set included 8 subsets partitioned by sex and the four age-classes when owls were first captured (J, S1, S2 and A). We tested the null hypothesis that survival probabilities were constant over time (model ϕ) versus alternatives that survival was time-dependent without a linear trend (model ϕ_t) and with a linear trend (model ϕ_T). Sex effects were considered in all hypotheses tested.

We initially modeled the ≥3-year old data with all 64 possible combinations of effect: no sex (s) effect, no time (t) effect, t, s, $s+t$, $s*t$, $s+T$, and $s*T$ for both ϕ and p. In addition, we examined models where recapture probabilities were structured on methodological constraints (p_c) as follows. During the first three years of the study (1985–1987) birds were physically recaptured each year to read their USFWS bands. During the rest of the study (1988–1993), owls were resighted through the use of color bands (Franklin et al. 1990). We, therefore, included models with p_c which represented a single estimate of p for 1986 and 1987 and one for 1988 through 1993.

Juvenile Northern Spotted Owls are capable of dispersing considerable distances (Gutiérrez et al. 1985). Therefore, we suspected that estimates of juvenile survival could be biased low because of permanent emigration of juveniles from our study area. Without the use of radio-telemetry, we were unable to quantitatively estimate this bias (e.g., Burnham et al. *this volume*). However, we examined this bias qualitatively by examining (1) distances moved by each age-class estimated from observed movements of banded birds between sites, and (2) the percentages of recaptures for each age-class which would have been missed if additional surveys had not been conducted by others outside the boundaries of areas we surveyed.

Estimates of age-specific fecundity (b_x, where x = age-class; number of female young fledged per female) were estimated according to Franklin et al. (*this volume*). In estimating fecundity, a 1:1 sex ratio was assumed. We tested this assumption using Fisher's Exact Test (Sokal and Rohlf 1981) on fledged young of known sex for 1992 (N = 48 young) and 1993 (N = 9 young) where sex was determined by chromosomal analysis of blood samples (Dvořák et al. 1992). Blood samples were analyzed by Zoogen, Inc., Davis, California. Trends in fecundity were examined using mixed-effect analysis of variance (ANOVA) models. We used PROC MIXED in program SAS (SAS Institute 1993) where age and time were fixed effects and occupied sites were random block effects (C. J. Schwarz, personal communication) because of possible lack of independence between years at a particular site. Using a linear contrast, we also tested an *a priori* hypothesis of $H_O : \mu$ for all years was equal versus $H_A : \mu_{1985-92} = \mu_{1993}$, based on the observation of a substantial decline in reproductive output in 1993.

ESTIMATING POPULATION TRENDS

We examined population trends by estimating the annual rate of population change (λ) as (1) a function of age- and sex-specific survival and fecundity (denoted as λ_d based on demographic parameters) and (2) changes in annual abundance (denoted as λ_n based on estimated annual counts of owls). We estimated λ_d by solving the characteristic equation resulting from a modified stage-based Leslie matrix (see Franklin et al. *this volume*). Size of the matrix was determined by the number of age-class groupings resulting from parameter estimation procedures for survival probabilities and fecundity.

We examined trends in abundance for females from (1) the Willow Creek study area combined with 21 selected sites that were consistently surveyed on the satellite areas from 1987 through 1993, and (2) both sexes on the Willow Creek study area only from 1985 through 1993. These two data sets were chosen *a priori* to achieve greatest possible statistical power. Abundance was estimated using open mark-recapture estimators (Pollock et al. 1990). We used the recapture probabilities (p) estimated from the analysis of survival probabilities to estimate numbers of individuals (N) in each year (t) as:

$$\hat{N}_t = \frac{(n_t + 1)\hat{M}_t}{m_t + 1} \quad \text{where} \quad \hat{M}_t = \frac{m_t}{\hat{p}_t}$$

and n_t (number of marked and unmarked owls captured on occasion t) and m_t (number of marked

owls captured on occasion t) were treated as constants (Pollock et al. 1990). Sampling variances for $\hat{M}_t$ and $\hat{N}_t$ were estimated using the delta method (Oehlert 1992). We felt estimating numbers in this manner was more reliable because we had more confidence in estimating $\hat{p}_t$ from the flexible modeling approach discussed in Franklin et al. (*this volume*) than using existing software (e.g., JOLLY and JOLLYAGE; Pollock et al. 1990). An annual change in population size (λ_i) between years t and $t + 1$ can be estimated as:

$$\hat{\lambda}_i = \frac{\hat{N}_{t+1}}{\hat{N}_t}$$

Estimates of SE(λ_i) tend to be negatively correlated because the numerator of one time interval becomes the denominator of the next time interval (Eberhardt 1970). For this reason, we regressed $\ln(\hat{N}_t)$ on time (Caughley and Birch 1971, Eberhardt 1985):

$$\ln(\hat{N}_t) = a + \beta t + \epsilon_t$$

where the slope of the regression (β) estimates r, and ϵ the error term is assumed N(0, σ^2). We used weighted regression in PROC GLM to estimate r and SE(r) where the inverse of SE($\hat{N}_t$) was used to weight $\hat{N}_t$ (SAS Institute 1990). The annual rate of change (λ_n) can then be estimated for a birth pulse population (Eberhardt 1985) as:

$$\hat{\lambda}_n = 1 + \hat{r} \quad \text{and} \quad \widehat{SE}(\hat{\lambda}_n) = \widehat{SE}(\hat{r})$$

We used a 1-tailed t-test of H_0: r $\geq$ 0 versus H_A: r < 0, which was equivalent to H_A: λ < 1.

We used the approach for estimating power from trends in abundance described by Gerrodette (1987). In the power calculations, we used parameters representative of the trends observed on the Willow Creek study area. These parameters represented the best-case scenario for detecting trends given our data and included an 8-year sampling period, an initial CV of 4.9% for the first estimate of abundance, and $\alpha = 0.05$. We assumed a 1-tailed t-test to detect a negative rate of change and that precision of the abundance estimates was relatively constant over time.

RESULTS

TRENDS IN SURVIVAL PROBABILITIES

From 1985 through 1993, we individually marked 274 juveniles, 46 1-year old birds (27 females, 19 males), 38 2-year old birds (19 females and 19 males), and 197 $\geq$3-year old birds (97 females and 100 males). Results of goodness-of-fit tests indicated the mark-recapture data adequately fit the global model for each data set (Table 1).

TABLE 1. RESULTS OF GOODNESS-OF-FIT TESTS FROM TESTS 2 AND 3 IN PROGRAM RELEASE FOR MARK-RECAPTURE DATA ON NORTHERN SPOTTED OWLS IN NORTHWESTERN CALIFORNIA FROM 1985 THROUGH 1993. GLOBAL MODELS CONTAIN ALL EFFECTS CONSIDERED WITHIN EACH DATA SET. REDUCED MODELS ARE MODELS SELECTED WITHIN EACH DATA SET BASED ON AIC AND LIKELIHOOD RATIO TESTS

| Data set | Model | TEST 2 + 3 | | | TEST 2 | TEST 3 |
		χ^2	df	P	P	P
≥3-year-olds	Global $\{\phi_{s \cdot t}, p_{s \cdot t}\}$	15.97	28	0.966	0.600	0.972
	Reduced $\{\phi_{s+T}, p_c\}$	36.18	55	0.977	0.846	0.976
Age-class	Global $\{\phi_{a \cdot s \cdot t}, p_{a \cdot s \cdot t}\}$[a]	40.53	50	0.828	0.451	0.875
	Reduced $\{\phi_t, p_c\}$[a]	7.16	16	0.970	0.985	0.994

[a] Juvenile age-class not included (see text for explanation).

Median date of capture for juveniles was not significantly different among years ($\chi^2 = 12.01$, df = 8, P = 0.15) suggesting that annual distributions of capture dates were similar from year to year. For birds ≥1 year old, median capture dates significantly differed ($\chi^2 = 37.01$, df = 1, P < 0.001) by 19 days in only two of the nine years (from 1987 to 1988 and from 1992 to 1993). Median capture dates for birds captured when ≥1-year old and birds captured as juveniles significantly differed by 37 days ($\chi^2 = 215.07$, df = 1, P < 0.001). We examined the effect of this bias in estimating annual rates of population change (λ_d).

Three competing models resulted from the analysis of the data containing owls first captured as ≥3-year olds, $\{\phi_{s+t}, p_c\}$, $\{\phi_{s \cdot t}, p_c\}$, and $\{\phi_{s+T}, p_c\}$, which were all within one AIC unit of each other (Table 2). The structure of the recapture probabilities constrained by capture methods (p_c) yielded the lowest AIC models without sex or other time effects. Although $\{\phi_{s \cdot T}, p_c\}$ had the lowest AIC, it was not significantly different from $\{\phi_{s+T}, p_c\}$ (Table 2) and the slope parameter for the interaction term was not significantly different from zero (Wald test: $\chi^2 = 2.02$, df = 1, P = 0.154). Therefore, we selected $\{\phi_{s+T}, p_c\}$ as the model which best explained the mark-recapture data because the interaction term in $\{\phi_{s \cdot T}, p_c\}$ was not supported. Model $\{\phi_{s+T}, p_c\}$ had significant time and sex effects (Table 2), still adequately fit the data based on goodness-of-fit tests (Table 1) and estimated slopes for sex ($\hat{\beta}_1 = 0.5126$, $\widehat{\text{SE}}(\hat{\beta}_1) = 0.2298$; $\chi^2 = 4.98$, df = 1, P = 0.03) and time ($\hat{\beta}_2 = -0.1307$, $\widehat{\text{SE}}(\hat{\beta}_2) = 0.0537$, $\chi^2 = 5.91$, df = 1, P = 0.02) that were significantly different from zero. Thus, we concluded that survival of owls first captured when ≥3-years old declined in a linear fashion, the trend differed according to sex, but survival in both sexes declined at the same rate (i.e., slopes were the same for both sexes; Fig. 2). The slope parameter for time ($\hat{\beta}_2$) was in terms of logit-transformed vari-

ables (Lebreton et al. 1992) which did not reflect a meaningful rate of decline. Therefore, we regressed the transformed estimates of annual survival against year to obtain the appropriate estimate (K. P. Burnham, personal communication) of $\hat{\beta}_2 = -0.0182$ ($\widehat{\text{SE}}(\hat{\beta}_2) = 0.004$), which indicated a 1.82% annual decline.

Based on analysis of 45 models that included all age-classes, model $\{\phi_{J,At}, p_{a4',c}\}$ had the lowest AIC (Table 2) where A included all birds ≥1 year old. Models that included separate estimates for 1-year, 2-year, and ≥3-year old age-classes had higher AICs (>1636) and were not considered further. Model $\{\phi_{J,At}, p_{a4',c}\}$ had significant variable time effects in adult survival estimates but sex or linear time effects were not supported (Table 2). Sex and time effects were not supported in estimating juvenile survival (Table 2). Therefore, model $\{\phi_{J,At}, p_{a4',c}\}$ was selected as the most parsimonious explanation of our mark-recapture data. This model indicated that (1) survival of owls >1-year old varied over time, (2) juvenile survival was constant over time, (3) there was no difference in survival by sex for any age-class, (4) recapture probabilities were different for the three years following initial capture as a juvenile, and (5) adults and subadults had similar capture probabilities regardless of sex but differed according to the method of capture during the study (Table 3, Fig. 2). We were unable to assess goodness-of-fit for this model because of the lack of identifiability of parameters when juveniles were treated as separate groups in TESTs 2 and 3 of RELEASE. However, an assessment of the portion of this model that included owls ≥1-year old indicated adequate goodness-of-fit (Table 1).

TRENDS IN FECUNDITY

Based on chromosomal analysis, the sex ratio of juveniles captured in 1992–1993 (28 males: 29 females) was not significantly different from a 1:1 sex ratio (Fisher's exact P = 1.00) which

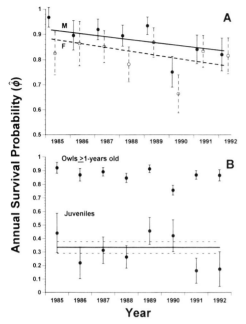

FIGURE 2. Estimates of juvenile and nonjuvenile survival (± 1 SE) for Northern Spotted Owls in northwestern California, 1985–1993. **A.** Estimates for birds first captured when ≥ 3-years old. Lines for males (solid) and females (dashed) represent linear time trends in estimates under model $\{\phi_{s+T}, p_c\}$ with an average standard error of 0.0301 for females and 0.0207 for males. Solid (males) and open (females) dots with 1 standard error are estimates under the variable time model $\{\phi_{s\cdot t}, p_c\}$. **B.** Estimates (± 1 SE) for juveniles and birds ≥ 1-year old under model $\{\phi_{J,At}, p_{a4',c}\}$. Estimates for juveniles is solid line with 1 SE represented by dashed lines under model $\{\phi_{J,At}, p_{a4',c}\}$ and dots under the variable time model $\{\phi_{Jt,At}, p_{a4',c}\}$.

supported our assumption of a 1:1 sex ratio in estimating fecundity. Fecundity differed significantly by age-class (F = 8.54; df = 2, 392; P = 0.0002) and time (F = 3.92; df = 8, 392; P = 0.0001), but the interaction between the two was not significant (F = 1.00; df = 15, 377; P = 0.45). Site effects were about 5% of the residual error for both sexes and were not significantly different from zero (z = 1.51, P = 0.13) which suggested that observations at a particular site were independent from year to year. Based on the *a priori* contrast, there was a significant difference (F = df = 22.35; 1, 444; P > 0.0001) in fecundity between 1993 and the other years combined (Fig. 3). We, therefore, concluded that fecundity differed by age-class (Table 4) but was relatively constant for all years except 1993 when fecundity declined significantly (Fig. 3).

TABLE 2. RESULTS OF LIKELIHOOD RATIO TESTS BETWEEN NESTED MARK-RECAPTURE MODELS USED TO ESTIMATE SURVIVAL PROBABILITIES. HYPOTHESES TESTED ARE H_O: REDUCED MODEL BEST EXPLAINS DATA, VERSUS H_A: MORE GENERAL MODEL BEST EXPLAINS DATA

H_O Model	K[a]	AIC[b]	H_A Model	K[a]	AIC[b]	Test χ^2	df	P	Effect tested	Decision
Owls banded as ≥ 3-year olds										
$\{\phi_{s+T}, p_c\}$	5	728.043	$\{\phi_{s+t}, p_c\}$	11	728.968	11.08	6	0.086	Variable time	Do not reject H_O
$\{\phi_s, p_c\}$	4	732.073	$\{\phi_{s\cdot T}, p_c\}$	6	728.018	2.03	1	0.155	Interaction term	Do not reject H_O
$\{\phi_T, p_c\}$	4	731.350	$\{\phi_{s+T}, p_c\}$	5	728.043	6.03	1	0.014	Linear time	Reject H_O
			$\{\phi_{s+T}, p_c\}$	5	728.043	5.31	1	0.021	Sex	Reject H_O
Owls banded in all age-classes										
$\{\phi_{J,At}, p_{a4'c}\}$	8	1633.976	$\{\phi_{J,At}, p_{a4c}\}$	14	1633.611	12.37	6	0.054	Linear time in A	Reject H_O
$\{\phi_{J,At}, p_{a4c}\}$	14	1633.611	$\{\phi_{J,As+t}, p_{a4c}\}$	15	1634.525	1.09	1	0.297	Sex in A	Do not reject H_O
$\{\phi_{J,A}, p_{a4c}\}$	7	1634.878	$\{\phi_{J,At}, p_{a4c}\}$	14	1633.611	15.26	7	0.033	Variable time in A	Reject H_O
$\{\phi_{Jt,At}, p_{a4',c}\}$	14	1633.611	$\{\phi_{Jt,At}, p_{a4',c}\}$	15	1635.495	0.12	1	0.733	Linear time in J	Do not reject H_O
			$\{\phi_{Js,At}, p_{a4',c}\}$	21	1639.151	8.46	7	0.294	Variable time in J	Do not reject H_O
			$\{\phi_{Js,At}, p_{a4',c}\}$	15	1635.105	0.51	1	0.477	Sex in J	Do not reject H_O

[a] Number of estimate parameters.
[b] Akaike's information criterion.

TABLE 3. ESTIMATES OF RECAPTURE PROBABILITIES (P) FOR THE SELECTED MARK-RECAPTURE MODEL $\{\phi_{J,At}, P_{A4',c}\}$ DESCRIBING AGE- AND SEX-SPECIFIC SURVIVAL PROBABILITIES FOR NORTHERN SPOTTED OWLS IN NORTHWESTERN CALIFORNIA FROM 1985–1993.

Class	Recapture probability	
	$\hat{p}$	$\widehat{SE}(\hat{p})$
Juveniles first recaptured as 1-year olds	0.2028	0.0467
Juveniles first recaptured as 2-year olds	0.3962	0.0693
J first recapture as ≥3-year olds	0.5654	0.0844
Owls ≥1-year old first recaptured in 1986–1987	0.7766	0.0379
Owls ≥1-year old first recaptured in 1988–1993	0.9182	0.0124

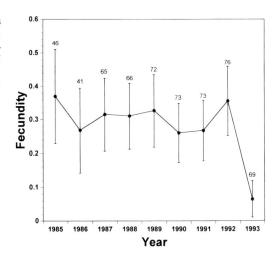

FIGURE 3. Estimates of fecundity (± 1 SE) for Northern Spotted Owls ≥1 year old in northwestern California, 1985–1993. Numbers above estimates represent sample sizes.

ESTIMATES OF POPULATION CHANGE

Trends based on demographic parameters

To estimate the annual rate of change based solely on demographic parameters (λ_d), we used estimates of fecundity and survival averaged over the period 1985–1993 (Table 4). For fecundity, we used the age-specific estimates from the ANOVA models and, for survival, we used the estimates of ϕ from model $\{\phi_{J,At}, p_{a4',c}\}$ of the mark-recapture analyses. Average survival of birds ≥1-year old was calculated by averaging the annual estimates from the variable time portion of the model with a standard error estimated using the delta method, which incorporated the annual standard error estimates and the covariances between years. Using our estimates of average demographic parameters, and their standard errors, in a 3-stage Leslie matrix, λ_d was 0.9656 ($\widehat{SE}(\hat{\lambda}_d) = 0.0138$) which was significantly different from a stationary population (1-tailed

$z = 2.08$, $P = 0.019$). Values for partial derivatives of each parameter estimate with respect to λ_d suggested that model sensitivity was highest for ≥1-year old survival followed by juvenile survival and adult fecundity which had roughly similar sensitivities (Table 4).

Our estimate of juvenile survival was probably biased low because of permanent emigration from our study area. Inter-site distances moved by 56 juveniles ($\bar{X} = 19.61$ km, SE = 2.70) were significantly higher (t-test with unequal variances: $t = -5.32$, df = 63, $P = 0.0001$) than the relatively short, with respect to study area size, distances moved by 45 ≥1-year old owls ($\bar{X} = 4.75$ km, SE = 0.73). We never observed marked juveniles on their natal sites, indicating they always

TABLE 4. AGE-SPECIFIC ESTIMATES AND STANDARD ERRORS OF DEMOGRAPHIC PARAMETERS, PARTIAL DERIVATIVES ($\delta\hat{\lambda}_d/\delta\theta$) FOR DEMOGRAPHIC PARAMETERS, AND ESTIMATES OF DEMOGRAPHIC PARAMETERS REQUIRED TO ACHIEVE A STATIONARY POPULATION ($\theta_{|\lambda=1}$) FOR FEMALE NORTHERN SPOTTED OWLS IN NORTHWESTERN CALIFORNIA, 1985–1993. PARAMETER ESTIMATES WERE USED TO CALCULATE THE ANNUAL RATE OF POPULATION CHANGE ($\hat{\lambda}_d$).

Parameter (θ)	$\hat{\theta}$	$\widehat{SE}(\hat{\theta})$	$\delta\hat{\lambda}_d/\delta\hat{\theta}$	$\theta_{|\lambda=1}$
Fecundity				
1-year old	0.0938	0.0669	0.0302	0.9613
2-year old	0.2046	0.0773	0.0272	1.2044
≥3-year old	0.3333	0.0292	0.2408	0.4858
Survival				
Juvenile	0.3295	0.0489	0.2690	0.4614
1-year old	0.8677	0.0115	0.0989	>1.0000
≥2-year old	0.8677	0.0115	0.9118	0.9053

moved. However, movements for owls ≥1-year old were relatively rare; they moved only 6.6% of the time based on number of movements detected divided by the number of their recaptures (45/685; Table 5). In terms of recaptures outside of our study areas, we would have missed 20.8% of juvenile recaptures, if other observers had not located them during their surveys (Table 5). In contrast, <1% of owls ≥1-year old were detected outside of the study area suggesting that emigration of these age-classes from our study area was very low. Regardless, juvenile survival would have to increase by 40.0% to achieve a stationary population (i.e., $\lambda = 1$) under the Leslie matrix model, given that all other parameter estimates remained the same (Table 4). Adult survival would have to increase by 4.3% to achieve the same effect.

To examine the effect of unequal sampling intervals on survival and, hence, estimates of λ_d, we corrected our single estimate of juvenile survival to obtain $\tilde{\phi}_J = 0.2907$ ($\widehat{SE}(\tilde{\phi}_J) = 0.0421$) and the two years included in average survival of ≥3-year olds to obtain a new average $\tilde{\phi}_A = 0.8661$ ($\widehat{SE}(\tilde{\phi}_A) = 0.0125$). We used these adjusted survival estimates, with the same fecundity estimates used before, to estimate $\tilde{\lambda}_d = 0.9535$ ($\widehat{SE}(\tilde{\lambda}_d) = 0.0169$) which was lower than our previous estimate.

Trends based on counts

Based on annual estimates of population size from counts of owls on the study area, trends for females on the Willow Creek study area plus the selected satellite areas ($\hat{\lambda}_n = 1.000$, $\widehat{SE}(\hat{\lambda}_n) = 0.014$, N = 6 years) was not significantly different (t = 0.02, df = 5, 1-tailed P = 0.491) from a stationary population (i.e., $\lambda = 1$). Trends for both sexes on the Willow Creek study area alone ($\hat{\lambda}_n = 1.009$, $\widehat{SE}(\hat{\lambda}_n) = 0.008$, N = 8 years) was also not significantly different (t = 1.16, df = 7, 1-tailed P = 0.145) from a stationary population. Estimates of N_t ranged from 55 to 62 for females in the larger sample, and 75 to 85 for both sexes on the Willow Creek study area alone, and were precise with CV's ranging from 1.3 to 4.9%. We achieved 100% power for detecting a linear annual decline of r = −0.034 (our point estimate of λ_d − 1), 80% power if r = −0.020, and 33% power if r = −0.010, given CV($\hat{N}_t$) = 0.049 remaining constant over an 8-year period and a 1-tailed t-test with $\alpha = 0.05$. The latter values of r were both within the upper 95% confidence interval of $\hat{\lambda}_d$. To detect an r = −0.01 with 80% power, would require 4 more years of monitoring.

DISCUSSION

Direct inferences from analysis of our data can, at most, be extended to the resident, territorial

TABLE 5. NUMBER OF RECAPTURES BETWEEN 1985 THROUGH 1993 OF NORTHERN SPOTTED OWLS THAT WERE DETECTED WITHIN AND OUTSIDE THE BOUNDARIES OF THE AREAS SURVEYED IN NORTHWESTERN CALIFORNIA. PERCENT MISSED (OUTSIDE ÷ {OUTSIDE + WITHIN}) REPRESENTS THE PERCENTAGE OF RECAPTURES WHICH WOULD HAVE BEEN MISSED IF ADDITIONAL SURVEYS BY OTHER OBSERVERS HAD NOT BEEN CONDUCTED OUTSIDE THE BOUNDARIES OF THE SURVEY AREAS.

| Age-class | Number of recaptures | | Percent missed |
	Within survey area	Outside survey area	
Juvenile	80	21	20.8
1–2 years old	156	6	3.7
≥3-years old	523	0	0

population of owls on public lands within northwestern California and, at the least, to specific Spotted Owl sites sampled within our study area because selection of study areas and Spotted Owl sites within the study area were not random. In both cases, we limited our inferences to the years when data were collected.

TRENDS IN DEMOGRAPHIC TRAITS

Survival of owls banded as ≥3-year olds decreased significantly over the period of our study. Possible hypotheses for this decrease included (1) a density-dependent response to changes in environmental conditions as the population adjusted to a new, lower carrying capacity; (2) a real decline in survival with the decline continuing to some lower level beyond which it will not recover; (3) a response to some environmental factor related to time; and (4) senescence. The latter hypothesis was partially supported (but not tested) by the fact that the decreasing trend in survival disappeared when younger age-classes were included in the mark-recapture models. If owls ≥3-years old were fairly old when first captured, then time would represent increasing age. This effect may have been masked when younger (1–2 years old) birds were included in the sample. If senescence was occurring, estimates of λ_d would be negatively biased (Noon and Biles 1990). The variable survival of owls ≥1-year old over time (based on the age-class models) suggested that external influences, such as weather, may affect survival. The decreasing nature of survival for owls ≥3-years old could, therefore, represent a trend imposed by environmental factors. The alternative hypotheses explaining decreasing survival need to be examined in greater detail and was beyond the scope of this paper. Therefore, we cannot ascribe a specific cause for this decrease in survival for owls ≥3-years old or for the variability of survival for owls ≥ 1-year old during our study period.

Although fecundity declined significantly in one year, we found it to be stable over the majority of years in this study in contrast to other populations of Northern (Forsman et al. 1984) and California Spotted Owls (*S. o. occidentalis*; Noon et al. 1992).

POPULATION TRENDS

Based on our estimate of λ_n, we found no evidence for a rate of change as low as -0.0334 $(1 - \hat{\lambda}_d)$, or even -0.02. We had sufficient statistical power to detect such trends. However, our estimates of λ_d and λ_n were subject to a number of biases that make estimating the exact rate of change difficult. Several alternatives exist that could explain the discrepancy between our estimate of λ_d, which indicated a declining population, and λ_n, which indicated a stationary population. One explanation of the projected decline under λ_d was that we underestimated juvenile survival because of permanent emigration from our study area. However, our estimate of juvenile survival would have to be substantially higher to achieve a stationary population. Understanding juvenile survival over the long term may be a key to understanding the demographics of Northern Spotted Owl populations. As estimated under the Leslie matrix model, changes in λ_d appear to be most sensitive to adult survival (see also Noon and Biles 1990). However, model sensitivity should not be confused with process sensitivity. Large-scale temporal changes in juvenile survival may be a process that ultimately regulates Spotted Owl populations. We believe this process can be examined best using radio-telemetry to estimate juvenile survival rather than through mark-recapture studies.

Another alternative to explain the discrepancies between our estimates of λ_d and λ_n was proposed by Franklin (1992), where a non-territorial "floating" population serves to stabilize the observed territorial population through immigration, even though the entire population as a whole may be declining. The Leslie model can include immigration if recruitment is used in lieu of fecundity and juvenile survival (Caswell 1989). Unfortunately, statistical models to estimate recruitment lack the current sophistication of those used to estimate survival and fecundity (see Pollock et al. 1990). True λ_d for the female portion of the population lies between 0.9385 and 0.9926 with a 95% probability. Therefore, decline in the female portion of the population could be less than 1% a year. If true λ_d was 1%, our study population of about 65 females would decline to 62 females after 5 years. With this magnitude of change, we lacked the power to detect this trend

when estimating λ_n. Additional years of monitoring will be required before such rates will be detectable with sufficient statistical power.

We believe appropriate inferences regarding rates of change of the Spotted Owl population in our study is that this population is currently not declining dramatically. The possibility exists that the population is either stationary or slightly declining. Estimates of λ_n are estimates of population change over the sample period only, whereas estimates of λ_d are properly interpreted as the rate of change in the population if the conditions during the study period were maintained indefinitely. Therefore, we do not know if estimated declines will continue past the time period when estimates of demographic traits and numbers were measured. We caution against attempts to forecast population trends using our estimates beyond the time period when the population was sampled because of uncertainty concerning the underlying causes of these trends. Even though there is considerable uncertainty in our estimates of population trends, our results suggest it would be prudent to exercise caution with management of Spotted Owl populations. Since our results suggest a slow rate of decline, management actions which may accelerate this decline should be avoided.

We believe that reliable information concerning the effects of land management activities on Northern Spotted Owl populations can be best achieved through well-designed experiments. For example, if logging continues in Spotted Owl habitat on public lands, different harvesting regimes could be applied to randomly selected control and treatment sites to examine the effects of such practices on survival, fecundity, (or their correlates) and, ultimately, fitness. Such a design could be incorporated into existing demographic studies. Demographic studies such as ours provide observational information for establishing the biologically-based hypotheses to be experimentally tested, as well as the initial pre-treatment data.

SUMMARY

A contentious point in the controversy surrounding Northern Spotted Owls is whether populations are declining or stationary. We estimated age- and sex-specific survival probabilities and fecundity rates from 1985 through 1993 in a population of Northern Spotted Owls on public lands in northwestern California. We used mark-recapture models to estimate survival probabilities and ANOVA models to estimate fecundity rates. We estimated annual rates of population change using average estimates of demographic parameters in a 3-stage Leslie matrix and by estimating counts of owls over time. We found a significant decline in survival for owls ≥3-years old in mark-recapture models which only included this age-class. However, survival of owls ≥1-year old was variable over time when all age-classes were included in the mark-recapture models. Estimates of juvenile survival and fecundity (with the exception of one year) were constant during the study period. Using our estimates of demographic parameters in a Leslie matrix, we estimated an annual rate of population change (λ) of 0.9656, which was significantly different (P = 0.019) from a stationary population. In contrast, trends in numbers of owls (λ = 1.000–1.009) were not different (P = 0.15–49) from a stationary population. A number of biases made estimation of population rates of change problematic and were possible explanations for the discrepancy between our estimates of λ. During the period of study, we concluded that the population of Spotted Owls in our study were not in dramatic decline, but may have been in either slight decline or stationary.

ACKNOWLEDGMENTS

This study would not have been possible over the years without the field assistance of D. Delaney, T. J. Evans, D. Fix, T. Hall, T. Heinz, M. Herrera, M. Kasper, C. Jewett, D. Lamphear, A. Padilla, K. White, J. Woodford, and K. E. Young. In addition, we are grateful to J. A. Blakesley, J. Hunter, C. Jewett and C. A. Moen for leading field crews and their assistance with data preparation and analysis. We also thank the many people at the Six Rivers, Shasta-Trinity, and Klamath National Forests, the Bureau of Land Management, and The Nature Conservancy for their help and encouragement. D. R. Anderson, K. P. Burnham and G. C. White provided insights for data analysis. D. R. Anderson, W. R. Clark, S. DeStefano, E. D. Forsman, T. M. Shenk and G. C. White reviewed earlier drafts of the manuscript. Funding for this project was provided by California Department of Fish and Game, Federal Aid in Wildlife Restoration Projects W-65-R-3 and 4 and California Environmental License Plate Funds; U.S. Forest Service, Pacific Southwest Forest and Range Experiment Station, Cooperative Agreement No. PSW-87–0011CA; and McIntire-Stennis Project No. 85.

Key words: California, demography, fecundity, Northern Spotted Owl, population trends, *Strix occidentalis caurina,* survival.

Studies in Avian Biology No. 17:92–101, 1996.

META-ANALYSIS OF VITAL RATES OF THE NORTHERN SPOTTED OWL

Kenneth P. Burnham, David R. Anderson, and Gary C. White

INTRODUCTION

Beginning in the mid-1980s a number of large "demographic" study areas were established within the range of the Northern Spotted Owl (*Strix occidentalis caurina*). Anderson and Burnham (1992) presented an analysis of data from five of these study areas. By the fall of 1993, 14 such demographic study areas had at least four years of capture-recapture and fecundity data. We provide results here for 11 of the 14 demographic data sets available; data from two studies areas in northern California conducted by the timber industry were not made available at the workshop, and the industry-sponsored study on the Wenatchee National Forest was withdrawn on the final day of the 12-day workshop. Thus, none of the three study areas sponsored by the timber industry was available for use in this paper. The 11 study areas where data were available are shown in Fig. 1 of Franklin et al. (*this volume*). These are large study areas, several are contiguous with others, and have as few as four years to as many as nine years of banding (Table 1) and fecundity data. The sample size for individual owls first banded as territorial "adults" (i.e., non-juvenile birds) was over 6,500 capture-and-releases events (Table 1).

Our main objective was to conduct a rigorous and objective analysis of the empirical population data available on the Northern Spotted Owl and provide the statistical inferences that were justified about the owl's vital rates. We emphasized a science-based, data analysis agenda during the 12-day workshop. Many quality controls were established, data were formally certified prior to analysis, analysis protocols were determined *a priori,* and these were followed. Several people with special expertise in capture-recapture and population dynamics theory were invited to supervise the analyses, and every effort was made to assure the integrity of the data analyses and inferences. Considerable published formal theory and computer software existed to guide the sophisticated analysis of these data. Direct inferences were limited to the years where data were available. Because of the number, large size, and wide distribution of the study areas, we assume the statistical inferences extend beyond these specific study areas to the range of this subspecies.

At and after the workshop we were asked repeatedly to provide insights to managers and policy people such as *"What do these results and inferences mean to managers?"* or *"Is Option 9 of the President's forest plan viable, given the results from these 11 studies?"* Those subjects lie beyond our expertise, and hence this chapter is a "science only" document with but few of our interpretations expressed. Other papers in this volume delve into these management issues (e.g., Gutiérrez *this volume,* Raphael et al. *this volume*).

METHODS

Most of the presentation of methods is in Franklin et al. (*this volume*). However, there are a few aspects of analyses herein that are not covered in Franklin et al. (*this volume*); it is these matters we cover below, in particular the estimation (and use of) emigration rate, *E,* from radio-tracking data.

Capture-Recapture Data

Most of the data analysis effort focused on the Northern Spotted Owl capture-recapture (CR) data sets from 11 studies (see Table 1). The CR data from each individual study were thoroughly analyzed as described in the previous chapters. Also several "meta-analyses" were done, because the data sets were partitioned into short- and long-term studies. The global model for a meta-analysis here is $\{\phi_{a \cdot s \cdot g \cdot t}, p_{a \cdot s \cdot g \cdot t}\}$. This model can have hundreds of parameters. No new ideas are introduced in doing a meta-analysis, but meta-analysis models are much more difficult because so many data are being dealt with. The advantage of such overall analyses is that we learn of effects and trends common in all the data sets. A meta-analysis is more powerful than the set of separate analyses.

The meta-analysis on the short term studies included the Wenatchee Demographic Study (N.E. Washington) data because those analyses were done, and could not be re-done, when the investigators withdrew their WDS data. They did, however, agree that the WDS data could remain in the meta-analysis.

The data used in the meta-analyses were the capture histories of just those birds initially caught as territory-holders; for simplicity we refer to

TABLE 1. SUMMARY INFORMATION ON SAMPLING EFFORT FOR 11 NORTHERN SPOTTED OWL DEMOGRAPHIC STUDIES. NUMBER BANDED IS THE NUMBER OF DISTINCT BIRDS CAUGHT AND BANDED, WHEREAS SAMPLE SIZE $N = R_1 + R_2 + \ldots + R_{K-1}$ IN THE CAPTURE-RECAPTURE *M*-ARRAY (LEBRETON ET AL. 1992). STUDY AREA ACRONYMS ARE DEFINED IN FRANKLIN ET AL. (*THIS VOLUME*)

Study area	First year	Number of years	Adults banded		Juveniles banded	Subadults banded	Adult sample size	
			Male	Female			Male	Female
CAL	1985	9	99	91	274	84	369	257
RSB	1985	9	262	214	429	117	692	520
SCS	1985	9	560	491	680	189	1032	823
SAL	1986	8	74	68	101	17	151	129
HJA	1987	7	123	109	226	57	294	286
OLY	1987	7	127	129	249	43	295	278
CLE	1989	5	60	56	186	30	131	96
EUG	1989	5	49	52	59	16	117	98
COO	1990	4	99	93	136	49	178	157
SIU	1990	4	82	72	72	25	135	112
SIS	1990	4	38	31	31	10	75	55
		Totals	1573	1406	2443	637	3469	2811

these birds here as adults although they can be <3 years old. Birds banded as juveniles that survived to be adults and were then re-encountered were not part of the data set used in the meta-analysis. These additional data were a minor part of all the possible data on territorial owls. In principle, program SURGE can use all the data in a meta-analyses; in fact, limitations of computer capability and the workshop time frame prevented us from using this additional information (known adults first banded as juveniles).

FECUNDITY DATA

The field studies involved finding and monitoring territorial females to determine their breeding success. The basic data are, for each territorial female (hence for potential breeders), the number of offspring that were fledged, which ranged from 0 to 3. A 50:50 sex ratio is assumed at fledging and is supported by genetic sex markers (see Franklin et al. *this volume*, Reid et al. *this volume*). The parameter of interest, fecundity rate b, is the average number of young fledged per territorial female, hence statistical analysis is straightforward. Despite the integer nature of the data, sample sizes are sufficient to justify ANOVA inference methods. Hence, data analysis was done using SAS PROCs MEANS, GLM, and VARCOMP (SAS Institute 1985). PROC MEANS was used to produce means and standard errors by various categories (e.g., female age, year, study area, age and study, etc.). PROC GLM, with area and time effects random (age is a fixed effect), was used to test for significance of effects and interactions. PROC VARCOMP, using option MIVQUE, was used to estimate variance components from the fecundity rates, $\hat{b}$, over years, areas, and for interactions.

POPULATION RATE OF CHANGE

For one study area, we can test $H_o : \lambda \geq 1$ vs. $H_a : \lambda < 1$ with a one-sided z-test (Franklin et al. *this volume*). With multiple studies a broader scope of inference is possible with an empirical t-test based on independent estimates of λ for each site. A less robust test is a z-test based on the estimated average $\hat{\bar{\lambda}}$ and its estimated theoretical standard error where

$$\hat{\bar{\lambda}} = \frac{1}{k} \sum_{i=1}^{k} \hat{\lambda}_i,$$

$$\widehat{SE}(\hat{\bar{\lambda}}) = \frac{1}{k} \sqrt{\sum_{i=1}^{k} \widehat{var}(\hat{\lambda}_i)}.$$

Hence, as an inference over all study areas, we can test $H_0 : \bar{\lambda} \geq 1$ vs. $H_a : \bar{\lambda} < 1$ with the one-sided z-test

$$z = \frac{1 - \hat{\bar{\lambda}}}{\widehat{SE}(\hat{\bar{\lambda}})}.$$

The corresponding t-test is more robust because it uses an empirical estimate of $SE(\bar{\lambda})$, but it can have less power for this same reason.

EMIGRATION ESTIMATION AND A COMMON λ

In recent years some juveniles have had radios attached so that their movements and fate could be determined. These radio-tracking data can be used to directly estimate juvenile emigration, based on counts of surviving juveniles in the next spring. Emigration is defined here as: the juvenile moves out of its original study area, where it would be at risk of capture, is not captured by any other researchers, and survives its first year. The radio-tracking data include counts of survivors in and out of the specific study areas, and include information on whether the emigrated birds were captured in other areas.

Let n be the total number of survivors in spring, year $t + 1$, of birds radioed in summer, year t. Then $n = n_s + n_{ed} + n_{en}$, where n_s = number that stayed in their natal study area and survived the year, n_{ed} = number that emigrated off the natal area, survived the year, and were detected by the routine CR study methods (with no aid from telemetry), and n_{en} = number that emigrated off the natal area, survived the year, and were not detected by the routine CR study methods. Then the emigration estimate is

$$\hat{E} = \frac{n_{en}}{n}, \text{ with } \widehat{\text{SE}}(\hat{E}) = \sqrt{\frac{\hat{E}(1 - \hat{E})}{n}}.$$

This estimator is robust to some problems that would bias an estimator of annual juvenile survival probability based on the radio-tracking data. Birds are radioed (on average) about a month after fledging and their survival is not always monitored until mid-June. Thus, a survival estimate covers a shorter time period than the requisite one year needed to match with adult survival probability in population dynamics evaluation. This emigration estimate is based only on birds surviving to spring. Assuming all emigration has occurred by then, and that by that spring, subsequent mortality of birds is the same for emigrants and non-emigrants, then it is not required that the survivors be monitored until mid-June to get a reliable emigration estimator.

Let S_s and S_e represent the annual survival probability of juveniles that stay and those that emigrate, respectively. Then true juvenile survival probability is

$$S_J = S_s (1 - E) + S_e E = \phi_J + S_e E.$$

Without reliable, large samples of radio-tracking data on annual survival probability of juveniles (residents vs. emigrants), to estimate E from these data it is necessary to assume $S_s = S_e \equiv S_J$. Then $S_J = \phi_J + S_e E$, and therefore

$$\hat{S}_J = \frac{\hat{\phi}_J}{1 - \hat{E}}.$$

To estimate SE($\hat{\lambda}$) we need the variances and covariance below (derived by the delta-method):

$$[\text{var}(\hat{S}_J)]^2 = (S_J)^2[[\text{cv}(\hat{\phi}_J)]^2 + [\text{cv}(1 - \hat{E})]^2],$$

$$\text{cov}(\hat{S}_J, \hat{\phi}_A) = \frac{\text{cov}(\hat{\phi}_J, \hat{\phi}_A)}{1 - \hat{E}}.$$

We note that while SE($\hat{E}$) $\equiv$ SE($1 - \hat{E}$),

$$\text{cv}(1 - \hat{E}) = \frac{\hat{E}}{1 - \hat{E}} \text{cv}(\hat{E}).$$

RESULTS

GOODNESS-OF-FIT TESTS FOR CAPTURE-RECAPTURE DATA

Table 2 gives the summarized results of the goodness-of-fit (GOF) tests to the global model $\{\phi_{a \cdot t}, p_{a \cdot t}\}$, separately for males and females and each study area, for the adult data. The CR data on releases of juveniles and subadults were also tested for goodness-of-fit; those tests are additive to the tests for the adult data. However, these latter data were so sparse in terms of captures that they contributed relatively little to the overall GOF test (a total of $\chi^2_{(36)} = 28.49$, P = 0.8095 for those test components with enough data to be reliable), and we therefore give the detailed results here only for the adults.

From Table 2, the overall GOF test result was $\chi^2_{(225)} = 292.47$, P = 0.0016. Given the sample size (about 3,000 individuals banded as adults) this is a decent fit for data of this magnitude and complexity. This judgment of a "decent fit" is based on the ratio $292.47/225 = 1.3$ (and $220.47/193 = 1.14$) being "near" 1 despite the huge sample size here (given sufficiently large sample size, one can get an extremely small P-value even for a trivial effect size). Lack of fit here comes from mostly the SCS and OLY areas. The GOF test components for these areas, and HJA and RSB, were carefully scrutinized. It was found that the significant test components were associated with only a few birds and failure to fit was not because of any systematic patterns that could be modeled with CR models more general than CJS. Much of the lack of fit for area SCS is attributed to about five birds that showed temporary emigration (one adult female was not seen for six years after initial banding, and this alone caused much of the GOF failure of the female data for SCS). In the case of OLY, there was one released cohort of 18 newly banded birds in 1992 that was captured in 1993 at a very different rate from previously banded birds. Basically, most of the lack of fit indicated in Table 2 can be related to about 30 to 40 birds out of 3,000. Without those few birds, the chi-squared to df ratio (i.e., a variance inflation factor) was 1.14. Therefore, we maintained that the global model was satisfactory and analysis could proceed without any compelling need for quasi-likelihood variance inflation.

MODELS OF THE CAPTURE-RECAPTURE DATA

The models with the minimum AIC value for each study area are summarized in Table 3 for data from owl adults and for all age-classes. Five of the 11 minimum AIC models contain a negative time trend in survival (i.e., ϕ_T) for the adult data, while three of the 11 show this negative trend for the data including all age-classes. Other

TABLE 2. GOODNESS-OF-FIT (GOF) TESTS FOR NORTHERN SPOTTED OWL ADULT CAPTURE-RECAPTURE DATA SETS. SEE FRANKLIN ET AL. (*THIS VOLUME*) FOR INFORMATION ABOUT THE TESTS USED

Study area	Sex	TEST 2 + 3			TEST 2 P	TEST 3 P
		χ^2	df	P		
CAL	Males	11.22	14	0.6688	0.2399	0.8382
	Females	4.75	14	0.9890	1.0000	0.9428
RSB[a]	Males	29.02	19	0.0656	0.0087	0.5393
	Females	26.93	20	0.1374	0.0831	0.3288
SCS[a]	Males	31.69	15	0.0071	0.0001	0.5714
	Females	40.54	17	0.0011	0.0000	0.5300
SAL	Males	12.89	14	0.5354	0.1420	0.8152
	Females	14.86	16	0.5350	0.9040	0.2753
HJA[a]	Males	16.23	12	0.1810	0.1239	0.3138
	Females	19.87	13	0.0984	0.5854	0.0482
OLY[a]	Males	19.89	12	0.0691	0.3937	0.0499
	Females	34.36	13	0.0011	0.2021	0.0008
CLE	Males	5.11	7	0.6466	0.3280	0.7185
	Females	6.03	7	0.5368	0.0612	0.9942
EUG	Males	0.85	4	0.9323	1.0000	0.9323
	Females	3.30	7	0.8559	1.0000	0.6539
COO	Males	2.98	4	0.5605	1.0000	0.3941
	Females	6.47	3	0.0910	0.0128	0.8787
SIU	Males	3.83	4	0.4295	1.0000	0.2804
	Females	1.15	4	0.8858	1.0000	0.7644
SIS	Males	0.50	3	0.9199	1.0000	0.9199
	Females	0.23	3	0.9734	1.0000	0.9734
Total χ^2 GOF		292.70	225	0.0016		
χ^2 GOF w/o SCS		220.47	193	0.0853		

[a] Examined in detail for lack of fit in the component tests (as per Burnham et al. 1987, Lebreton et al. 1992).

study areas had negative time trends in survival for models within 1 or 2 AIC units of the low-AIC model. Thus, even for individual data sets, where sample size is small and statistical power is expected to be low, there are indications of negative time trends in survival probabilities.

There is also evidence in these and other analyses of time trends in the capture probabilities, although this has no relevance to owl population dynamics. In general, within a study capture probabilities tended to increase over time because funding and field experience tended to increase.

ESTIMATES OF AGE-SPECIFIC SURVIVAL UNDER THE MINIMUM AIC MODELS

Estimated apparent juvenile survival ($\hat{\phi}_J$) varied from 0.140 (CLE) to 0.418 (RSB), excluding SIS, which had little data for the estimation of this parameter (Table 4). An unweighted average across study areas yielded an estimate of apparent juvenile survival of 0.258 (empirical SE = 0.036). These estimates include the rate at which juvenile birds left the area and survived a year (i.e., $\phi_J = S_J (1 - E)$). Adults had estimated survival probabilities varying over a small range from 0.821 (HJA) to 0.868 (CAL). The unweighted average survival of adults was 0.844

(empirical SE = 0.0052) (Table 4). Emigration is a minor issue in territorial birds (see chapters on individual studies). The effect of emigration and senescence produce negative and positive bias,

TABLE 3. SUMMARY OF THE MODEL WITH THE MINIMUM AIC VALUE BY STUDY AREA, FOR THE NORTHERN SPOTTED OWL. "ADULTS ONLY" USE ONLY CR DATA ON BIRDS INITIALLY BANDED AS AN ADULT; "AGE MODELS" USE ALL THE DATA. NOTATION IS EXPLAINED IN THE APPENDIX

Study area	Best model, adults only	Best model, age models
CAL[a]	$\{\phi_{s \cdot T}, p_c\}$	$\{\phi_{J,At}, p_{a4',Ac}\}$
RSB	$\{\phi_T, p_{s+T}\}$	$\{\phi_{a2}, p_{a4'+s}\}$
SCS	$\{\phi_T, p_s\}$	$\{\phi_{a2}, p_{a4'+s}\}$
SAL	$\{\phi_T, p\}$	$\{\phi_{a2+T}, p_{a4'+s}\}$
HJA	$\{\phi, p_{s+T}\}$	$\{\phi_{a2+t}, p_{a3'+s}\}$
OLY	$\{\phi_s, p_T\}$	$\{\phi_{a2}, p_{a5'+T}\}$
CLE	$\{\phi_T, p_s\}$	$\{\phi_{a2+T}, p_{s+T}\}$
EUG[b]	$\{\phi_{t_1=t_2,t_3,t_4}, p_{t+s}\}$	$\{\phi_{a2+T}, p_{a2+s \cdot T}\}$
COO	$\{\phi_t, p_s\}$	$\{\phi_{a2+T}, p_{a2+s}\}$
SIU	$\{\phi, p_{s+t}\}$	$\{\phi_{a2}, p_{a2}\}$
SIS	$\{\phi, p_T\}$	$\{\phi, p_T\}$

[a] Capture technique (c): a binary variable to index physical recapture vs. resighting.
[b] Here $\phi_{t_1=t_2,t_3,t_4}$ denotes model $\{\phi_t\}$ with the constraint that survival probabilities are same over time periods 1 to 2 and 2 to 3 (i.e., $\phi_1 = \phi_2$).

TABLE 4.   ESTIMATES OF JUVENILE AND ADULT SURVIVAL PROBABILITIES, FROM THE BEST MODEL, FOR THE
NORTHERN SPOTTED OWL DATA. NOTATION IS EXPLAINED IN THE APPENDIX

Study area	Best model, age models	Juvenile survival		Adult survival	
		$\hat{\phi}_J$	$SE(\hat{\phi}_J)$	$\hat{\phi}_A$	$SE(\hat{\phi}_A)$
CAL	$\{\phi_{J,At}, p_{a4',Ac}\}$	0.330	0.043	0.868	0.012[a]
RSB	$\{\phi_{a2}, p_{a4'+s}\}$	0.418	0.042	0.843	0.010
SCS	$\{\phi_{a2}, p_{a4'+s}\}$	0.320	0.038	0.824	0.009
SAL	$\{\phi_{a2+T}, p_{a4'+s}\}$	0.402	0.105[a]	0.851	0.022[a]
HJA	$\{\phi_{a2+t}, p_{a3'+s}\}$	0.288	0.052[a]	0.821	0.016[a]
OLY	$\{\phi_{a2}, p_{a5'+T}\}$	0.245	0.064[a]	0.862	0.017[a]
CLE	$\{\phi_{a2+T}, p_{s+T}\}$	0.140	0.026[a]	0.850	0.031[a]
EUG	$\{\phi_{a2+T}, p_{a2+s \cdot T}\}$	0.232	0.078[a]	0.853	0.026[a]
COO	$\{\phi_{a2+t}, p_{a2+s}\}$	0.218	0.045[a]	0.862	0.019[a]
SIU	$\{\phi_{a2}, p_{a2}\}$	0.243	0.092	0.822	0.027
SIS	$\{\phi, p_T\}$	0.000	—	0.830	0.045
Mean, and empirical SE on 10 *df*		0.258	0.036	0.844	0.005

[a] Standard error is an approximation based on the nearest (in AIC) model with no time effects on survival probability; we did not have general enough software to get exact standard errors in these cases.

respectively; thus, for adults (these were all territory holders, due to the sampling methods) we assumed $\phi_A = S_A$. The average survival of adults is very precisely estimated, cv = 0.6%.

META-ANALYSIS OF SURVIVAL

Anderson and Burnham (1992) conducted a comprehensive "meta-analysis" of the data from adult females on the five study areas available at that time. Because more data are used in the estimation of parameters, there is greater power to detect various "effects" and reveal more structure in the data. Here, we partitioned the study areas into six short-term data sets (<6 years; the WDS data were included in this analysis, with the investigators consent) and six long-term data sets (>6 years) to test the null hypothesis that there were no decreasing time trends in survival against the one-sided alternative that survival was decreasing. Thus, interest was focused on three models for survival $\{\phi, \phi_T, \text{ and } \phi_t\}$, while allowing the minimum AIC parameterization of the capture probabilities (e.g., $p_{g \cdot T}$). The data were in no way "pooled" during this analysis; rather, the data from several study areas were jointly used to estimate the same parameter set.

Long-term study areas

We tested for a time trend in survival of females captured as adults using a likelihood ratio test of model $\{\phi, p_{g \cdot T}\}$ vs. model $\{\phi_T, p_{g \cdot T}\}$ and found evidence of a time trend ($\chi^2_{(1)} = 4.889$, P = 0.0270). A further test of model $\{\phi_T, p_{g \cdot T}\}$ vs. model $\{\phi_t, p_{g \cdot T}\}$ was also significant ($\chi^2_{(6)} = 15.015$, P = 0.0201). Some of this additional time variation in ϕ_t (beyond just a linear time effect) is related to study area effects. This general

finding is shown in Fig. 1 where a nearly linear negative trend in adult female survival is seen (it is linear on logit(ϕ)) corresponding to model $\{\phi_T, p_{g \cdot T}\}$ and the year-specific estimates are also plotted, corresponding to model $\{\phi_t, p_T\}$. The average standard error for points along the line was 0.014, cv $\doteq$ 1.7%.

A similar finding was made for a joint analysis of males and females captured as adults. That is,

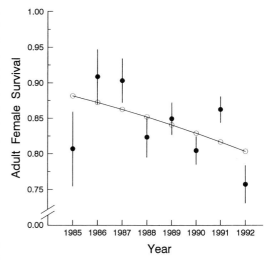

FIGURE 1.   Estimated survival probability of adult female Northern Spotted Owls as a function of years, 1985–1992. A significant negative time trend (open circles) is indicated by the nearly linear line (estimated under model $\{\phi_T, p_{g \cdot T}\}$). The solid circles are estimates under model $\{\phi_t, p_{g \cdot T}\}$ with one standard error plotted. The standard error for points along the line averaged 0.014.

TABLE 5. NUMBER OF RECORDS OF NORTHERN SPOTTED OWL FEMALES THAT PRODUCED 0, 1, 2, OR 3 YOUNG, BASED ON DATA COMBINED OVER 11 STUDY AREAS, BY YEAR.

Year	Number of young produced				Totals
	0	1	2	3	
1985	79	14	22	1	116
1986	60	26	39	0	125
1987	154	19	44	0	217
1988	153	63	68	1	285
1989	264	66	89	2	421
1990	431	216	192	0	839
1991	660	146	194	3	1003
1992	469	280	466	31	1246
1993	1013	61	51	0	1125
Totals	3283	891	1165	38	5377

a significant negative time trend in survival was shown ($\chi^2_{(1)} = 15.307$, P = 0.0001), testing model $\{\phi, p_{g \cdot T + s}\}$ vs. $\{\phi_T, p_{g \cdot T + s}\}$. Less evidence was found for a similar negative time trend in the survival of adult males ($\chi^2_{(1)} = 2.053$, P = 0.1519), testing model $\{\phi, p_{g \cdot t}\}$ vs. model $\{\phi_T, p_{g \cdot t}\}$.

Short-term study areas

Power to detect time trends from the short-term study areas is surely low, because so few years were available and sample sizes tended to be low (Table 2.). A negative time trend in survival was detected only for females ($\chi^2_{(1)} = 3.476$, P = 0.0623), testing model $\{\phi, p_{g+t}\}$ vs. model $\{\phi_T, p_{g+t}\}$. The result for the joint analysis of males and females was inconclusive ($\chi^2_{(1)} = 1.707$, P = 0.1914), as was that for the males alone ($\chi^2_{(1)} = 0.754$, P = 0.3852). Two points are of interest here, first a significant negative trend was shown for females and second, the sign of the non-significant relationships for males and females and males alone was negative in both cases.

FECUNDITY DATA

Across all 11 studies and years, there were 5,377 females checked for reproduction. Of these, 3,283

TABLE 6. ANALYSIS OF VARIANCE RESULTS, AND YEARLY MEANS, FOR NUMBER OF FEMALE YOUNG FLEDGED PER TERRITORIAL FEMALE. THE EXACT F-TESTS USE EXPECTED MEAN SQUARES TO CONSTRUCT A DENOMINATOR MEAN SQUARE; VARIANCE COMPONENTS ESTIMATED BY THE MIVQUE METHOD IN SAS PROC VARCOMP (AGE IS A FIXED-EFFECT, HENCE FOR IT THERE IS NO VARIANCE COMPONENT)

Source	df	SS	Mean square	F-value	P
AGE	2	9.4096	4.7048	8.18	0.0003
		(exact F-test based on expected mean squares		8.14	0.0004)
YEAR	8	39.5056	4.9382	8.58	0.0001
		(exact F-test based on expected mean squares		5.07	0.0001)
AGE*YEAR	16	14.5058	0.9068	1.58	0.0665
STUDY	11	12.4231	1.1294	1.96	0.0280
		(exact F-test based on expected mean squares		1.84	0.0534)
AGE*STUDY	21	5.7360	0.2731	0.47	0.9791
YEAR*STUDY	57	129.9290	2.2795	3.96	0.0001
ERROR	4406	2534.4290	0.5752		

Variance components estimates

Var(YEAR)	0.02087
Var(STUDY)	0.00256
Var(YEAR*STUDY)	0.00000
Var(YEAR*AGE)	0.02682
Var(STUDY*AGE)	0.00000
Var(ERROR)	0.13932

Average yearly fecundity

Year	Mean	N
1985	0.2630	116
1986	0.4160	125
1987	0.2466	217
1988	0.3544	285
1989	0.2969	421
1990	0.3576	839
1991	0.2707	1003
1992	0.5237	1246
1993	0.0725	1125

TABLE 7. ESTIMATES OF AGE-SPECIFIC FECUNDITY (B_X) FOR FEMALE NORTHERN SPOTTED OWLS (B_X = THE NUMBER OF JUVENILE FEMALES FLEDGED/FEMALE OF AGE X)

Study area	Subadult 1 (12 mos.)		Subadult 2 (24 mos.)		Adult ($\geq$36 mos.)	
	$\hat{b}_1$	SE($\hat{b}_1$)	$\hat{b}_2$	SE($\hat{b}_2$)	$\hat{b}_A$	SE($\hat{b}_A$)
CAL	0.094	0.067	0.205	0.077	0.333	0.029
RSB	0.080	0.056	0.144	0.062	0.321	0.022
SCS	0.013	0.019	0.145	0.056	0.313	0.016
SAL[a]	0.500	0.408	0.500	0.408	0.381	0.051
HJA[a]	0.154	0.102	0.154	0.102	0.348	0.034
OLY[a]	0.206	0.106	0.206	0.106	0.380	0.036
CLE[a]	0.360	0.126	0.360	0.126	0.565	0.061
EUG[a]	0.167	0.236	0.167	0.236	0.272	0.049
COO	0.156	0.124	0.167	0.113	0.323	0.044
SIU[a]	0.071	0.101	0.071	0.101	0.231	0.043
SIS[a]	0.000	0.000	0.000	0.000	0.282	0.072
Average[b]	0.068	0.027	0.205	0.034	0.339	0.010

[a] Data for subadults 1 and 2 were pooled, to estimate a common fecundity, because of small sample size ($n_1 + n_2 < 30$ for total sample size of subadults).
[b] These averages are based directly on all the data pooled over ages, not on averaging the column means.

(61.1%), 891 (16.6%), 1,165 (21.7%), and 38 (0.7%) had fledged 0, 1, 2 and 3 young, respectively (Table 5). These data were converted into fecundity values (see Franklin et al. *this volume*) for subsequent analyses.

Key results for the fecundity data are given in Table 6, along with the overall means for each year. These means are numbers of female young fledged per territorial (hence potentially breeding) female; these yearly means use all data (known and unknown aged females). Table 7 gives estimates of fecundity (b) by study area and age of parent female; these means use only data from known-aged female parents. The variance components in Table 6 are for females fledged per territorial female.

From the ANOVA results in Table 6, age of the female parent and year are significant factors in variation among true fecundities. There may be small, but real, differences in fecundity by study area (P = 0.0534). With year and study area effects and interactions of these effects treated as random, the estimated variance components are given in Table 6. Because of the large year effects, Table 6 also gives the mean fecundity by year. The most striking features of these means are the high fecundity in 1992 and low fecundity in 1993. We believe no meaningful linear trend in fecundity is observed over these 9 years; formal regression-based statistical tests for a linear trend are strongly influenced by the results in 1993 (these data points have very high leverage) and therefore tend to have a negative trend.

As Table 7 shows, fecundity of 1–2 year old birds is much less than for birds 3+ years old (P = 0.0004). Within the subadult age class, 2-year old females are more productive than 1-year old birds (P = 0.0045).

JUVENILE EMIGRATION (RADIO-TRACKING DATA)

The only radio-tracking data available for these analyses relative to emigration were from post-fledging juveniles in the OLY and RSB areas in 1991 and 1992 (Forsman, unpublished data; Reid, unpublished data). These data were analyzed to see if estimates of juvenile survival could be obtained that would validly apply to the same annual time period as the CR data. Because the radios were put on 3–6 weeks after fledging and there was a lot of censoring (radio failure and birds that were lost), we did not obtain an estimate of S_J from the radio-tracking data. However, it became apparent during the workshop that these data did allow estimation of the parameter E needed to adjust the CR estimator, $\hat{\phi}_J$, for permanent emigration.

To estimate E we need only counts of juveniles surviving until after emigration occurs (plus the unavoidable assumption that the annual survival probability is the same for emigrating and not emigrating juveniles). The relevant data are given below:

Area	Year	n_{en}	n
OLY	1991	8	11
OLY	1992	3	8
RSB	1991	2	26
RSB	1992	11	31
Totals:		24	76

Based on these data, $\hat{E}$ = 24/76 = 0.3158, with SE($\hat{E}$) = 0.05332 and a 95% confidence interval of 0.2113 to 0.4203.

POPULATION RATE OF CHANGE, λ

Our estimates of λ based on $\hat{\phi}_J$ (Table 8) are biased low because of the confounding effect of

TABLE 8. ESTIMATES OF THE RATE OF ANNUAL POPULATION CHANGE, λ, FOR FEMALE NORTHERN SPOTTED OWLS IN 11 INDEPENDENT STUDY AREAS THROUGHOUT THEIR RANGE. ALSO SHOWN ARE TEST STATISTICS AND P-VALUES FOR THE TEST OF THE NULL HYPOTHESIS THAT $\lambda \geq 1$ VS. THE ALTERNATIVE THAT $\lambda < 1$

Study area	$\hat{\lambda}$	SE($\hat{\lambda}$)	t or z	P
CAL	0.9656	0.0165	2.08	0.0188
RSB	0.9570	0.0146	2.94	0.0016
SCS	0.9105	0.0121	7.39	0.0000
SAL	1.0191	0.0729	−0.26	0.6064
HJA	0.9106	0.0212	4.22	0.0000
OLY	0.9472	0.0255	2.07	0.0192
CLE	0.9240	0.0323	2.35	0.0094
EUG	0.9134	0.0314	2.76	0.0029
COO	0.9274	0.0223	3.25	0.0006
SIU	0.8738	0.0312	4.04	0.0000
SIS	0.8302	—	—	—
Simple average and t-test, 10 df	0.9253	0.0148	5.04	0.0003
Simple average and z-test	0.9349[a]	0.0103	6.32	0.0000

[a] Excludes SIS area because no theoretical SE($\hat{\lambda}$) could be obtained for that area.

emigration. Still, it is worth testing these $\hat{\lambda}$ against 1 because if, with such a test, they are not significantly less than 1 we may conclude we do not have statistical evidence that λ is less than 1. Given that the results in Table 8 suggest true λ might be less than 1, we computed Table 9 results. Table 9 allows a subjective assessment of whether it is reasonable or not to believe $\lambda < 1$. Overall, to believe $\lambda \geq 1$, one must believe average juvenile survival probability (S_J) is ≥ 0.565, or (equivalently) that emigration probability is ≥ 0.51. In the previous section we derived $\hat{E} = 0.3158$ with a 95% confidence interval of 0.2113 to 0.4203. This is indirect, but strong, evidence that, on average, $\lambda < 1$ during the years of these studies.

Given this data-based estimate of E, we can adjust $\hat{\phi}_J$ for emigration to obtain $\hat{S}_J$ and compute a less biased $\hat{\lambda}$. We did not do this for each area because we do not have area-specific $\hat{E}$. Instead, we obtained averages of the vital rates over time and study areas to use with the single estimate $\hat{E}$ to get one bias-adjusted $\hat{\lambda}$. This $\hat{\lambda}$ applies in general, as an average over the years 1985 to 1993, to Northern Spotted Owls. From Table 7 the fecundities are (standard errors in parentheses), $\hat{b}_1 = 0.068$ (0.027), $\hat{b}_2 = 0.205$ (0.034), $\hat{b}_A = 0.339$ (0.010). Sampling correlations among these estimates are 0. From Table 4, $\hat{\phi}_J = 0.2579$ (0.03563), $\hat{S}_A = \hat{\phi}_A = 0.8441$ (0.00519), with empirical correlation between these estimates of 0.130 (note, we are using empirical not theoretical variances for the above point estimates). From above, we get $\hat{E} = 0.3158$ (0.05332), hence $\hat{S}_J = 0.3769$ (0.05979), and the estimated correlation between adult and juvenile survival estimates ($\hat{S}_A$, $\hat{S}_J$) is 0.13. Using these parameter

estimates (and associated variances and covariances) we find $\hat{\lambda} = 0.9548$, SE($\hat{\lambda}$) = 0.01731. Because we used empirical variances we will consider that the standard error of $\hat{\lambda}$ is based on 10 df and do a one sided t-test, as well as construct a 95% confidence interval. This is conservative in the sense of producing a less powerful test and a wider interval than might be justified by a more exact evaluation of degrees of freedom to associate with the standard error of $\hat{\lambda}$. The t-test (H_o:

TABLE 9. THE VALUE OF JUVENILE SURVIVAL PROBABILITY NEEDED TO PRODUCE $\lambda = 1$, DENOTED AS $S_{J|\lambda=1}$ IS PRESENTED. THE CALCULATION OF $S_{J|\lambda=1}$ IS BASED ON THE ESTIMATES OF ADULT SURVIVAL (TABLE 4) AND FECUNDITY (TABLE 7) USED TO COMPUTE $\hat{\lambda}$ IN TABLE 7 (AND REPEATED BELOW). SIMILARLY, WE PRESENT THE JUVENILE EMIGRATION PROBABILITY ($E_{|\lambda=1}$) THAT WOULD RESULT IN THE OBSERVED $\hat{\phi}_J$ ESTIMATES GIVEN IN TABLE 5 UNDER THE ASSUMPTION THAT $\lambda = 1$. THIS INFORMATION IS USEFUL IN ASSESSING THE PLAUSIBLE DEGREE OF BIAS IN THE $\hat{\lambda}$ VALUES DUE TO EMIGRATION OF JUVENILE BIRDS

Study area	$\hat{\lambda}$	$S_{J|\lambda=1}$	$E_{|\lambda=1}$
CAL	0.9656	0.461	0.29
RSB	0.9570	0.607	0.31
SCS	0.9105	0.746	0.75
SAL	1.0191	0.360	−0.12
HJA	0.9106	0.630	0.54
OLY	0.9472	0.413	0.41
CLE	0.9240	0.297	0.53
EUG	0.9134	0.603	0.61
COO	0.9274	0.492	0.56
SIU	0.8738	0.995	0.77
SIS	0.8302	0.607	1.00
Means	0.9253	0.565	0.51

: $\bar{\lambda} \geq 1$ vs. $H_a : \bar{\lambda} < 1$) is $t_{10} = 2.61$, $P = 0.0130$. The 95% confidence interval on $\bar{\lambda}$ (uses 97.5 percentile $t_{10} = 2.228$) is 0.9162 to 0.9934.

DISCUSSION

The first important result was that annual survival probabilities of females capture as adults have declined at a significant, negative rate. Several individual data sets revealed this negative time trend, as did the meta-analyses for both the short-term and long-term data sets. This is an important finding and must be weighed heavily in decisions concerning land management policy in the future and in view of the fact that this is a Threatened subspecies under the Endangered Species Act. The survival results for adult males were less convincing, but the pattern of declining survival was still there. The meta-analysis of males and females also showed a highly significant negative time trend. The adult female population component is the most important, and it is this component where the evidence is strongest for a negative time trend (Fig. 1) (we again note that λ applies only to the female owls).

We did not detect any trend in juvenile survival probabilities; these data are somewhat sparse and the power to detect a trend was low. Several areas did seem to show a negative time trend in ϕ_J (Table 3), but we will not pursue this further here. We found no time trends that we felt were biologically significant in fecundity, but note that 1993 was a year of very poor production.

We make here two comments on methodology. Firstly, the tests for time trend in survival are based on a ideas of fixed time effects, because we are not making any inference to other time periods. To be consistent with this philosophy, the ANOVAs on the fecundity data could have treated time main-effects as fixed (Table 6). Inferences about fecundity would not have changed under a fixed time-effects model.

Secondly, the issue was raised about whether tag loss or senescence could be factors confounded with time, hence mislead us about a true time decline in adult survival rates. We have considered these issues. There was no loss of leg bands. The design of the studies, especially in regards to the sample sizes, over time, of numbers of newly banded adults precludes senescence as a confounding factor with time-effects.

The second important result is that average λ, corrected for juvenile emigration, is significantly <1. We will restrict our inference to the specific years of study; we do not intend that this $\hat{\lambda}$ be used to project the size or rate of change of the population into the distant future (≥ 10 years). We use λ to answer the following question, *"given a population with estimated average vital rates*

for females (i.e., the $\hat{\bar{S}}_x$ and $\hat{\bar{b}}_x$, where $x = age$), what is the rate of population change if these rates remained constant over an appropriately long time period?" Thus, these estimates of λ answer a hypothetical question that remains of prime interest. No assumptions concerning a stationary age distribution are required under this interpretation. Finally, $\hat{\lambda}$ relates to the population of resident, territorial female birds. In this sense, λ answers the question, *"Have the resident, territorial female birds replaced themselves?"* This is an inference to the entire population of owls, not just the banded birds.

The ability to make definitive statements concerning λ is hampered by undetected emigration of some juvenile birds to places outside the study areas. To the degree that juvenile owls emigrate from the study area, survive the year, and are not captured, a negative bias exists if one takes $\hat{\phi}_J$ as an estimator of the parameter S_J, because of the relationship $\phi_J = S_J (1 - E)$. To evaluate the bias in $\hat{\phi}_J$, we have given the value of S_J required for $\lambda = 1$ (see Table 9). In addition, during 1991 and 1992 there were birds fitted with radio transmitters, which allowed an estimate of emigration probability (E). This also leads to insights concerning the degree to which $\lambda < 1$ may be true. Generally, we conclude from Table 8 that the population of resident females is declining on most of the 11 areas (perhaps SAL is an exception; but note the large estimated standard error for SAL).

Past studies (e.g., Anderson and Burnham 1992) have shown significant rates of immigration (much of this may be recruitment from a floater component of the owl population) and this seems likely to be the case here. Time constraints did not permit the estimation of these rates during the December, 1993, workshop. Thus, if a census could be done over several years to completely enumerate all the birds within some study area boundary, it is likely that these numbers might be fairly stationary (i.e., $N_1 \doteq N_2 \doteq N_3 \doteq \ldots \doteq N_k$). This hypothetical result is not inconsistent with our findings that $\lambda < 1$ and that populations of resident territorial birds are declining. In this latter case, the population within a particular bounded study area is being temporarily augmented by recruitment into the territorial population.

The third important result is that the rate of population decline is accelerating. This result stems from the fact that λ is estimated using time-averages of the vital rates (the $\bar{\phi}_x$ and $\hat{b}_x$, where $x = age$); however, it is clear that the survival probability of territorial females has a significant, negative time trend (Fig. 1). Thus, we conclude that the rate of population decline is accelerating. This acceleration was not expected by, for example, the Interagency Scientific Committee (Thomas et al. 1990) or other groups who have examined these general issues. If the next 100 years are thought to be "highly risky" for the owl, then the findings concerning accelerating declines offer no comfort for the long-term viability for this subspecies.

SUMMARY

We used all available demographic data on the northern spotted owl to estimate vital rates of this population to assess the current status of the subspecies. We used capture-recapture analysis and information-theoretic methods to analyze survival data from 1985–1993 on the Northern Spotted Owl from 11 large study areas. That analysis of all the capture-recapture data showed a declining annual survival rate for adult Northern Spotted Owls on the study areas during 1985–1993. We used general linear models to analyze recruitment data; no time trend was found. Survival and recruitment rates were combined in a Leslie matrix demography analysis. Using data from the 11 study areas we estimated $\hat{\lambda} = 0.9548$ ($\text{SE} = 0.017$). This is the average annual rate of population change under the estimated vital rates. We rejected the null hypothesis that $\lambda \geq 1$ vs. the one-sided alternative hypothesis that $\lambda < 1$ ($t = 2.61$, $P = 0.0130$). We restrict our interpretation of $\hat{\lambda}$ to the specific years of the studies; $\hat{\lambda}$ should not be used to project the size, or rate of change, of the population into the distant future (10+ years). From either the trend in adult survival rate, or $\hat{\lambda}$, there is a plausible inference of a declining population during the study period. This inference concerning declining populations of resident, territorial female owls applies to the entire population, not just the banded birds on the 11 study areas. Based on the capture-recapture analyses alone, the annual survival probability of adult female owls declined during the study years. Therefore, we conclude that the rate of population decline is accelerating.

ACKNOWLEDGMENTS

This paper is a result of the 12 day workshop held in Fort Collins, in December, 1993. Our sincere appreciation is extended to many people who participated in that fascinating workshop. Ms. B. Klein and Ms. B. Williams (Colorado State University) and Ms. B. O'Connell (USFS) provided excellent administrative support. The funds for the workshop came from the Interagency EIS Team. We especially thank the many biologists who brought their data for analysis and weathered the entire 12 days. Special thanks to those that helped in coordination in various ways, including R. Anthony and S. DeStefano (Oregon Cooperative Fish and Wildlife Research Unit), E. D. Forsman (USFS), A. B. Franklin (Colorado Cooperative Fish and Wildlife Research Unit), C. Meslow (Oregon Cooperative Fish and Wildlife Research Unit), and M. Raphael (USFS). So many helped in this effort it is hard to stop in acknowledging valued assistance, but we must include R. Lande (University of Oregon), J. D. Nichols, J. E. Hines, B. Noon (USFS), E. A. Rexstad (University of Alaska), and T. Shenk and K. Wilson (Colorado State University). Dr. J. Clobert traveled from Paris, France to join the analysis team; R. Pradel, also from France, attended some of the workshop on his move from Maryland to Vancouver, BC. Dr. J. Bart (Ohio Cooperative Fish and Wildlife Research Unit) and L. Goldwasser (University of California at Santa Barbara) attended the evening session on the estimation and interpretation of λ.

Numerous persons provided review comments on drafts of this paper (which is based on the full workshop report). We thank these people for their reviews and helpful suggestions: A. N. Arnason, M. J. Conroy, S. DeStefano, E. D. Forsman, R. J. Gutiérrez, J. D. Nichols and C. J. Schwarz.

Key words: capture-recapture, Cormack-Jolly-Seber models, Leslie matrices, Northern Spotted Owl, survival estimation, threatened species.

Studies in Avian Biology No. 17:102–112, 1996.

USE, INTERPRETATION, AND IMPLICATIONS OF DEMOGRAPHIC ANALYSES OF NORTHERN SPOTTED OWL POPULATIONS

Martin G. Raphael, Robert G. Anthony, Stephen DeStefano, Eric D. Forsman, Alan B. Franklin, Richard Holthausen, and Barry R. Noon

INTRODUCTION

Demographic analyses of Northern Spotted Owl (*Strix occidentalis caurina*) populations have generated much discussion and debate among scientists, conservationists, managers, and representatives of the timber industry (Gutiérrez et al. *this volume*). The results of these analyses appear clear: populations of territorial adult female Northern Spotted Owls have been in decline for the past 8–10 years, and the rate of decline is accelerating (Burnham et al. *this volume*). Debate, however, has focused on at least three topics: (1) analysis and interpretation of results (reliability of the data, analytical techniques involved, potential biases, and, interpretation of the results); (2) the relationship between demography and habitat alteration; and (3) given the results of this research, the implications for land management.

Our objectives are to discuss the uses and limitations of demographic data for the management of spotted owl populations, provide additional interpretations of the spotted owl demographic data from a management perspective, and make recommendations for additional analyses and future monitoring efforts. We also will attempt to link inferences from demographic analyses to habitat management.

USES OF DEMOGRAPHIC DATA

Role of Demographic Data in Understanding Population Ecology

Studies of population ecology of terrestrial vertebrates show that demographic parameters of populations can be affected by an array of environmental variables, including weather; abundance, availability and quality of food and breeding sites; plant-herbivore and predator-prey interactions; rates of emigration and immigration; and habitat quality. These and other factors may act additively or synergistically on populations. In the case of the Northern Spotted Owl, extensive and intensive alteration of late-seral forests, perhaps in conjunction with other variables, has likely played a significant role in the demography of the species during the last century. Obtaining a better understanding of relationships between population growth or stability in relation to habitat conditions is one of the key goals in population research (Van Horne 1983, Vickery et al. 1992a,b, Conroy 1993).

Mark-recapture or mark-recovery techniques have been used to correlate survival with habitat types where birds were either marked or recaptured (Conroy 1993). Other studies attempted to correlate survival with food supply (Koenig and Mumme 1987, Estes 1990, Dinerstein and Price 1991, Marzluff and Balda 1992) or water (Heitmeyer and Fredrickson 1981, Cowardin et al. 1985, Raveling and Heitmeyer 1989). Relationships between survival and reproduction and the dispersion or availability of resources (e.g., wetlands) have also been examined (Rotella and Ratti 1992, Thompson and Fritzell 1989).

Among raptors, availability of nest sites and prey, and territoriality may act to regulate populations (Newton 1976). Newton (1986) documented a relationship among population levels, reproductive success, and habitat quality for the European Sparrowhawk (*Accipiter nisus*) during long-term studies in England. Higher quality habitats were occupied by nesting pairs in all or most years. As numbers of breeders rose, however, lower quality habitats were occupied, until ultimately the breeding population was limited. Raptors also show numerical and functional responses based on abundance of prey (Newton 1976, Adamcik et al. 1978). Red-tailed Hawks (*Buteo jamaicensis*), which tend to be prey generalists, however, showed functional (high nestling mortality), but not numerical responses to fluctuations in hare populations (Adamcik et al. 1979).

Although many studies have examined correlations between food supply and survival rates or reproductive rates of birds (e.g., Wilson et al. 1986, Koenig and Mumme 1987, Marzluff and Balda 1992, Taylor et al. 1992,) there are few examples where demographic parameters have been linked with habitat amount, distribution, or quality at the nest-site or landscape level. Methods have been proposed that utilize resighting data from radiotelemetry studies to assess relationships between survival rates and habitat (Conroy 1993). Although these methods are relatively new and untested in field studies, they appear to offer some promise for assessing relationships between habitat conditions and survival.

DETERMINATION OF RECOVERY AND DELISTING

Delisting of endangered or threatened species by the U.S. Fish and Wildlife Service has generally been based on numeric goals for population abundances rather than on changes in basic demographic rates. A recent example is the delisting of the gray whale (*Eschrichtius glaucus*), now relatively common along the Pacific Coast after being nearly eradicated by over-harvest in the late 1800's. However, demographic data could be used as a more reliable indicator of population trend and status. For example, the recovery plan for the desert tortoise (*Gopherus agassizi*) included a requirement that the population must exhibit a statistically significant upward trend or remain stationary for at least 25 years before delisting would be considered (USDI 1994). The draft recovery plan for the Northern Spotted Owl proposed the use of demographic data to assess recovery (USDI 1992a).

INTERPRETATION OF EXISTING NORTHERN SPOTTED OWL DATA

Burnham et al. (*this volume*) synthesized results from 11 large scale Spotted Owl demography studies in a meta-analysis and estimated an average rate of population decline of 4.5% per year (with a 95% confidence interval of 0.6% to 8.4%) after adjusting estimates of juvenile survival for permanent emigration. Based on this analysis, Burnham et al. (*this volume*) concluded that the finite rate of population change (λ) was probably <1.0 for the population of territorial females, based on the years of study (see Franklin et al. *this volume*). The most parsimonious statistical model in a meta-analysis of adult survival indicated adult female survival rates were declining over time (Burnham et al. *this volume*). Based on this finding, the rate of population decline was apparently accelerating during the period of study.

Although the meta-analysis conducted by Burnham et al. (*this volume*) indicated an overall decline in survival rates of adult females, estimated rates of adult survival varied among individual study areas. The best capture-recapture models identified in the individual study areas indicated declining linear trends in adult survival

in some areas, constant rates of adult survival in other areas, and non-linear trends in others. However, the individual studies were unable to achieve the same statistical power to detect underlying trends as the meta-analysis.

MODEL-BASED VERSUS SURVEY-BASED ESTIMATES OF POPULATION TREND

The conclusion by Burnham et al. (*this volume*) that the territorial owl population was declining has been controversial because (1) estimates of population trend from counts of owls (derived from annual surveys of the population of owls within density study areas) do not clearly demonstrate a population decline (Thomas et al. 1993a); and (2) estimates of λ may be biased low because of bias in survival rates (Bart 1995a; Forsman et al. *this volume*). However, other factors (see below) may result in positive biases in estimates of λ.

It is not surprising that survey-based estimates of trends in owl numbers deviate from estimates based on capture-recapture models of population growth rates for long-lived species experiencing rapid declines in habitat. The empirical estimate of population stability from counts of owls does not directly account for the number of additions (births) and losses (deaths) in a population. For example, by this measure of growth a population whose death rate far exceeded its birth rate could appear stable if it was maintained by recruits from the local population of nonbreeding owls (floaters), by outside immigration, or both (see Franklin 1992).

In contrast, estimates of λ from capture-recapture models are functions of survival rates and *in situ* recruitment (birth rates). These model-based estimates are particularly useful because they are capable of discriminating a subpopulation on a study area that appears stable due to recruitment from outside the study area from one that is inherently stable due to a balance between birth and death rates. For the Northern Spotted Owl, we are specifically interested in whether a local population is stable ($\lambda \geq 1.0$) in the absence of immigration/emigration dynamics.

Another factor contributing to the disparity between density and model-based estimates of population trend is the response of the territorial component of the owl population to habitat loss. During periods of rapid decline in amounts of late-successional forests, owls were presumably displaced from previously occupied habitats (Forsman et al. 1984, Forsman 1988). Many of these individuals did not die immediately, but became nonterritorial floaters or replaced territorial owls that in turn became floaters. Such circumstances could result in "packing" of adult owls into the remaining suitable habitat and this could lead to decreased reproductive and survival rates of territorial owls. Therefore, one might expect to infer declining populations ($\lambda <$ 1.0) from demographic studies under circumstances of density-induced declines in survival and reproduction.

LIMITATIONS AND POTENTIAL BIASES OF DEMOGRAPHIC DATA

Demographic analyses are subject to potential biases depending on the assumptions on which they are based and the reliability of parameter estimates. Interpretation of demographic results may also be limited to certain geographic segments of the population because the study areas may be small in comparison to the geographic range of a species or parts of the species' range may not be adequately represented. These considerations are important in the interpretation of the demographic characteristics of Northern Spotted Owl.

At least seven simulation models of spotted owl populations have been developed (see Lande 1988; Noon and Biles 1990; Lamberson et al. 1992, 1994; Carroll and Lamberson 1993; Bart 1995a), and one of these is a spatially explicit population model (McKelvey et al. 1992). These simulation models have suggested alternative scenarios for the dynamics of spotted owl populations. The models by Lande (1988) and Noon and Biles (1990) are most comparable to the demographic analyses here because they are deterministic models based on Lotka-Leslie methods. Bart (1995a) used a stochastic simulation model to evaluate the effects of errors in estimates of reproductive and survival rates on estimates of the annual rate of population change.

WHAT SEGMENT OF THE POPULATION DOES THE CAPTURE-RECAPTURE MODEL REPRESENT?

There is disagreement as to whether an inference about rate of population change applies to only the territorial population (Anderson and Burnham 1992; Franklin et al. *this volume*; Burnham et al. *this volume*) or the entire population (Bart 1995a) of Spotted Owls. Because data on reproductive rates and estimates of adult survival are collected from territorial owls, Anderson and Burnham (1992) and Burnham et al. (*this volume*) contend that the annual rate of population change refers to only the territorial segment of the population. In contrast, Bart (1995a) has suggested that the results pertain to the entire population because of the exchange of owls between the territorial and floater components. However, how floaters contribute to or regulate spotted owl population dynamics is unknown. Whereas floaters have been incidentally observed in spotted owl populations (Franklin 1992), certain conditions must be met for floaters to have a substantial regulatory capacity in population dynamics (see Klomp 1972, Patterson 1980, Sinclair 1989).

Although it is not entirely clear which segment of the population is represented by the demographic results, we believe the results in Burnham et al. (*this volume*) and the other papers in this volume primarily represent the dynamics of the territorial population when survival rates are adjusted for permanent emigration (see below). However, some of the data used in the Lotka-Leslie models to estimate λ were collected from juvenile owls who have been part of the nonbreeding segment of the population. For example, of 1,169 juvenile owls banded on four study areas (H.J. Andrews, Olympic Peninsula, Siuslaw National Forest, Southern Oregon), 145 (12%) were reobserved; 58 (40%) were resighted for the first time 1 year after banding; 54 (37%) 2 years after banding; 25 (17%) 3 years after banding; 6 (4%) 4 years after banding; and 2 (1%) 5 years after banding. Approximately 60% of the banded and resighted juveniles were not observed for 2 or more years after banding. Presumably these individuals were either part of the nonterritorial population for this period of time or they temporarily emigrated to another territorial population. Obviously, we know little about the fate of banded juveniles (only 12% have been reobserved) and when they do appear in the territorial population, they may show up 2–5 years after they are banded. These facts tend to make interpretations of λ less certain, but the key here is that only the territorial birds breed. The question is whether these birds are replacing themselves. If not, the population, as a whole, will decline in the long run.

PROJECTION OF POPULATION CHANGES

As indicated by Burnham et al. (*this volume*), the results from the demographic analyses apply only to the years during which data on reproductive rates and survival were collected. Forecasts of future population trends depend on assumptions (1) that the population would maintain a stable age distribution and (2) rates of survival and reproduction would remain the same as the period when these data were collected. Because these assumptions are not valid for Spotted Owl populations (Burnham et al. *this volume*), forecasting into the past or future more than several years beyond the period of data collection is risky. Even predictions 2–3 years into the future will be biased if rates of reproduction or survival change considerably, although such forecasts are obviously more defensible than long-term forecasts.

POTENTIAL BIASES

Lambda (λ) is estimated as a function of birth and death rates; therefore, the reliability of any estimated rate of population change reflects the bias and precision of these estimates. These potential biases include violation of any assumptions of the underlying Lotka-Leslie model, as well as biased estimation of reproductive rates, survival rates, the influence of senescence on survival and reproductive rates, the effects of emigration of juveniles and adults from study areas, and longevity of studies.

Assumptions of the Lotka-Leslie model

Violations of the assumptions of the Lotka-Leslie model may create biases in the estimate of λ (see Franklin et al. *this volume*), but the degree and direction of bias varies considerably among the different assumptions. Calculation of λ from an eigenanalysis of the projection matrix (see Caswell 1989) assumes a stable age (stage) distribution if inferences are extended to forecasting trends (see Franklin et al. *this volume*). This is not a problem if inferences are limited to projections because convergence to a stable distribution is asymptotically exponential (Caswell 1989:70). If the vital rates vary stochastically, or are time-dependent, then the assumption of a stable stage distribution is invalid. To date, all calculations of λ for spotted owls have been based on mean (i.e., constant) values of the vital rates (Burnham et al. *this volume*).

Falsely invoking the assumption that birth and death rates are constant over time in the analysis of owl demographic data would lead to an overestimate of λ. Adult female survival rate has shown a significant negative time trend (Burnham et al. *this volume*), thus this assumption is clearly violated. If the annual rate of population change varies with time, then growth of that population is described by the product of a sequence of projection matrices. In the special case of independent matrices (i.e., independent environments), population growth rate is equivalent to the dominant eigenvalue (λ) of the projection matrix based on mean values for the vital rates (Tuljapurkar 1982). However, under time-dependent or stochastic conditions, the average growth rate of the population may be a misleading indicator of population stability. This occurs because the distribution of population sizes from time-varying projection matrices is approximately lognormal (Tuljapurkar and Orzack 1980). A property of lognormal distributions is that the modal population size will always be smaller than that based on the mean values of the vital rates (Gerrodette et al. 1985). Thus, the actual growth rate of any single population with time-varying rates is always $\leq$ the growth rate estimated from

mean values of the projection matrices (Cohen et al. 1983). However, the magnitude of the positive bias arising from annual variation in survival or reproductive rates appears to be small (Noon and Biles 1990).

Duration of studies

Shorter study duration may underestimate survival. For example, survival rates of juvenile owls (Burnham et al. *this volume*) were higher for the 6 long-term ($\bar{x} = 0.334$, SE $= 0.027$) versus 5 short-term ($\bar{x} = 0.208$, SE $= 0.047$) study areas (t $= 3.26$, P $= 0.011$). Estimates of adult survival rates did not differ between long-term and short-term studies (USDA and USDI 1994a, Burnham et al. *this volume*). These differences in the estimates of juvenile survival for long-term versus short-term studies resulted in higher mean values of λ for the six long term ($\bar{x} = 0.952$, SE $= 0.040$) versus five short term ($\bar{x} = 0.894$, SE $= 0.041$) study areas (t $= 2.36$, P $= 0.043$). We offer three possible explanations for these differences in survival rates for long-term versus short-term studies: (1) survival rates may have actually decreased during the later years; (2) longer study duration provided better estimates of survival, particularly for juveniles; or (3) survival rates differed between the geographic areas represented by the sets of long-term and short-term study areas. Both point estimates of juvenile survival rates and their standard errors may be particularly sensitive to duration of studies because it takes a number of years for juveniles to appear in the territorial population. Because banded adults are most often territorial and have high resighting probabilities, their survival estimates are much less sensitive to study duration (USDA and USDI 1994a, Burnham et al. *this volume*).

Senescence

A decrease in survival and/or reproductive rates in older owls will overestimate survival and reproductive rates and result in an inflated estimate of λ. The particular form of the age-specific survival and reproductive rates used in the demographic analyses assumed that senescence was not occurring. Anderson et al. (1990), Noon and Biles (1990), and Bart (1995a) simulated the effects of senescence on the estimates of λ. Bart (1995a) found that moderate senescence may cause an overestimate in λ by as much as 0.02. Noon and Biles (1990) found the effects of senescence to be most pronounced when adult survival rates were high, juvenile survival rates were low, and values of λ were >0.7. The effects of senescence at ages <21 years of age were dramatic, so failure to account for senescence could result in significant overestimates of λ. The extent to which senescence occurs in owl populations is unknown, so the magnitude of the potential bias is unknown at present.

Estimation of reproductive rates

The estimation of reproductive rates may be biased in several ways. First, death of some young owls may occur prior to detection, leading to an underestimate of fecundity (but an overestimate of survival rates of juveniles). Second, most of the demographic studies did not include pairs of owls in fecundity estimates unless the age of the female was known. The majority of pairs in which age of females was unknown were pairs that appeared to produce no young and that could not be located enough times to confirm the age and identity of the female. Exclusion of these females from the estimates of fecundity may have caused a positive bias in estimates of fecundity (Reid et al. *this volume*). Third, Bart and Robson (1992: 9) showed that λ may be overestimated by as much as 0.027, assuming nonterritorial female owls comprise up to about 30% of the population but are not observed. However, we believe the inferences from λ apply primarily to the territorial female component of owl populations (Franklin et al. *this volume*) so the influence of this potential bias is probably not great.

Permanent emigration and estimates of survival

Another potential bias is permanent emigration of juveniles or adults which would result in underestimates of juvenile survival rates. The Cormack-Jolly-Seber estimates (Pollock et al. 1990) of survival cannot discriminate between undetected emigrants and individuals that have died (see Franklin et al. *this volume*). To the extent that banded owls emigrate, survive at least one year, and are never observed again, Cormack-Jolly-Seber models will underestimate survival rates on local study areas. As a result, estimates of λ will be biased low.

Based on the results of radio-telemetry studies, undetected emigration of banded juvenile owls, followed by their subsequent survival, occurs frequently (Forsman personal communication). The bias in survival estimates of juveniles caused by such movements is probably greater for study areas that are relatively isolated (e.g., H.J. Andrews in the Oregon Cascades) versus study areas that are surrounded by other study areas. In larger or more contiguous study areas (e.g., Oregon Coast Range), emigrating owls are more readily detected. Burnham et al. (*this volume*) recognized the potential bias in estimates of juvenile survival and computed the necessary rates of juvenile survival to result in λ = 1.0, given the estimates of other vital rates. They found that juvenile survival and emigration must be in the range of 0.57 and 0.51, respectively, for owl pop-

ulations to be stationary. Both of these rates are substantially greater than the actual rates estimated on most of the study areas, but a juvenile emigration rate of 0.60 was reported from the Olympic study area (Forsman et al. *this volume*). Although the estimates of emigration rates were based on small samples from only two years of data, they do suggest that, in some years and on some areas, rates of emigration were relatively high. It is clear, however, that rates of emigration estimated from one year of telemetry data will not be adequate for long-term estimates of permanent emigration. It is likely, for example, that some proportion of juveniles that emigrate during their first year of life will continue to move around (i.e., disperse [Miller 1989]) and will eventually be detected when they acquire territories. In these cases, emigration will be temporary, and the negative bias on estimated juvenile survival will be reduced when they reappear as territorial adults.

Permanent emigration by adult owls appears to be infrequent. However, even occasional permanent emigration by adults is an important consideration because model estimates of λ are especially sensitive to changes in survival rates of adults (Lande 1988, Noon and Biles 1990). Therefore, a relatively small, negative bias in estimates of adult survival due to emigration could cause underestimates of λ. Telemetry studies of adult owls have indicated some emigration, and this may have an influence on estimates of adult survival on study areas that are isolated from other study areas (Thrailkill et al. *this volume*, Wagner et al. *this volume*).

Net effect of the potential biases on estimates of λ

Bart (1995a) evaluated the potential biases on λ from permanent emigration and senescence with a stochastic simulation model. Bart suggested that the results of the spotted owl demographic analyses may have underestimated λ by 0.03 to 0.13. We believe his results should be viewed cautiously because some of his assumptions do not reflect the field situation. For example, his simulations estimated the extreme bias in λ only when it was assumed that neither senescence nor overestimation of fecundity rates were occurring. Including these factors would increase the estimate of λ, which would counter the negative biases of permanent emigration. Also, the most important source of bias in estimates of λ in Bart's simulations was the proportion of sites monitored, which affected the estimation of emigration rates. For example, he assumed that the proportion of territories that were monitored in each study area was 0.2 or 0.4 in the first year of marking and increased linearly to 0.8 in the fifth year. He also assumed that any bird that left the study area had a recapture probability of 0. His assumed proportion of sites monitored is lower than actual proportions in most demographic study areas, and there is no support for the assumption that the proportion monitored increases linearly with time or that recapture probability is 0 when birds leave the area. In fact, in the present demographic studies, many emigrants are recaptured after they leave study areas. Collectively, we believe these assumptions may have led to an extreme estimate of the negative bias in λ.

As discussed previously, estimates of λ are probably most affected by the negative bias in the estimate of juvenile survival. However, Burnham et al. (*this volume*) adjusted their estimate of juvenile survival to account for emigration followed by survival. Permanent emigration of adult owls is rare. Therefore, we believe the most current estimates of λ for spotted owls (Burnham et al. *this volume*) have largely addressed Bart's (1995a) concern.

From the above it should be obvious that there are both positive and negative biases that may effect estimates of λ, but the relative magnitude of these biases are currently unknown. This is likely to be a lively topic of research and debate in the future.

APPLICABILITY TO THE RANGE-WIDE POPULATION

The Spotted Owl demographic studies reported in this volume were initiated by different researchers and agencies with little coordinated effort to ensure equal representation of the different ecological provinces within the range of the owl. For example, there are two study areas in the western Cascades of Oregon, whereas there are no demographic studies in the western Washington Cascades, eastern Oregon Cascades, western Washington lowlands, or the California Cascades. In contrast, there are seven demographic study areas in the Coast Range and Klamath Provinces of western Oregon and northern California. The eastern Washington Cascades is well represented by two demographic studies. Until studies and data are available from other areas, it is unknown if the existing data adequately represent the dynamics of the entire population. However, the current studies encompass a large portion of the Northern Spotted Owl's geographic range in the United States (Franklin et al. *this volume*).

INFERENCES FROM A HETEROGENEOUS POPULATION

An additional problem that may complicate interpretation of the demographic data is the extent to which inferences from estimates of λ apply to heterogeneous subpopulations consisting of a mixture of source and sink territories. We believe this is an important issue. Virtually all extensive studies of lifetime reproductive success among birds, for example, have shown that relatively few individuals in a population produce most of the offspring (see Newton 1979), and this has been observed among Spotted Owls as well (Verner et al. 1992b:74). Spotted Owl subpopulations in the study areas also may be heterogeneous because the amount and distribution of suitable habitat remaining and the degree of habitat fragmentation varies considerably over the owl's range. The overall estimate of λ for a heterogeneous subpopulation is a weighted average with the weights determined by the relative numbers of the source and sink territories in the sample. Various combinations of source and sink proportions could yield a weighted estimate of $\lambda < 1.0$ even though a portion of the subpopulation may be stable or increasing.

If one could partition a population into its source and sink components, it is obvious that the long-term dynamics (assuming constant vital rates) in a deterministic analysis is determined by the persistence of the source component of the population. The problem of drawing the correct biological inference (population is declining, stable, or increasing), however, is not this easily addressed. For example, consider the case where the source component of the population is small and the vital rates are time-dependent. Estimates of λ based on mean values of the vital rates could have a substantial positive bias (Cohen et al. 1983), and the researcher could incorrectly infer a stable or growing population.

Given the above, valid insights into the persistence likelihood of a heterogeneous population must come from analyzing other relevant factors—for example, the smallest source population size or number of source territories needed for local stability. As described by Lamberson et al. (1994), the threshold number of territories may be determined by considering the limits of demographic and environmental stochasticity and the spatial distribution of breeding pairs. At a larger geographic scale, overall persistence of a population may be determined by the number and spatial distribution of locally stable source populations. The latter constraint is imposed by rare, catastrophic events that require many local populations, widely dispersed, so that adverse effects are not experienced simultaneously by all local populations.

IS THE CURRENT LEVEL OF HABITAT FRAGMENTATION BEYOND THE EXTINCTION THRESHOLD?

Based on their interpretation of the Burnham et al. (1994b) report, some prominent scientists and conservation groups have suggested that the

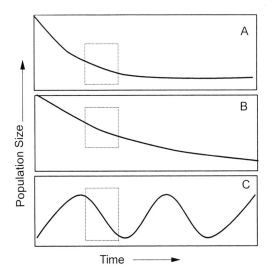

FIGURE 1. Graphic representation of three hypothetical scenarios for Northern Spotted Owl populations. Dashed boxes represent plausible periods when declining populations were detected by current studies. Explanation of scenarios is in text.

declining adult survival rate may indicate a population that has passed a persistence threshold and is declining toward extinction. Consistent with this interpretation would be the observation that populations are declining more rapidly than the rate of habitat loss (Lande 1987, Lamberson et al. 1992). Accelerating rates of population decline might also suggest that a threshold had been passed.

The assumption that the Spotted Owl will reach an eventual positive, stable equilibrium in the context of a continuing overall decline in carrying capacity requires the demographic rates of the territorial owls in the remaining habitat be relatively unaffected by habitat losses occurring elsewhere. Under this scenario, the population is in decline largely because juveniles cannot find territorial vacancies and the rate of juvenile survival is depressed. As the amount and distribution of habitat stops declining or increases, juvenile survival rate will increase and the population will approach an equilibrium. Simulation studies (Raphael et al. 1994) support this scenario. Under these conditions, however, the decline in population cannot exceed the rate of habitat loss and will generally lag behind it (Lamberson et al. 1992).

The evidence provided by papers in this volume support the hypothesis that Northern Spotted Owl populations are declining across a large proportion of their range and that adult survival is also declining. Since these declines have been

documented only over the last 5–10 years, which is less than the average generation length of spotted owls, forecasting the future is difficult. A number of scenarios can be suggested concerning the future fate of Spotted Owl populations:

1. Northern Spotted Owl populations will decline but reach an equilibrium at some lower population level (Fig. 1A). If habitat across the range of the Spotted Owl stabilizes at some equilibrium amount and configuration, Spotted Owl populations will eventually reach an equilibrium and remain stable at a lower population size. This hypothesis assumes (1) survival rates are density dependent and will show a compensatory increase as population densities decline, and/or (2) survival and reproductive rates increase as the amount and quality of habitat within home ranges in reserved areas increases.

2. Northern Spotted Owl populations will continue to decline to extinction (Fig. 1B). There are at least 3 ways this could arise: (1) current habitat loss and fragmentation is so severe that Spotted Owl populations have passed a persistence threshold arising from difficulties in finding suitable territories and mates (Lande 1988); (2) habitat quality has been so depressed that birth and survival rates will not support a stable population; or (3) populations are so small as to be inescapably vulnerable to stochastic extinction events. For all these scenarios, the overall owl population will continue to decline to extinction at some unknown rate and over some unknown period of time.

3. Observed declines in Northern Spotted Owl populations are part of a natural, long-term fluctuation in numbers (Fig. 1C). Observed declines are a result of natural fluctuations in numbers that are unrelated to the amount and distribution of suitable habitat, and the present studies have merely estimated population trends during a transient period of natural decline. We do not view this as a plausible scenario.

The management plans proposed by Thomas et al. (1990), USDI (1992b), and USDA and USDI (1994a) all assumed that scenario 2 had not occurred and that scenario 1 was a likely outcome once a condition of no-net-loss of habitat was reached. Researchers have attempted to discriminate among these scenarios with sophisticated computer projections (Lamberson et al. 1992, 1994; McKelvey et al. 1992; Raphael et al. 1994; Holthausen et al., 1995). However, these models are characterized by simplifying assumptions, uncertainty in parameter estimates, and unknown aspects of spotted owl behavior. Therefore, continued monitoring of spotted owl population trends with demographic analyses and monitoring of changes in amount and distribution of habitat is a prudent approach to discriminate among these possible outcomes.

RECOMMENDATIONS FOR ADDITIONAL ANALYSES

MODIFYING DEMOGRAPHIC STUDY AREAS

Design criteria

Given the legal and social significance of the status and trend of Spotted Owl populations and the high cost of obtaining demographic information, agencies should strive to acquire reliable, range-wide information on the status of owl populations. With limited funding, it is important to determine the most efficient study design that will meet this objective. We are aware of 17 different studies, including the 11 described in this volume. Because of the biases and other limitations cited above, we believe the current design of the program of demographic studies can and should be improved.

Several factors should be considered. First, if inferences are to apply to the entire geographic range of the Northern Spotted Owl, the demographic study areas must be more representative of range-wide conditions. As discussed above, some physiographic provinces are omitted and others are well represented by current study areas. Other important environmental criteria for study area selection and design should include habitat quality (for example, representation of all relevant elevation zones, forest composition, and structural features), large-scale land ownership patterns, and land allocations (proportions of wilderness, national parks, and other large areas withdrawn from timber cutting, as well as lands available for timber cutting).

Second, each study area should be large enough to reduce the biases in estimates of juvenile and adult survival due to undetected emigration (Franklin et al. 1990). Not only size, but shape of study area should be reexamined. Some of the areas are long and narrow (e.g., Siskiyou), some include a collection of small, scattered sites (e.g., northwestern California), and some are surrounded by other study areas; these irregular shapes likely exacerbate emigration biases (see Franklin et al. *this volume*). Ideally, study areas should be shaped to minimize the ratio of edge to area.

In addition, many of the current study areas are not surveyed with equal effort over their entire extent. As a result, banded birds, especially juveniles, may emigrate to unsurveyed sites within the study area where they may survive but not be reobserved. If study areas were consolidated to reduce such effects, more reliable inferences might be obtained.

Finally, we recommend use of radio-telemetry to estimate rates of emigration and survival of juvenile and adult owls on a larger sample of study areas. Although labor-intensive and expensive, such studies appear to be the only feasible way to evaluate the effects of emigration on estimates of survival from capture-recapture studies.

Selection criteria

Several additional considerations are relevant in deciding whether to drop or add demographic study areas. First, certain study areas may be critical to understanding dynamics of isolated or unique owl populations, such as on the Olympic Peninsula. Second, some study areas offer opportunities for integration with other ongoing efforts, such as Adaptive Management Areas (Thomas et al. 1993b) where demographic response of owls to silvicultural techniques might be tested using carefully designed experiments. Study duration also should be considered, with retention of longer-term studies a high priority. We recommend development of a screening process to evaluate each current study area against the above criteria to assess the value of the information they provide. Such screening should be undertaken by knowledgeable but objective scientists.

ROLE OF DEMOGRAPHIC STUDIES IN MONITORING

At present, the ongoing demographic studies are the basis of the regional monitoring strategy for the Northern Spotted Owl. It is unlikely that a single measure of population status will be accepted by all parties so estimates of parallel changes in related factors will raise confidence in estimated population trends. Other components of a regional monitoring strategy could include monitoring trend in amount and pattern (size, shape, and arrangement) of habitat over time, monitoring density of territorial owls, and conducting periodic large-scale surveys or counts to estimate changes in abundance (USDI 1992b). Each of these is discussed below.

Habitat trend

Loss of habitat due to logging and other disturbance is usually cited as the fundamental cause of declining populations of the Northern Spotted Owl (Anderson et al. 1990, Thomas et al. 1990, Murphy and Noon 1992). We believe that any plan must monitor trends in the amount and distribution of suitable habitat. Ideally, these habitat data will cover all ownerships, perhaps using remotely sensed information. Given these data, relationships between status and trend of owl populations can be tested against trends in habitat attributes. Evidence that net loss of habitat is no longer occurring will be critical in delisting the owl as a threatened species.

Local density studies

Estimates of population trend based on complete surveys of selected study areas may be an important element of a monitoring strategy. Such surveys on density study areas are an ongoing component of many of the studies reported in this volume (see Franklin et al. *this volume*). Direct estimates of density, in conjunction with model-based results of demographic analyses, may strengthen a monitoring program.

Regional surveys or density estimates

The Northern Spotted Owl recovery team recommended a large-scale survey to estimate population size and trend (USDI 1992b). Various designs of such a survey have been suggested, including call counts at a sample of several thousand stations with single visits (USDI 1992b) and randomly selected quadrats with multiple visits (Noon et al. 1993; Holthausen et al. 1995, Seaman et al., unpublished data). The former design might yield a yearly estimate of relative abundance, whereas the latter might yield a yearly density estimate. The latter technique has the advantage that multiple visits can be used to estimate sighting probability, but is more costly than the former method. Both approaches suffer from bias associated with use of calls to elicit responses from owls. If biases can be understood or sufficiently reduced, it may be possible to directly estimate the annual rate of population change from the ratio of populations from one year to the next where estimates of population sizes are estimated from density studies and regional surveys, using open- or closed-population mark-recapture estimators (Noon et al. 1993).

The major advantage of a regional survey is that it provides a robust means to validate inferences from the demographic studies. With an adequate design, regional surveys can yield broad statistical inferences, and can directly estimate population trend and provide information on the geographic distribution of owls. The demographic studies would continue to provide independent estimates of trends and provide essential information on the processes responsible for these trends.

LINKING DEMOGRAPHIC ANALYSES TO HABITAT

Importance of habitat relationships

Limitations on the extrapolation of demographic data into the future have both research and management implications. Controversy over Northern Spotted Owls focuses on the future status of the owl population, and management ef-

forts focus on the future status of owl populations under different habitat management scenarios. Thus, while demographic information may be useful in determining the past and current status of populations, it has not been very helpful in resolving questions about the future effects of current management decisions.

To improve the formulation of testable hypotheses, management is increasingly turning to simulation models (Raphael et al. 1994, Holthausen et al. 1995). The simulation models that are most germane to management questions are those that link population attributes (density, birth and death rates) to habitat conditions, and thus base future population performance on projected future habitat conditions (e.g., McKelvey et al. 1992). An improved understanding of the relationship between habitat and population performance is essential to the use of simulation models in the formulation of hypotheses and the refinement of habitat management plans. Unless we can test responses of demographic parameters to habitat condition, management plans are no better than our hypotheses.

Simulation models are useful for testing assumptions or assessing relative risk to populations under alternative scenarios. However, limitations of these models must be clearly understood. As discussed by Holthausen et al. (1995), simulation results are entirely dependent on the structure of the model, its underlying assumptions, and the input data supplied to them. These models are inevitably a simplification of reality and do not take into account the myriad interactions that influence real populations.

EXISTING INFORMATION

To date, demographic studies have yielded only limited information on relationships between variation in the vital rates and habitat. Such relationships are currently being studied at a number of scales including the nest site, the home range, and larger areas encompassing entire local populations. At the scale of individual territories, occupancy, fecundity, and persistence of owls on territories have been significantly correlated with amounts of suitable habitat in the territories (Thomas et al. 1990, Lehmkuhl and Raphael 1993, Bart 1995b). At a larger scale, fecundity of breeding pairs and survival of adults have been correlated with percent habitat in variously-sized areas that included individual or multiple nest sites of pairs (Bart and Forsman 1992, Bart 1995b). Finally, at the scale of entire demographic study areas, Raphael et al. (unpublished data) found no correlations between average habitat conditions on study areas and rates of fecundity and survival estimated for those study areas. The lack of association at this scale may result from selective use of higher-quality sites. Spotted Owls have been shown to select home ranges where superior habitat conditions are located so that habitat within home ranges is of higher quality than the average conditions on the larger landscape (Ripple et al. 1991, Lehmkuhl and Raphael 1993). Alternatively, the lack of correlation between vital rates and habitat may indicate that the amount and distribution of habitat is not limiting population processes and vital rates.

Results of these studies, and a consideration of the ways that owls use habitat, suggest the following scale-dependent relationships between habitat and demography: (1) studies at scales smaller than individual home ranges may provide some insight about patterns of occupancy, but cannot reveal relationships of habitat conditions to actual population performance; (2) studies at the scale of individual home ranges are most likely to reveal relationships of population performance to habitat if such relationships exist; and (3) studies completed at landscape scales may mask relationships of population performance to habitat unless habitat conditions and prey abundance are homogeneously distributed within study areas.

We conclude that the relationships between habitat and demographics may be most significant at the scale of individual home ranges. This is the scale at which such relationships have been modeled in recent computer simulations reported by McKelvey et al. (1992) and Raphael et al. (1994).

Analytical technique

The parameters of most interest in an analysis of habitat effects on population performance are fecundity, juvenile survival, and adult survival. Persistence of birds on home ranges is of less interest, but may be used to provide insight into survival if capture history information is not available. To associate these parameters with habitat at the scale of individual home ranges, it is necessary to determine the area within which habitat should be measured. Ideally, radio telemetry would be used to determine the actual boundaries of pair home ranges, and habitat would then be measured within those boundaries. In practice, using radio telemetry for a large number of owls is impractical, too expensive, and potentially disruptive to the owls. Therefore, circles chosen to represent mean home range sizes of territorial pairs in the geographic area being studied should be drawn around nest sites and used as surrogates for true home ranges. Circles are clearly crude approximations for actual home ranges, but when sample sizes of homes ranges

are large, the circles provide a reasonable approximation of conditions within home ranges (Lehmkuhl and Raphael 1993).

Fecundity and persistence on home ranges

The relationships between demography and habitat variation at the scale of a home range can most readily be estimated for fecundity and persistence on territories (e.g., Bart 1995b). The habitat parameter used by Bart was the percent suitable habitat within single or multiple home range-sized areas. Where areas were large enough to include more than one home range, they were chosen based on homogeneity of habitat conditions. Habitat was used either as a continuous variable, allowing correlation (Bart 1995b), or as a categorical variable, allowing investigation for significant differences among categories (Bart and Forsman 1992). Utility of the results for simulation modeling is probably enhanced by treating habitat as a continuous variable.

Survival

Determining the relationship between habitat and survival is the most difficult. Survival values estimated in the demographic studies are the result of the capture-recapture histories of hundreds of owls (Franklin et al. *this volume*). Raphael et al. (unpublished data) attempted to relate habitat to survival on entire demographic study areas, but found little correlation. The lack of pattern may have been a consequence of scale— the areas actually used by individual owls are much smaller and may be different from the overall conditions of the study areas—or lack of variation in survival among areas. At smaller scales, habitat variables can be attached to individual or groups of capture histories using a number of modeling approaches (Lebreton et al. 1992, Conroy 1993, Skalski et al. 1993). The demographic studies reported in this volume provide large sample sizes and may allow detection of even moderate differences in habitat configuration provided such variation is present within study areas. A meta-analysis incorporating study areas would be the strongest approach.

EPILOGUE

To develop a comprehensive management plan for the Northern Spotted Owl and other species associated with older forests, the Clinton administration convened an interagency team of scientists, managers, and technicians in 1993 and instructed them to develop a series of options for management of federal lands within the range of the Northern Spotted Owl. Collectively referred to as the Forest Ecosystem Management Assessment Team (FEMAT), this team proposed

10 different options, ranging from a plan that would have followed the forest plans in effect at that time, to a plan that would have allowed no future harvest of mature or old-growth forests on federal lands (Thomas et al. 1993b). After reviewing the options, the President instructed the federal agencies to adopt an intermediate option (Alternative 9) that would protect large areas of mature and old-growth forest, but that would also allow some harvest of older forests.

The President's proposed plan was almost immediately challenged in federal court by industry and environmental groups who argued, respectively, that the plan was illegal and that it was not adequate to protect the spotted owl and other wildlife. The interpretation of the demographic data described in this series of papers played a central role in this litigation. The government was convinced that the available demographic data indicated a declining owl population and that this decline called for conservation of much of the owl's remaining habitat.

We have discussed at length the potential biases associated with parameter estimation using mark-recapture methods, and limits to inference from the analysis of the parameterized projection matrices. Despite remaining uncertainty, these methods are the best currently available and provide the most reliable insights into the population dynamics of wild animal populations. The methods do not provide exact rates of population change. We believe, however, that the estimated direction of change for the Spotted Owl, decline, is reliable; the magnitude of this decline remains in question. Further, a probable mechanism causing the population decline can be described: extensive loss and fragmentation of an estimated 80% of late-seral stage forest within the last 40 years (Bolsinger and Waddall 1993). Therefore, conservation efforts (Thomas et al. 1990) and changes in land management (Thomas et al. 1993b) are clearly justified by the results of the Spotted Owl demographic studies.

Finally, we believe it is critical to continue to monitor the owl population over time to document the response of the population to future changes in the amount and distribution of suitable habitat. In this context, we believe the demographic studies will continue to provide a foundation for our understanding of the status and trend of the Northern Spotted Owl.

SUMMARY

Ongoing demographic studies have played a leading role in estimating the status and trend of populations of the Northern Spotted Owl. Interpreting results of these studies is controversial because of debate about the reliability of the data and the analytical techniques used. In this paper we discuss the uses of demographic data, outline some of the potential biases in estimates of demographic parameters, and suggest ways to reduce biases. Major sources of bias include permanent emigration of juveniles (marked birds that leave the area, survive at least a year, and remain undetected), senescence, estimates of reproductive rates, and study duration. Biases can be either positive or negative. Although we know the direction of bias associated with each source, the net effect of these biases on the estimated rate of population change, λ, remains difficult to assess, and further work is needed to better understand their cumulative effect. We recommend modifications to the current study designs to reduce biases and to ensure a better representation of range-wide habitat conditions. We believe the ongoing demographic studies are a key to understanding the relationship of the owls to variation in habitat and to change in amount and distribution of habitat, and that these studies are a major component of a long-term monitoring strategy. A priority for future research is to establish relationships between fitness and habitat conditions measured at different scales, and to synthesize these results across the individual home ranges.

ACKNOWLEDGMENTS

We thank M. J. Conroy, R. J. Gutiérrez, D. R. Anderson, G. C. White, K. P Burnham, and two anonymous reviewers for comments on earlier drafts. We also thank J. L. Jones, M. Coday, and B. M. Galleher for help preparing the manuscript.

Key words: demography, emigration, habitat, management, mark-recapture estimators, Northern Spotted Owl, *Strix occidentalis caurina,* survival estimators.

LITERATURE CITED

ADAMCIK, R. S., A. W. TODD, AND L. B. KEITH. 1978. Demographic and dietary responses of Great Horned Owls during a snowshoe hare fluctuation. Can. Field-Nat. 92:156–166.

ADAMCIK, R. S., A. W. TODD, AND L. B. KEITH. 1979. Demographic and dietary responses of Red-tailed Hawks during a snowshoe hare fluctuation. Can. Field-Nat. 93:16–27.

AGEE, J. K. 1993. Fire ecology of the Pacific Northwest forests. Island Press, Washington, DC.

AKAIKE, H. 1973. Information theory and an extension of the maximum likelihood principle. Pp. 267–281 in B. N. Petran and F. Csaki (eds.), International symposium on information theory. Second edition. Akademiai Kiadi, Budapest, Hungary.

ALVAREZ-BUYLLA, E. R., AND M. SLATKIN. 1994. Finding confidence limits on population growth rates: three real examples revised. Ecology. 75:255–260.

ANDERSON, D. R., J. BART, T. C. EDWARDS, JR., C. B. KEPLER, AND E. C. MESLOW. 1990. 1990 Status review: Northern Spotted Owl (Strix occidentalis caurina). USDI Fish and Wildl. Serv., Portland, OR.

ANDERSON, D. R., AND K. P. BURNHAM. 1992. Demographic analysis of Northern Spotted Owl populations. Pp. 319–328 in Draft recovery plan for the Northern Spotted Owl. USDI Fish and Wildl. Serv., Portland, OR.

ANDERSON, D. R., K. P. BURNHAM, AND C. G. WHITE. 1985. Problems in estimating age-specific survival rates from recovery data of birds ringed as young. J. Anim. Ecol. 54:89–98.

ANDERSON, D. R., K. P. BURNHAM, AND C. G. WHITE. 1994. AIC model selection in overdispersed capture-recapture data. Ecology 75:1780–1793.

ANONYMOUS. 1982. Average annual precipitation, 1960–1980, in southwest Oregon. Oregon State Univ. Extension Serv., Oregon State Univ., Corvallis OR.

ATZET, T., AND L. A. McCRIMMEN. 1990. Preliminary plant associations of the southern Oregon Cascades Province. USDA For. Serv., Siskiyou National Forest, Grants Pass, OR.

ATZET, T., AND D. L. WHEELER. 1984. Preliminary plant associations of the Siskiyou Mountain Province. USDA For. Serv., Siskiyou National Forest, Grants Pass, OR.

BALDWIN, J. L. 1973. Climates of the United States. U.S. Dep. Commerce, Washington, DC.

BARROWCLOUGH, G. F., AND R. J. GUTIÉRREZ. 1990. Genetic variation and differentiation in the Spotted Owl (Strix occidentalis). Auk 107:737–744.

BARROWS, C. W. 1980. Summer roost selection by Spotted Owls: an adaptation to heat stress. M.S. thesis. California State Univ., Long Beach, CA.

BARROWS, C. W. 1981. Roost selection by Spotted Owls: an adaptation to heat stress. Condor 83:302–309.

BARROWS, C. W. 1985. Breeding success relative to fluctuations in diet for spotted owls in California. Pp. 50–54 in R. J. Gutiérrez and A. B. Carey (eds.), Ecology and management of the spotted owl in the Pacific Northwest. USDA For. Serv. Gen. Tech. Rep. PNW-185. Portland, OR.

BARROWS, C. W. 1987. Diet shifts in breeding and nonbreeding Spotted Owls. J. Raptor Res. 21:95–97.

BARROWS, C., AND K. BARROWS. 1978. Roost characteristics and behavioral thermoregulation in the Spotted Owl. West. Birds 9:1–8.

BART, J. 1995a. Evaluation of population trend estimates calculated using capture-recapture and population projection methods. Ecol. Appl. 5:662–671.

BART, J. 1995b. Amount of suitable habitat and viability of Northern Spotted Owls. Conserv. Biol. 9:943–946.

BART, J., AND S. EARNST. 1992. Suitable habitat for Northern Spotted Owls: an update. Pp. 281–317 in Draft recovery plan for the Northern Spotted Owl, USDI, Fish and Wildl. Serv., Portland, OR.

BART, J., AND E. D. FORSMAN. 1992. Dependence of Northern Spotted Owls Strix occidentalis caurina on old-growth forests in the western USA. Conserv. Biol. 62:95–100.

BART, J., AND D. S. ROBSON. 1992. Methods and recommendations for population monitoring. Pp. 1–16 (Appendix A) in Draft recovery plan for the Northern Spotted Owl, Vol. 2. U.S. Dep. Interior, Washington, DC.

BENT, A. C. 1938. Life histories on North American birds of prey. Part 2. U.S. Natl. Mus. Bull. No. 170. Washington, DC.

BLAKESLEY, J. A., A. B. FRANKLIN, AND R. J. GUTIÉRREZ. 1992. Spotted Owl roost and nest site selection in northwestern California. J. Wildl. Manage. 56:388–392.

BLONDEL, J., A. GOSLER, J. D. LEBRETON, AND R. H. McCLEERY (EDS.). 1990. Population biology of passerine birds: an integrated approach. Springer-Verlag, Berlin.

BOLSINGER, C. L., AND K. L. WADELL. 1993. Area of old-growth forests in California, Oregon and Washington. USDA For. Serv. Res. Bull. PNW-RB-197.

BOTSFORD, L. W., T. C. WAINWRIGHT, J. T. SMITH, S. MASTRUP, AND D. F. LOTT. 1988. Population dynamics of California quail related to meteorological conditions. J. Wildl. Manage. 52:469–477.

BOYCE, M. S. 1987. A review of the U.S. Forest Service's viability analysis for the Spotted Owl. National Council of the Paper Industry for Air and Stream Improvement, Inc., Corvallis, OR.

BOYCE, M. S., J. S. MEYER, AND L. IRWIN. 1994. Habitat-based PVA for the Northern Spotted Owl. Pp. in N. Ferguson and B. F. J. Manly (eds.), Proc. conference on statistics in ecology and environmental monitoring. Univ. Otago, Dunedin, New Zealand.

BROWNIE, C., D. R. ANDERSON, K. P. BURNHAM, AND D. S. ROBSON. 1985. Statistical inference from band recovery data: a handbook. USDI Fish and Wildl. Serv., Resour. Publ. 156.

BROWNIE, C., AND J. D. NICHOLS. 1983. Estimation of time-specific survival rate from tag-resighting samples: a generalization of the Jolly-Seber Model. Biometrics 39:437–45.

BUCHANAN, J. B. 1991. Spotted Owl nest site characteristics in mixed conifer forests of the eastern Cascade Mountains, Washington. M.S. thesis. Univ. Washington, Seattle.

BUCHANAN, J. B., L. L. IRWIN, AND E. L. McCUTCHEN.

1993. Characteristics of Spotted Owl nest trees in the Wenatchee National Forest. J. Rapt. Res. 27: 1–7.

BUCHANAN, J. B., L. L. IRWIN, AND E. L. MCCUTCHEN. 1995. Within-stand nest site selection by Spotted Owls in the eastern Washington Cascades. J. Wildl. Manage. 59:301–310.

BURNHAM, K. P., AND D. R. ANDERSON. 1992. Data-based selection of an appropriate biological model: the key to modern data analysis. Pp. 16–30 in D. R. McCullough and R. H. Barrett (eds.), Wildlife 2001: populations. Elsevier Applied Science, London.

BURNHAM, K. P., D. R. ANDERSON, AND G. C. WHITE. 1994a. Evaluation of the Kullback-Leibler discrepancy for model selection in open population capture-recapture models. Biometrical J. 36:299–315.

BURNHAM, K. P., D. R. ANDERSON, AND G. C. WHITE. 1994b. Estimation of vital rates of the Northern Spotted Owl. Pp. 1–44 (Appendix J) in Final supplemental environmental impact statement, on management of habitat for late-successional and old-growth forest related species within the range of the Northern Spotted Owl. Vol. 2. USDA For. Serv., Portland, OR.

BURNHAM, K. P., D. R. ANDERSON, AND G. C. WHITE. 1995a. Model selection strategy in the analysis of capture-recapture data. Biometrics 51:888–898.

BURNHAM, K. P., D. R. ANDERSON, AND G. C. WHITE. 1995b. Selection among open population capture-recapture models when capture probabilities are heterogeneous. J. Appl. Stat. 22:611–624.

BURNHAM, K. P., D. R. ANDERSON, G. C. WHITE, C. BROWNIE, AND K. H. POLLOCK. 1987. Design and analysis methods for fish survival experiments based on release-recapture. American Fisheries Society Monogr. 5.

CALIFORNIA FORESTRY ASSOCIATION. 1993. A petition to remove the California Spotted Owl from the federal list of threatened species. California Forestry Assoc., Sacramento, CA.

CAMPBELL, R. W., E. D. FORSMAN, AND B. M. VAN DER RAAY. 1984. An annotated bibliography of literature on the spotted owl. Land Manage. Rept. No. 24. British Columbia Ministry of Forests, Victoria, Canada.

CAREY, A. B., S. P. HORTON, AND B. L. BISWELL. 1992. Northern Spotted Owls: influence of prey base and landscape character. Ecological Monogr. 62:223–250.

CAREY, A. B., AND K. C. PEELER. 1995. Spotted Owls: resource and space use in a mosaic landscape. J. Rapt. Res. 29: In press.

CAREY, A. B., J. A. REID, AND S. P. HORTON. 1990. Spotted Owl home range and habitat use in southern Oregon coast ranges. J. Wildl. Manage. 54:11–17.

CARROLL, J. E., AND R. H. LAMBERSON. 1993. The owl's odyssey, a continuous model for the dispersal of territorial species. J. Appl. Mathematics 53:205–218.

CARROLL, R. J., AND D. RUPPERT. 1988. Transformation and weighting in regression. Chapman and Hall, New York.

CASWELL, H. 1989. Matrix population models: construction, analysis, and interpretation. Sinauer Assoc., Inc., Sunderland, MA.

CAUGHLEY, G. 1977. Analysis of vertebrate populations. J. Wiley and Sons, New York.

CAUGHLEY, G. AND L. C. BIRCH. 1971. Rate of increase. J. Wildl. Manage. 35:658–663. Caughley G., and A. R. E. Sinclair. 1994. Wildlife ecology and management. Blackwell Sci., Cambridge MA.

CHÁVEZ-LEÓN, G. 1989. Characteristics of fragmented habitats used by the Northern Spotted Owl (Strix occidentalis caurina) in northwestern California. M.S. thesis. Humboldt State Univ., Arcata, CA.

CLOBERT, J., J. D. LEBRETON, AND D. ALLAINE. 1987. A general approach to survival rate estimation by recaptures or resightings of marked birds. Ardea 75: 133–142.

COHEN, J. E., S. W. CHRISTENSEN, AND C. P. GOODYEAR. 1983. A stochastic age-structured population model of striped bass (Morone saxatilis) in the Potomac River. Can. J. Fisheries and Aquatic Sci. 40:2170–2183.

COHEN, W. B., T. A. SPIES, AND M. FIORELLA. 1995. Estimating the age and structure of forests in a multi-ownership landscape of western Oregon, USA. Int. J. Remote Sensing 16:721–746.

CONROY, M. J. 1993. Testing hypotheses about the relationship of habitat to animal survivorship. Pp. 331–342 in J. D. Lebreton and P. M. North (eds.), Marked individuals in the study of bird population. Birkhäuser Verlag, Basel.

CORMACK, R. M. 1964. Estimates of survival from the sighting of marked animals. Biometrika 51:429–438.

COWARDIN, L. M., D. S. GILMER, AND C. W. SHAIFFER. 1985. Mallard recruitment in the agricultural environment of North Dakota. Wildl. Monogr. 92.

COX, D. R. 1983. Some remarks on overdispersion. Biometrika 70:269–274.

DAWSON, W. L. 1923. The birds of California. Booklovers Edition, Vol. 3. South Moulton Company, San Diego, Los Angeles and San Francisco, CA.

DAWSON, W. R., J. D. LIGON, J. R. MURPHY, J. P. MYERS, D. SIMBERLOFF, AND J. VERNER. 1987. Report of the scientific advisory panel on the Spotted Owl. Condor 89:205–229.

DINERSTEIN, E., AND L. PRICE. 1991. Demography and habitat use by greater one-horned rhinoceros in Nepal. J. Wildl. Manage. 55:401–411.

DIXON, W. J., M. B. BROWN, L. ENGELMANN, AND R. I. JENNRICH. 1990. BMDP statistical software manual, Vol. 1. Univ. Calif. Press, Berkeley, CA.

DOAK, D. 1989. Spotted Owls and old growth logging in the Pacific Northwest. Conserv. Biol. 3:389–396.

DUNBAR, D. L., B. P. BOOTH, E. D. FORSMAN, A. E. HETHERINGTON, AND D. WILSON. 1991. Status of the Spotted Owl (Strix occidentalis) and Barred Owl (Strix varia) in southwestern British Columbia. Can. Field-Nat. 105:464–468.

DUNCAN, J. R. 1992. Influence of prey abundance and snow cover on Great Gray Owl breeding dispersal. Ph.D. diss. Univ. Manitoba, Winnipeg, MB.

DVORÁK, J., J. L. HALVERSON, P. GULICK, K. A. RAUEN, U. K. ABBOTT, B. J. KELLEY, AND F. T. SHULTZ. 1992. cDNA cloning of a Z- and W-linked gene in gallinaceous birds. J. Heredity 83:22–25.

EASTERBROOK, G. 1994. The Birds. The New Republic 210:22–29.

EBERHARDT, L. L. 1970. Correlation, regression, and density dependence. Ecology 51:306–310.

EBERHARDT, L. L. 1985. Assessing the dynamics of wild populations. J. Wildl. Manage. 49:997–1012

EFRON, B. 1982. The jackknife, the bootstrap and other resampling plans. Soc. Industrial and Appl. Math. Series 38.

ESTES, J. A. 1990. Growth and equilibrium in sea otter populations. J. Anim. Ecol. 59:385–401.

FERNANDEZ-DUQUE, E., AND C. VALEGGIA. 1994. Meta-analysis: a valuable tool in conservation research. Conserv. Biol. 8:555–561.

FITTON, S. D. 1991. Vocal learning and call structure of male Northern Spotted Owls in northwestern California. M.S. thesis. Humboldt State Univ., Arcata, CA.

FOLLIARD, L. 1993. Nest site characteristics of Northern Spotted Owls in managed forests of northwest California. M.S. thesis. Univ. Idaho, Moscow, ID.

FORSMAN, E. D. 1976. A preliminary investigation of the Spotted Owl in Oregon. M.S. thesis. Oregon State Univ., Corvallis, OR.

FORSMAN, E. D. 1980. Habitat utilization by Spotted Owls in the west-central cascades of Oregon. Ph.D. diss. Oregon State Univ., Corvallis, OR.

FORSMAN, E. D. 1981. Molt of the Spotted Owl. Auk 98:735–742.

FORSMAN, E. D. 1983. Methods and materials for locating and studying Spotted Owls. USDA For. Serv. Gen. Tech. Rep. PNW-162.

FORSMAN, E. D. 1988. A survey of Spotted Owls in young forests in the northern coast range of Oregon. Murrelet 69:65–68.

FORSMAN, E. D., C. R. BRUCE, M. A. WALTER, AND E. C. MESLOW. 1988. A current assessment of the Spotted Owl population in Oregon. Murrelet 68:51–54.

FORSMAN, E. D., A. R. GIESE, D. J. MANSON, AND S. G. SOVERN. 1995. Renesting by Spotted Owls. Condor 97:1078–1080.

FORSMAN, E. D., AND E. C. MESLOW. 1986. The Spotted Owl. Pp. 742–761 in Audubon wildlife report: 1986. Nat. Aud. Soc., New York.

FORSMAN, E. D., E. C. MESLOW, AND M. J. STRUB. 1977. Spotted Owl abundance in young versus old-growth forests, Oregon. Wildl. Soc. Bull. 5: 43–47.

FORSMAN, E. D., I. A. OTTO, D. AUBUCHON, J. C. LEWIS, S. G. SOVERN, K. J. MAURICE, AND T. KAMINSKI. 1994. Reproductive chronology of the northern flying squirrel. Northwest Sci. 68:273–276.

FORSMAN, E. D., E. C. MESLOW, AND H. M. WIGHT. 1984. Distribution and biology of the Spotted Owl in Oregon. Wildl. Monogr. 87:1–64.

FOSTER, C. C., E. D. FORSMAN, E. C. MESLOW, G. S. MILLER, J. A. REID, F. F. WAGNER, A. B. CAREY, AND J. B. LINT. 1992. Survival and reproduction of radio-marked adult Spotted Owls. J. Wildl. Manage. 56:91–95.

FRANKLIN, A. B. 1992. Population regulation in Northern Spotted Owls: theoretical implications for management. Pp. 815–827 in D. R. McCullough and R. H. Barrett (eds.), Wildlife 2001: populations. Elsevier Applied Sciences, London, England.

FRANKLIN, A. B., J. P. WARD, R. J. GUTIÉRREZ, AND G. I. GOULD, JR. 1990. Density of Northern Spotted Owls in northwest California. J. Wildl. Manage. 54:1–10.

FRANKLIN, J. F., AND C. T. DYRNESS. 1973. Natural vegetation of Oregon and Washington. USDA For. Serv. Gen. Tech. Rept. PNW-GTR-8.

GAO (GENERAL ACCOUNTING OFFICE). 1989. Endangered species: Spotted Owl petition evaluation beset by problems. RCED 89–79. U.S. General Accounting Office, Washington, DC

GARCIA, E. R. 1979. A survey of the Spotted Owl in southwestern Washington. Pp. 18–28 in P. P. Schaeffer, and S. M. Ehlers (eds.), Owls of the west: their ecology and conservation. Proc. Nat. Aud. Soc. Symposium. Nat. Aud. Soc. Western Education Ctr., Tiburon, CA.

GERRODETTE, T. 1987. A power analysis for detecting trends. Ecology 68:1364–1372.

GERRODETTE, T., D. GOODMAN, AND J. BARLOW. 1985. Confidence limits for population projections when vital rates vary randomly. Fisheries Bull. 83:207–215.

GOODMAN, L. A. 1960. On the exact variance of products. J. Am. Stat. Assoc. 55:708–713.

GOODMAN, L. A. 1968. An elementary approach to the population projection-matrix, to the population reproductive value, and to related topics in the mathematical theory of population growth. Demography 5:382–409.

GOULD, G. I., JR. 1977. Distribution of the Spotted Owl in California. West. Birds 8:131–146.

GRINNELL, J., AND A. H. MILLER. 1944. The distribution of the birds of California. Pacific Coast Avifauna, No. 27. The Nuttall Ornithological Club, Berkeley, CA.

GUTIÉRREZ, R. J. 1985. An overview of recent research on the Spotted Owl. Pp. 39–49 in R. J. Gutierrez and A. B. Carey (eds.), Ecology and management of the Spotted Owl in the Pacific Northwest. USDA For. Serv. Gen. Tech. Rep. PNW-185.

GUTIÉRREZ, R. J. 1994a. Changes in the distribution and abundance of Spotted Owls during the past century. Studies in Avian Biol. 15:293–300.

GUTIÉRREZ, R. J. 1994b. Conservation planning: lessons from the Spotted Owl. Pp. 51–58 in W. W. Covington and L. F. DeBano (eds.), Sustainable ecological systems: implementing an ecological approach to land management. USDA For. Serv. Gen. Tech. Rept. RM-247.

GUTIÉRREZ, R. J., AND A. B. CAREY (TECH EDS.). 1985. Ecology and management of the Spotted Owl in the Pacific Northwest. USDA For. Serv. Gen. Tech. Rept. PNW-185.

GUTIÉRREZ, R. J., A. B. FRANKLIN, AND W. S. LAHAYE. 1995. "Spotted owl." A. Poole and F. Gill (eds.), The birds of North America no. 179. The Academy of Natural Sciences, Philadelphia, PA, and The American Ornithologists' Union, Washington, DC.

GUTIÉRREZ, R. J., A. B. FRANKLIN, W. LAHAYE, V. J. MERETSKY, AND J. P. WARD. 1985. Juvenile Spotted Owl dispersal in northwestern California: preliminary results. Pp. 60–65 in R. J. Gutiérrez and A. B. Carey (eds.), Ecology and management of the Spotted Owl in the Pacific Northwest. USDA For. Serv. Gen. Tech. Rep. PNW-185.

GUTIÉRREZ, R. J., AND S. HARRISON. In Press. Applications of metapopulation theory to Spotted Owl management: a history and critique. *In* D. R. McCullough (ed.), Wildlife metapopulations. Island Press, Covelo, CA.

GUTIÉRREZ, R. J., D. M. SOLIS, AND C. SISCO. 1984. Habitat ecology of the Spotted Owl in northwestern California: implications for management. Pp. 368–373 *in* Proceedings of 1993 annual convention of the Society of American Foresters. Soc. Am. Foresters, Bethesda, MD.

HAMER, T. E. 1988. Home range size of the Northern Barred Owl and Northern Spotted Owl in western Washington. M.S. thesis. Western Washington Univ., Bellingham, WA.

HAMER, T. E., E. D. FORSMAN, A. D. FUCHS, AND M. L. WALTERS. 1994. Hybridization between Barred and Spotted Owls. Auk 111:487–492.

HARRISON, S., A. STAHL, AND D. DOAK. 1993. Spatial models and Spotted Owls: exploring some biological issues behind recent events. Conserv. Biol. 7:950–953.

HENDERSON, J. A., D. H. PETER, R. D. LESHER, AND D. C. SHAW. 1989. Forested plant associations of the Olympic National Forest. USDA For. Serv. Ecological Tech. Paper R6-ECOL-TP 001–88.

HOLTHAUSEN, R. S., M. G. RAPHAEL, K. S. MCKELVEY, E. D. FORSMAN, E. E. STARKEY, AND D. E. SEAMAN. 1995. The contribution of federal and nonfederal habitat to persistence of the Northern Spotted Owl on the Olympic Peninsula, Washington: report of the reanalysis team. USDA For. Serv. Gen. Tech. Rept. PNW-GTR-352.

HOSMER, D. W., AND S. LEMESHOW. 1989. Applied logistic regression. John Wiley and Sons, New York, NY.

HUNTER, J. E. 1994. Habitat configuration around Spotted Owl nest and roost sites in northwestern California. M.S. thesis. Humboldt State Univ., Arcata, CA.

HUNTER, J. E., R. J. GUTIÉRREZ, AND A. B. FRANKLIN. 1995. Habitat configuration around Spotted Owl sites in northwestern California. Condor 97:684–693.

JOHNSON, D. H. 1980. The comparison of usage and availability measurements for evaluating resource preference. Ecology 61:65–71.

JOHNSON, D. H. 1992. Spotted Owls, Great Horned Owls, and forest fragmentation in the central Oregon Cascades. M.S. thesis. Oregon State Univ., Corvallis, OR.

JOHNSON, K. N., J. F. FRANKLIN, J. W. THOMAS, AND J. GORDON. 1991. Alternatives for management of late-successional forests in the Pacific Northwest—a report to the Agriculture Committee and the Merchant Marine and Fisheries Committee of the United States House of Representatives.

JOLLY, G. M. 1965. Explicit estimates from capture-recapture data with both death and immigration-stochastic model. Biometrika 52:225–247.

JOLLY, G. M. 1982. Mark-recapture models with parameters constant in time. Biometrics 38:301–321.

KEYFITZ, N. 1972. On future population. J. Amer. Stat. Assoc. 67:347–363.

KLOMP, H. 1972. Regulation of the size of bird populations by means of territorial behavior. Netherlands J. Zool. 22:456–488.

KOENIG, W. W., AND R. L. MUMME. 1987. Population ecology of the cooperatively breeding Acorn Woodpecker. Princeton Univ. Press, Princeton, NJ.

KOSTRZEWA, A., AND R. KOSTRZEWA. 1990. The relationship of spring and summer weather with density and breeding performance of the buzzard *Buteo buteo*, Goshawk *Accipiter gentilis* and Kestrel *Falco tinnunculus*. Ibis 132:550–559.

KROEL, K. W., AND P. J. ZWANK. 1992. Renesting of Mexican Spotted Owl in southern New Mexico. J. Raptor Res. 26:267–268.

KÜCHLER, A. W. 1977. The map of the natural vegetation of California. Pp. 909–938 *in* M. Barbour and J. Majors (eds.), Terrestrial vegetation of California. J. Wiley and Sons, New York, NY.

LAHAYE, W. S. 1988. Nest site selection and nesting habitat of the Northern Spotted Owl (*Strix occidentalis caurina*) in northwestern California. M.S. thesis. Humboldt State Univ., Arcata, CA.

LAMBERSON, R. H., R. MCKELVEY, B. R. NOON, AND C. VOSS. 1992. A dynamic analysis of Northern Spotted Owl viability in a fragmented forest landscape. Conserv. Biol. 6:505–512.

LAMBERSON, R. H., B. R. NOON, C. VOSS, AND K. S. MCKELVEY. 1994. Reserve design for territorial species: effects of patch size and spacing on the viability of the Northern Spotted Owl. Conserv. Biol. 8:185–195.

LANDE, R. 1987. Extinction thresholds in demographic models of territorial populations. Amer. Natur. 130:624–635.

LANDE, R. 1988. Demographic models of the Northern Spotted Owl. Oecologia 75:601–607.

LANDE, R., G. ORIANS, AND J. WIENS. 1994. A best guess scenario—Spotted Owl demography and option 9. Inner Voice 6:6–7.

LAYMON, S. A. 1988. Ecology of the Spotted Owl in the central Sierra Nevadas, California. Ph.D. diss. Univ. California, Berkeley, CA.

LEBRETON, J. D., K. P. BURNHAM, J. CLOBERT, AND D. R. ANDERSON. 1992. Modeling survival and testing biological hypotheses using marked animals: a unified approach with case studies. Ecol. Monogr. 62:67–118.

LEFKOVITCH, L. P. 1965. The study of population growth in organisms grouped by stages. Biometrics 21:1–18.

LEHMKUHL, J. F., AND M. G. RAPHAEL. 1993. Habitat pattern around Northern Spotted Owl locations on the Olympic Peninsula, Washington. J. Wildl. Manage. 57:302–315.

LESLIE, P. H. 1945. On the use of matrices in certain population mathematics. Biometrika 33:183–212.

LESLIE, P. H. 1948. Some further notes on the use of matrices in population mathematics. Biometrika 35:213–245.

LEWIS, J. C., AND B. C. WALES. 1993. Northern Spotted Owl pair successfully renests. J. Field Ornithol. 64:323–325.

LOERY, G., K. H. POLLOCK, J. D. NICHOLS, AND J. E. HINES. 1987. Age-specificity of Black-Capped Chickadee survival rates: analysis of capture-recapture data. Ecology 68:1038–1044.

LUNDBERG, A. 1980. Vocalizations and courtship

feeding of the Ural Owl (*Strix uralensis*). Ornis Scand. 11:65–70.

MARSHALL, J. T., JR. 1942. Food and habitat of the Spotted Owl. Condor 44:66–67.

MARZLUFF, J. M., AND R. P. BALDA. 1992. The Pinyon Jay: behavioral ecology of a colonial and cooperative corvid. Academic Press Inc., San Diego, CA.

MAX, T. A., R. A. SOUTER, AND K. A. O'HALLORAN. 1990. Statistical estimators for monitoring Spotted Owls in Oregon and Washington in 1987. USDA Forest Service Research Paper PNW-RP-420. Pacific Northwest Research Station, Portland, OR.

McCULLAGH, P., and J. A. NELDER. 1983. Generalized linear models. Chapman and Hall, New York, NY.

McCULLOUGH, D. R. 1982. Population growth rate of the George Reserve deer herd. J. Wildl. Manage. 46:1079–1083.

McDONALD, D. B., AND H. CASWELL. 1993. Matrix methods for avian demography. Pp. 139–185 *in* D. M. Power (ed.), Current ornithology, Vol. 10. Plenum Press, New York, NY.

McKELVEY, K., B. R. NOON, AND R. H. LAMBERSON. 1993. Conservation planning for species occupying fragmented landscapes: the case of the Northern Spotted Owl. Pp. 424–450 *in* P. Kareiva, J. Kingsolver, and R. Huey (eds.), Biotic interactions and global change. Sinauer Assoc., Sunderland, MA.

MEARNS, R., AND I. NEWTON. 1988. Factors affecting breeding success of Peregrines in south Scotland. J. Anim. Ecol. 57:903–916.

MESLOW, E. C. 1993. Spotted Owl protection: unintentional evolution toward ecosystem management. Endangered Species Update 3/4:34–38.

MIELKE, P. W., K. J. BERRY, P. J. BROCKWELL, AND J. S. WILLIAMS. 1981. A class of nonparametric tests based on multiresponse permutation procedures. Biometrica 68:720–724.

MILLER, G. S., K. NELSON, AND W. C. WRIGHT. 1985. Two-year-old female Spotted Owl breeds successfully. West. Birds 16:69–73.

MILLER, G. S. 1989. Dispersal of juvenile Northern Spotted Owls in western Oregon. M.S. thesis. Oregon State Univ., Corvallis, OR.

MILLS, L. S., R. J. FREDRICKSON, AND B. B. MOORHEAD. 1993. Characteristics of old-growth forests associated with Northern Spotted Owls in Olympic National Park. J. Wildl. Manage. 57:315–321.

MOEN, C. A., A. B. FRANKLIN, AND R. J. GUTIÉRRÉZ. 1991. Age determination of subadult Northern Spotted Owls in northwest California. Wildl. Soc. Bull. 19:489–493.

MORRIS, W. G. 1934. Forest fires in western Oregon and western Washington. Oregon Historical Quarterly 35(4):313–339.

MUNGER, T. T. 1930. Ecological aspects of the transition from old forests to new. Science 72:327–332.

MURPHY, D. D., AND B. R. NOON. 1992. Integrating scientific methods with habitat conservation planning: reserve design for Northern Spotted Owls. Ecol. Appl. 2:3–17.

NELSON, L. J., D. R. ANDERSON, AND K. P. BURNHAM. 1980. The effect of band loss on estimates of annual survival. J. Field Ornith. 51:30–38.

NERO, R. W. 1980. The Great Gray Owl: phantom of the northern forest. Smithsonian Institution Press, Washington, DC.

NEWTON, I. 1976. Population limitation in diurnal raptors. Can. Field-Nat. 90:274–300.

NEWTON, I. 1979. Population ecology of raptors. Poyser, Berkhamsted, England.

NEWTON, I. 1986. The sparrowhawk. T. and A. D. Poyser, Calton, England.

NEWTON, I., I. WYLLIE, AND P. ROTHERY. 1993. Annual survival of sparrowhawks *Accipter nisus* breeding in three areas of Britain. Ibis 135:49–60.

NOAA. 1990–1994. Climatological data for Washington, Vols. 93–96. U.S. National Oceanic and Atmospheric Administration, Asheville, NC.

NICHOLS, J. D., B. R. NOON, S. L. STOKES, AND J. E. HINES. 1981. Remarks on the use of mark-recapture methodology in estimating avian population size. Pp. 121–136 *in* C. J. Ralph and J. M. Scott (eds.), Estimating the numbers of terrestrial birds. Studies in Avian Biol. 6.

NOON, B. R., AND C. M. BILES. 1990. Mathematical demography of Spotted Owls in the Pacific northwest. J. Wildl. Manage. 54:18–27.

NOON, B. R., K. S. McKELVEY, D. W. LUTZ, W. S. LAHAYE, R. J. GUTIÉRREZ, AND C. A. MOEN. 1992. Estimates of demographic parameters and rates of population change. Pp. 175–186 *in* J. Verner, K. S. McKelvey, B. R. Noon, R. J. Gutiérrez, G. I. Gould, Jr., and T. W. Beck (eds.), The California Spotted Owl: a technical assessment of its current status. USDA For. Serv. Gen. Tech. Rep. PSW-GTR-133.

NOON, B. R., AND J. R. SAUER. 1992. Population models for passerine birds: structure, parameterization and analysis. Pp. 441–464 *in* D. R. McCullough and R. H. Barrett (eds.), Wildlife 2001: populations. Elsevier Applied Sciences, London, England.

NORTH, P. M. 1993. Stand structure and truffle abundance associated with Northern Spotted Owl habitat. Ph.D. diss. Univ. Washington, Seattle, WA.

NORUŠIS, M. J. 1990. SPSS/PC+ Statistics 4.0 for the IBM PC/XT/AT and PS/2. SPSS Inc., Chicago, IL.

OEHLERT, G. W. 1992. A note on the delta method. Am. Statistician 46:27–29.

OLSEN, P. D., AND J. OLSEN. 1989a. Breeding of the Peregrine Falcon *Falco peregrinus*: II. Weather, nest quality, and the timing of egg laying. Emu 89:1–5.

OLSEN, P. D., AND J. OLSEN. 1989b. Breeding of the Peregrine Falcon *Falco peregrinus*: III. Weather, nest quality, and breeding access. Emu 89:6–14.

PATON, P. W. C., C. J. ZABEL, D. L. NEAL, G. N. STEGER, N. G. TILGHMAN, AND B. R. NOON. 1991. Effects of radio tags on Spotted Owls. J. Wildl. Manage. 55:617–622.

PATTERSON, I. J. 1980. Territorial behavior and the limitation of population density. Ardea 68:53–62.

PETERMAN, R. M. 1990. Statistical power analysis can improve fisheries research and management. Can. J. Fish. and Aquatic Sci. 47:2–15.

PITELKA, F. A., P. Q. TOMICH, AND G. W. TREICHEL. 1955. Ecological relations of jaegers and owls as lemming predators near Barrow, Alaska. Ecol. Monogr. 25:85–117.

POLLOCK, K. H. 1981a. Capture-recapture models

allowing for age-dependent survival and capture rates. Biometrics 37:521–529.

POLLOCK, K. H. 1981b. Capture-recapture models: a review of current methods, assumptions and experimental design. Pp. 426–435 in C. J. Ralph and J. M. Scott (eds.), Estimating the numbers of terrestrial birds. Studies in Avian Biol. 6.

POLLOCK, K. H., J. E. HINES, AND J. D. NICHOLS. 1985. Goodness-of-fit tests for open capture-recapture models. Biometrics 41:399–410.

POLLOCK, K. H., J. D. NICHOLS, C. BROWNIE, AND J. E. HINES. 1990. Statistical inference from capture-recapture experiments. Wildl. Monogr. 107.

PRADEL, R. J., J. CLOBERT, AND J. D. LEBRETON. 1990. Recent developments for the analysis of multiple capture-recapture data sets: an example concerning two Blue Tit populations. The Ring 13:193–204.

RAPHAEL, M. G., J. A. YOUNG, K. McKELVEY, B. M. GALLEHER, AND K. C. PEELER. 1994. A simulation analysis of population dynamics of the Northern Spotted Owl in relation to forest management alternatives. Appendix J3 in Final environmental impact statement of management of habitat for late-successional and old-growth forest related species within the range of the Northern Spotted Owl, Vol. 2. USDA For. Serv. and USDI Bur. Land Manage., Portland, OR.

RAVELING, D. G., AND M. E. HEITMEYER. 1989. Relationships of population size and recruitment of Pintails to habitat conditions and harvest. J. Wildl. Manage. 53:1088–1103.

RICHARDS, J. E. 1989. Spotted Owl food habits and prey availability on the east slope of the Washington Cascades. M.S. thesis. Colorado State Univ., Fort Collins, CO.

RICHARDSON, E. 1980. BLM's billion-dollar checkerboard. Forest History Soc., Santa Cruz, CA.

RIPPLE, W. J., D. H. JOHNSON, K. T. HERSHEY, AND E. C. MESLOW. 1991. Old-growth and mature forests near Spotted Owl nests in western Oregon. J. Wildl. Manage. 55:316–318.

ROSENBERG, D. K. 1991. Characteristics of northern flying squirrel and Townsend's chipmunk populations in second- and old-growth forests. M.S. thesis. Oregon State Univ., Corvallis, OR.

ROTELLA, J. J., AND J. T. RATTI. 1992. Mallard brood survival and wetland habitat conditions in southwestern Manitoba. J. Wildl. Manage. 56:499–507.

RUSCH, D. H., E. C. MESLOW, P. D. DOERR, AND L. B. KEITH. 1972. Response of Great Horned Owl populations to changing prey densities. J. Wildl. Manage. 36:282–296.

RYAN, B. F., B. L. JOINER, AND T. A. RYAN, JR. 1980. Minitab handbook. Second edition. Duxbury Press, Boston, MA.

SANDLAND, R. L., AND P. KIRKWOOD. 1981. Estimation of survival in marked populations with possibly dependent sighting probabilities. Biometrika 68:531–541.

SAS INSTITUTE. 1990a. SAS® Language: Reference, Vers. 6, 1st ed. SAS Institute, Inc., Carey, NC.

SAS INSTITUTE. 1990b. SAS/STAT® User's Guide, Ver. 6, 4th ed., Vol. 2. SAS Institute, Inc., Carey, NC.

SAS INSTITUTE. 1993. SAS/STAT® Software: Changes and Enhancements, Release 6.07. SAS Tech. Rep. P-229. SAS Institute, Inc., Carey, NC.

SEBER, G. A. F. 1965. A note on the multiple recapture census. Biometrika 52:249–259.

SEBER, G. A. F. 1973. Estimation of animal abundance and related parameters. Griffin, London, England.

SEBER, G. A. F. 1982. The estimation of animal abundance and related parameters. Second edition. Macmillan, New York, NY.

SEBER, G. A. F. 1986. A review of estimating animal abundance. Biometrics 42:267–292.

SIMBERLOFF, D. 1987. The Spotted Owl fracas: mixing academic, applied, and political ecology. Ecology 68:766–772.

SINCLAIR, A. R. E. 1989. Population regulation in animals. Pp. 197–241 in J. M. Cherrett (ed.), Ecological concepts. Blackwell Scientific Publ., Oxford, England.

SISCO, C. L. 1990. Seasonal home range and habitat ecology of Spotted Owls in northwestern California. M.S. thesis. Humboldt State Univ., Arcata, CA.

SKALSKI, J. R., A. HOFFMAN, AND G. S. SMITH. 1993. Testing the significance of individual- and cohort-level covariates in animal survival studies. Pp. 9–28 in J. D. Lebreton and P. M. North (eds.), Marked individuals in the study of bird populations. Birkhäuser Verlag, Basel, Switzerland.

SMITH, D. R., AND D. R. ANDERSON. 1987. Effects of lengthy ringing periods on estimators of annual survival. Acta Ornithol. 23:69–76.

SOKAL, R. R., AND F. J. ROHLF. 1981. Biometry. 2nd ed. W. H. Freeman and Co., San Francisco, CA.

SOLIS, D. M., JR. 1983. Summer habitat ecology of Spotted Owls in northwestern California. M.S. thesis. Humboldt State Univ., Arcata, CA.

SOLIS, D. M. AND R. J. GUTIÉRREZ. 1990. Summer habitat ecology of Northern Spotted Owls in northwestern California. Condor 92:739–748.

SOUTHERN, H. N. 1970. The natural control of a population of Tawny Owls (Strix aluco). J. Zool. London 162:197–285.

SOVERN, S. G., E. D. FORSMAN, B. L. BISWELL, D. N. ROLPH, AND M. TAYLOR. 1994. Diurnal behavior of the Spotted Owl in Washington. Condor 96:200–202.

STOKES, S. L. 1984. The Jolly-Seber model applied to age-stratified populations. J. Wildl. Manage. 48:1053–1059. (also see the corrigendum in J. Wildl. Manage. 49:282).

TAYLOR, A. L., AND E. D. FORSMAN. 1976. Recent range expansion of the Barred Owl in western North American, including the first records for Oregon. Condor 78:560–561.

TAYLOR, B. L., AND T. GERRODETTE. 1993. The uses of statistical power in conservation biology: the vaquita and Northern Spotted Owl. Conserv. Biol. 7:489–500.

TAYLOR, I. R., A. DOWELL, AND G. SHAW. 1992. The population ecology and conservation of Barn Owls (Tyto alba) in coniferous plantations. Pp. 16–21 in A. Galbraith et al. (eds.), The ecology and conservation of European owls. U.K. Nature Conservation No. 5, Joint Nature Conservation Committee, Peterborough, U.K.

TEENSMA, P. D. A., J. T. RIENSTRA, AND M. A. YEITER. 1991. Preliminary reconstruction and analysis of change in forest stand age classes of the Oregon Coast Range from 1850 to 1940. USDI Bur. Land Manage., Oregon State Office, Tech. Note T/N OR-9.

THOMAS, J. W., E. D. FORSMAN, J. B. LINT, E. C. MESLOW, B. R. NOON, AND J. VERNER. 1990. A conservation strategy for the Northern Spotted Owl. Report of the Interagency Scientific Committee to address the conservation of the Northern Spotted Owl. USDA For. Serv., USDI Bur. Land Manage., Fish and Wildl. Serv., and Natl. Park Serv. U.S. Government Printing Office 791-171/20026, Washington DC.

THOMAS, J. W., ET AL. 1993a. Viability assessments and management considerations for species associated with late-successional and old-growth forests of the Pacific Northwest. The report of the Scientific Analysis Team. USDA For. Serv., Portland, OR.

THOMAS, J. W., M. G. RAPHAEL, R. G. ANTHONY, E. D. FORSMAN, A. G. GUNDERSON, R. S. HOLTHAUSEN, B. G. MARCOT, G. H. REEVES, J. R. SEDELL, AND D. M. SOLIS. 1993b. Forest ecosystem management: an ecological, economic, and social assessment. Report of the Forest Ecosystem Management Assessment Team. USDA For. Serv. and USDI Bur. Land Manage., Portland OR.

THOMPSON, F. R., III, AND E. K. FRITZELL. 1989. Habitat use, home range, and survival of territorial male Ruffed Grouse. J. Wildl. Manage. 53:15–21.

TULJAPURKAR, S. D. 1982. Population dynamics in variable environments. 11. Correlated environments, sensitivity analysis, and dynamics. Theoretical Pop. Biol. 21:114–140.

TULJAPURKAR, S. D., AND S. H. ORZACK. 1980. Population dynamics in variable environments, 1. Long-run growth and extinction. Theoretical Pop. Biol. 18:314–342.

USHER, M. B. 1972. Developments in the Leslie matrix model. Pp. 29–60 in R. Jeffers (ed.), Mathematical models in ecology. Blackwell, Oxford, England.

USDA. 1988. Final supplement to the environmental impact statement for an amendment to the Pacific Northwest regional guide, 2 Vols. USDA For. Serv., Portland, OR.

USDA. 1989. Siskiyou National Forest land and resource management plan. USDA For. Serv., Grants Pass, OR.

USDA. 1992. Final environmental impact statement on management for the Northern Spotted Owl in the national forests. USDA For. Serv., Portland, OR.

USDA AND USDI. 1994a. Final supplemental environmental impact statement on management of habitat for late-successional and old-growth forest related species within the range of the Northern Spotted Owl, 2 Vols. USDA For. Serv. and USDI Bur. Land Manage., Portland, OR.

USDA AND USDI. 1994b. Record of decision for amendments to Forest Service and Bureau of Land Management planning documents within the range of the Northern Spotted Owl. USDA For. Serv. and USDI Bur. Land Manage., Portland, OR.

USDC. 1994. Climatological data annual summary, Oregon 1993. Vol. 99, No. 13. National Oceanic and Atmospheric Administration, U.S. Dep. Commerce, Asheville, NC.

USDI. 1973. Threatened wildlife of the United States. USDI Fish and Wildl. Serv. Resource Publ. 114 (Rev. Resour. Publ. 34).

USDI. 1990. Endangered and threatened wildlife and plants: determination of threatened status for the Northern Spotted Owl. Fed. Register 55:26114–26194.

USDI. 1992a. Draft recovery plan for the northern spotted owl. U.S. Dep. Interior, Washington, DC.

USDI. 1992b. Final draft recovery plan for the Northern Spotted Owl, 2 Vols. U.S. Dep. Interior, Washington, DC.

USDI. 1994. Desert tortoise (Mojave population) recovery plan. USDI Fish and Wildl. Serv., Portland, OR.

USDI BUREAU OF LAND MANAGEMENT. 1992a. Roseburg District resource management plan and environmental impact statement. Draft. Vol. 1. Roseburg, OR.

USDI BUREAU OF LAND MANAGEMENT. 1992b. Salem District draft resource management plan and environmental impact statement, 2 Vols. USDI Bur. Land Manage., Salem, OR.

USDI BUREAU OF LAND MANAGEMENT. 1995. Final Medford District resource management plan and environmental impact statement. Vol. 1. USDI Bur. Land Manage., Medford, OR.

VAN BALLENBERGHE, V. 1983. Rate of increase of white-tailed deer on the George Reserve: a re-evaluation. J. Wildl. Manage. 47:1245–1247.

VAN HORNE, B. 1983. Density as a misleading indicator of habitat quality. J. Wildl. Mange. 47:893–901.

VERNER, J., R. J. GUTIÉRREZ, AND G. I. GOULD. 1992. The California Spotted Owl: general biology and ecological relations. Pp. 55–78 in J. Verner, K. S. McKelvey, B. R. Noon, R. J. Gutierrez, G. I. Gould, Jr., and T. W. Beck (tech. coords.), The California spotted owl: a technical assessment of its current status. USDA For. Serv. Gen. Tech. Rep. PSW-GTR-133.

VICKERY, P. D., M. L. HUNTER, JR., AND J. V. WELLS. 1992a. Is density an indicator of breeding success? Auk 109:706–710.

VICKERY, P. D., M. L. HUNTER, JR., AND J. V. WELLS. 1992b. Use of a new relationship index to evaluate relationship between habitat quality and breeding success. Auk 109:697–705.

WARD, J. P., JR. 1990. Spotted Owl reproduction, diet and prey abundance in northwest California. M.S. thesis. Humboldt State Univ., Arcata, CA.

WARD, J. P., A. B. FRANKLIN, AND R. J. GUTIÉRREZ. 1991. Using search time and regression to estimate abundance of territorial Spotted Owls. Ecol. Appl. 1:207–214.

WEDDERBURN, R. W. M. 1974. Quasi-likelihood functions, generalized linear models, and the Gauss-Newton method. Biometrika 61:439–447.

WHITE, G. C. 1983. Numerical estimation of survival rates from band-recovery and biotelemetry data. J. Wildl. Manage. 47:716–728.

WILSON, R. R., M. P. WILSON, AND J. W. DURKIN.

1986. Breeding biology of the Barn Owl (*Tyto alba*) in central Mali. Ibis 128:81–90.

ZABEL, C. J., K. MCKELVEY, AND J. P. WARD, JR. 1995. Influence of primary prey on home range size and habitat use patterns of Spotted Owls (*Strix occidentalis*). Can. J. Zool. 73:433–439.

ZAR, J. H. 1984. Biostatistical analysis, 2nd edition. Prentice-Hall, Englewood Cliffs, New Jersey, USA.

Studies in Avian Biology No. 17:121–122, 1996.

APPENDIX

Symbols and Acronyms

Glossary of terms, symbols, and notation (adapted from Burnham et al. 1987). Although appropriate for general applications, definitions are placed in the context of the studies presented in this volume. Additional descriptions and citations are in the text.

Symbols for Parameters

The following symbols are generally subscripted.

b fecundity; the number of female young fledged per territorial female owl.

λ annual rate of population change; $\lambda = 1$ indicates a stationary population; $\lambda < 1$, a declining population; and $\lambda > 1$, an increasing population; and $\lambda - 1$, the annual magnitude of change.

E permanent emigration rate; for an owl in a study area at the start of a year, the annual probability of it leaving the area where surveys occur and never returning.

F fidelity rate ($= 1 - E$); annual probability of an owl remaining on a study area.

ϕ apparent survival ($= 1 - $ [mortality rate $+ [S \times E]$); the probability that an owl alive in year t survives and remains within a study area to year $t+1$.

p recapture probability; the probability that an owl alive in year t is recaptured or resighted in year t.

q $1 - p$; the probability that an owl alive in year t is not recaptured in year t.

S true survival rate ($= 1 - $ mortality rate); the probability that an owl alive in year t survives to year $t+1$.

θ a generic parameter, e.g., ϕ, S, λ, or p. Used when discussing parameters in general terms.

Subscripts for Parameters

A   owls that are ≥ 3 years old.

i capture occasion for which parameter is estimated.

J   juvenile age-class; includes fledged young of the year that are <1 year old.

t year for which parameter is estimated.

S1   owls that are ≥ 1 and <2 years old.

S2   owls that are ≥ 2 and <3 years old.

x age-class; a generic symbol to denote either juvenile (J), 1-year old (S1), 2-year old (S2), or ≥ 3-year old (A) age-classes.

Statistical Symbols and Acronyms

AIC   Akaike's Information Criterion; AIC $= -2\ln(L) + 2K$.

$E(\hat{\theta})$ expected value of the estimator $\hat{\theta}$.

^   placed above a symbol denotes an estimate or estimator.

H_O Null hypothesis.

H_A Alternate hypothesis.

k number of capture occasions; in this case, the number of years where owls were captured.

K number of estimable parameters in a mark-recapture model.

L   likelihood function.

$\ln(\ )$ natural logarithm (base 2.718).

$\ln(L)$ natural logarithm of the likelihood function.

$\widehat{SE}(\hat{\theta})$ estimated standard error of a parameter estimate where $\widehat{SE}(\hat{\theta}) = \sqrt{\widehat{var}(\hat{\theta})}$.

X   capture history matrix where columns are years (capture occasions), rows represent individual owls, and cells represent whether an owl was captured (1) or not captured (0).

z a test statistic distributed normally with mean $= 0$ and standard error $= 1$ under the null hypothesis.

χ^2 a test statistic distributed as chi-square with n degrees of freedom under the null hypothesis.

Symbols Used in Model Notation

a categorical age effects for four age classes.

an   categorical age effects for n age classes where n ≤ 4.

an'   categorical age effects for birds initially banded as juveniles where n is the number of age classes over which restrictions apply, e.g., $p_{a2'}$ indicates recapture probabilities for juveniles that differ over the 2 next age-classes in which juveniles are recaptured.

g categorical study area effects.

s categorical sex effect.

t categorical time effects.

T time effects are modeled as being linear over time.

+ when used between effect subscripts indicates that effects are additive (no interactions), e.g., $s + t$ indicates rates modeled by sex which vary similarly over time.

* when used between effect subscripts indicates that interaction between effects are included, e.g., $s*t$ indicates rates are modeled by sex and time and the interaction between the two.

Specific Terms

DSA Density Study Area—A defined area within which the objective is to estimate the total number of resident owls present each year. The entire area is systematically searched 3-6 times each year, using calling stations spaced at close intervals.

fecundity the number of female young fledged per territorial female owl per year.

floater an unpaired, nonbreeding owl which does not exhibit territorial behavior.

GSA General Study Area—A geographic region within which information on owl demographic performance is collected. Entire area is not necessarily searched for owls. Rather, the focus is on specific areas with a history of occupancy by Spotted Owls.

juvenile a fledged young of the year; an owl <1 year of age.

non-juvenile any owl ≥1 year of age.

mousing method in which observers place live mice in front of owls and then watch to see if the owls eat, cache, or take the mice to nests or fledged young. Used to determine reproductive output in owls.

permanent emigration owls leave a study area and do not return; denoted by E.

reproductive output the total number of young fledged per territorial female owl per year.

site area where Spotted Owls exhibited territorial behavior on ≥2 separate occasions ≥ one week apart within a given year.

stable demographic parameters (such as survival and fecundity) which do not change over time.

stationary a population whose numbers remain constant over time ($\lambda = 1$).

temporary emigration owls leave a study area for at least one year and then return to the study area.